AVIONICS

Patrick Stephens Limited, part of Thorsons, a division of the Collins Publishing Group, has published authoritative, quality books for enthusiasts for more than twenty years. During that time the company has established a reputation as one of the world's leading publishers of books on aviation, maritime, military, model-making, motor cycling, motoring, motor racing, railway and railway modelling subjects. Readers or authors with suggestions for books they would like to see published are invited to write to: The Editorial Director, Patrick Stephens Limited, Thorsons Publishing Group, Wellingborough, Northants, NN8 2RQ.

AVIONICS

The story and technology of aviation electronics

Bill Gunston

Patrick Stephens Limited

First published in 1990

British Library Cataloguing in Publication Data
Gunston, Bill, 1927-
    Avionics.
    1. Aircraft. Electronic equipment
    I. Title
    629.135'6

ISBN 1-85260-133-7

Patrick Stephens Limited is part of the
Thorsons Publishing Group, Wellingborough,
Northamptonshire NN8 2RQ, England.

Typeset by Burns and Smith Ltd, Derby

Printed by The Bath Press, Bath, Avon

10 9 8 7 6 5 4 3 2 1

CONTENTS

ACKNOWLEDGEMENTS

I would like to thank over thirty companies for responding to requests for information. Special thanks are due to L.F.E. Coombs, and to Hughes Radar Systems Group, who are acknowledged as the source of no fewer than 36 diagrams. Others who gave permission to use proprietary material included Ferranti Defence Systems and the Oxford Air Training School. Amazingly, while companies send out expensive colour brochures by the truckload, they are highly resistant to specific requests for reproducible black/white photos or diagrams — in one case after five airmail letters, five faxes and three phone calls!

INTRODUCTION

One of my books for PSL is an Encyclopaedia of Aero Engines. It was easy to write, because each company appears in its correct alphabetical place; then the engines of each company are discussed in chronological order. This is what most people wanted. They did not, so far as I am aware, want the totally different kind of book that would result from having chapters with such titles as 'the design of big ends' or 'the advantages of digital control'.

With avionics (aviation electronics) the situation is quite different. Not many people would want a company-by-company catalogue, and in any case these are periodically available from trade magazines and other sources such as the annual *Jane's Avionics*. PSL and I believe that the main requirement is an overview of the whole subject, explaining how things work, not assuming too much prior knowledge, but at the same time not so simplistic or 'popular' as to deter the serious reader (or even the PhD in solid-state devices). But what a challenge!

Few people would disagree with my belief that you can't just plunge in at the deep end with 1990s' technology; you need some historical background describing where we have come from. But we seem to have come some distance! I can't help being wry-ly amused by a 1939 author who wrote 'The challenge [of describing modern aircraft] is awesome in its complexity'. If only I could leave off the subject of avionics at the 1939 level I could omit at least 99 per cent of this book. Today I sometimes feel the complexities really are 'awesome'. The other day I got an invitation to a seminar on XA. You don't know what that is? Shame on you! To explain, this is the opening of the accompanying blurb (I haven't altered a word):

'MVS and VM system performance can be significantly improved by exploiting the features of XA. Relief from storage and I/O constraints and improved availability and response for TSO, IMS, DB2 and other subsystems can be achieved through specific SRM tuning options, creative use of expanded storage and advanced 31-bit programming. Use of the 3090 vector facility, linear VSAM files, and other architectural enhancements can secure many non-obvious benefits...'

There's a lot more in the same vein, but this will suffice to demonstrate that 1939 perhaps wasn't so complex after all. Yet, at the most fundamental level, we didn't know what an electron was in 1939 and we don't know what it is half a century later. All we can claim is that we know a lot more about how to make them work for us. Certainly, the development of electronics is perhaps the greatest of man's (we don't have a word meaning 'man's and woman's') technical success stories. It is at least able to rank alongside molecular biology, genetic engineering, new materials or anything else — even flying machines. Electronics is certainly one of the 'leading edge' technologies, and avionics is one of its most important branches, responsible for driving more than half the current research programmes.

In putting this book together I often had agonizing doubts that I had got the structure right. The chapter headings seemed obvious enough, until I realized — for example — that everything tends to be inter-related. Thus Chapter 6 RADAR FOR AT-TACK talks about automatic terrain-following, and you cannot do this without discussing automatic flight-control systems, but these are covered in Chapter 14. Again the same chapter cannot omit reference to radar for detecting submarine periscopes or snorkels, but ASW systems come in Chapter 7. This kind of difficulty cannot be avoided. Certainly the worst problem appeared to be that most chapters deal with a wide range of wavelengths, and it was often hard to decide which was best for a particular topic. Suppose we are interested in NVGs (night-vision goggles). I put them

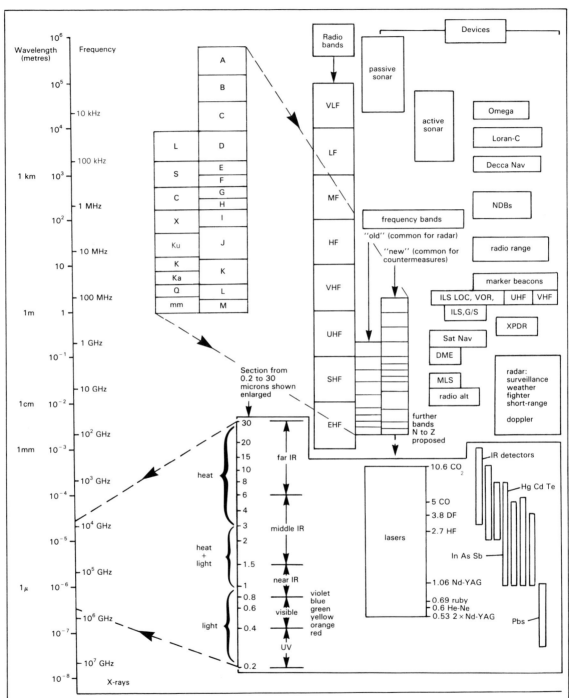

This diagram shows the entire usable EM (electromagnetic) spectrum. Wavelength is shown in metres, and in other units ranging from kilometres to Ångströms. Corresponding frequencies are shown ranging from Hertz (cycles per second) through kilohertz and megahertz to gigahertz. The part of the spectrum ranging from far-IR (far infra-red) to UV (ultraviolet) is shown enlarged.

in Chapter 7 TACTICAL DEVICES, but they could be used by a civilian pilot. They could equally well come under NAVIGATION (they enable you to map-read on a clear night), or RECON-NAISSANCE SYSTEMS (you can see the ground, ditto) or DISPLAYS. Frequently I felt like restructuring the whole book and having a big chapter on infra-red, another on lasers and electro-optics, and so on.

It was obvious from the start that it would be impossible to include everything. I believe most interest centres on things that go into manned aircraft. Accordingly I have left out numerous very worthwhile topics, among them ground stations and air-traffic control (though of course I have included the airborne elements), runway visibility measurement, test equipment, telemetry, simulators, training devices, missile and space guidance, computer-aided design and manufacture, modelling techniques.... There's still quite enough left to fill a book.

Why avionics?

The first chapter, 'Electronics', plunges straight into an inevitably very technical subject, and might prove heavy going for many readers, so I am grateful to the publisher for suggesting that it ought to be preceded by an addition to the introduction explaining why all today's avionics are needed. I certainly do not wish to make anyone give up and put the book down as being too difficult and I hope that this will ease the reader into the subject more gently.

I am not sure if it helps to suggest that, to the modern aircraft, avionics are like the eyes, ears, nose, taste buds, tactile nerve endings and voice (for example) are to a human being. This may be misleading, because the Tiger Moth with no avionics is not exactly deaf, dumb and blind; but it is severely restricted in where it can go and the weather it can fly in. In any case, most avionic systems do not have directly comparable systems in the human body (though — and please don't give up and put the book down — our bodies do have something even more complex than a MIL-STD-1553B data bus, but working in almost exactly the same way, for example in feeding billions of bits of pictorial information every second from our eyes to our brains).

As explained in Chapter 2, the first electronic system to be taken aloft in an aircraft was radio. It is so obviously useful to be able to talk to people on the ground, such as an air traffic controller, that I am sure it will not be long before every aircraft capable of sustained flight, which includes microlights, will have two-way radio. There is no real problem with the required electric power, antennas or the size or weight of the radio. In the 1960s I was shown a very normal looking domestic radio receiver and was then shown that the whole set was in one of the tuning knobs; the rest was an empty dummy! Millions of enthusiasts use airband transceivers weighing about 1lb and not much bigger than a pack of cards, and these are increasingly being used in ultralights and other simple aircraft. But warplanes need much cleverer, longer-ranged radios, whose messages remain absolutely secure against eavesdropping by clever enemies.

The next chapter deals with navigation. Like most pilots, the author knows what it's like to be well and truly lost in the sky (though he appreciates the comment of the SR-71A pilot who said 'You've never been really lost until you're lost at Mach 3!'). Even at 150 knots your face comes out in prickly perspiration as you worry about time, fuel state and possible consequences. You can't stop and ask the way, but modern avionics — again often not much bigger than a pack of cards — can make all the difference. When I was an RAF pilot at the end of World War 2 we had to learn 'nav' the hard way, with plotting charts, pencils and rulers, protractors and laborious triangles of velocities. I sometimes wonder if — anywhere in the world — all this is still done. Over the years navaids have got ever smaller, more versatile and more useful, and today it is hard to imagine any serious private owner (by which I mean one who uses his aircraft in order to go somewhere) failing to have what is often called a 'complete suite'. Thanks to microelectronics these suites, which fit into the instrument panel and thus give rise to the term 'a well-panelled aircraft', have become not only smaller but also much, much cheaper. In the 1950s only rich pilots could afford a radio. Today if you can afford to fly at all you can afford a suite which not only handles your communications and bad-weather navigation but also helps you to land in bad weather.

What today's lightplane — as distinct from light twin or bizjet — does not have is any avionic sensors. Unless we include cameras, which are avionic in the sense that they use electromagnetic radiation at visual, UV or IR wavelengths to record images on film, the first avionic sensors to be installed in aircraft were radars. Over the past half century radars have revolutionized aviation. Today aircraft are flying with many contrasting kinds of radar, working in several totally different ways and doing many contrasting tasks. Some radars provide a picture of clouds, rain, storms, turbulence and dangerous windshear ahead. Some guide aircraft at high speed along the undulations of the Earth's surface. Some detect and lock-on to hostile aircraft, or 'illuminate' such aircraft for radar-homing missiles. Some watch everything that moves (or not) in a million cubic miles of sky. Some make marvellous pictures of the Earth's surface, and whatever is on it, perhaps 80 or 100 miles away. But these radars are not for lightplanes!

Other sensors, often doing generally similar things, work by TV, or 'low-light TV', or IR (infra-red) or at laser wavelengths, which can be IR or can be in the visual optical waveband we call light. Many of these sensors are used in military reconnaissance systems. Since to every action there is an equal and opposite reaction, many sensors are designed to detect avionic systems belonging to an enemy, and to interfere with them in some way. We can jam them to stop them working or, if we are cleverer, we can interfere with their output so that the information the enemy receives is not reliable. All these activities are grouped under the general heading of EW (electronic warfare), which is one of the more exciting and varied branches of avionics, even if its objective is to be unhelpful (most avionics are 100% helpful).

Around 1914 Geoffrey de Havilland took off in a B.E. in thick fog. It did not occur to him that this was suicidal; it was an experiment to investigate visibility at various heights, but as soon as he was airborne he realized the implications, and most of the next half hour was stark terror. He soon got 'on top' and enjoyed the serene cloudscapes and warm sunshine, but the terror remained, because he knew he could not remain there. He was very lucky indeed to spot a darkish patch which proved to be a kind of vertical tunnel through the cloud, through which he could see the ground, far below (on which he soon force-landed). Today a small package removes all the fear, though you usually have to go to a runway equipped with an ILS (instrument landing system). Avionics has made bad-weather flying safe and indeed routine. Indeed, some modern combat aircraft can land in essentially blind conditions on airfields where there are no aids whatsoever; the aircraft's own avionics do everything. This is only to be expected from aircraft which can fly blind within a few feet of the Earth's surface at close to the speed of sound!

In modern lightplanes the avionics usually comprise a quite small 'nav/com' system which in a few minutes, with the aid of a screwdriver, could be removed. Not so today's fighter or jetliner, where literally hundreds of 'black boxes' are linked together by a data bus which, as I said earlier, somewhat resembles the human nervous system. What is a 'bus'? Most of it looks quite simple: just a pair of fine insulated wires twisted together. What is less obvious is that the total system is so complex that it needs thousand-page manuals to describe it. After all, a pair of railway lines kept 4 ft $8\frac{1}{2}$ in apart is not complicated, but the control system for a national rail network is. And to pass many millions of 'bits' of information along a bus network so that (1) everything gets to the right place (and only the right place) at the right time, and (2) important things take priority over others, and (3) the data are not degraded even if parts of the bus are damaged (for example, a bare wire could touch the airframe), is a real challenge. The bus simply has to work; in many aircraft that's how the signals get from the pilot's flight controls to the aircraft control surfaces. And, as avionics is a 'leading edge' technology, thrusting ahead with fantastic speed to get smaller, more reliable and cheaper, tip-to-tip digital buses are bound to be taken for granted on simple lightplanes well before year 2000.

Nobody can see any limit to what avionics can do. Unfortunately, the technology of book production cannot rival that of avionics. If this book has a new edition in year 2000 it will not be a tiny 'microbook' but probably twice as big as the one you are holding today.

Bill Gunston
Haslemere, Surrey

1
ELECTRONICS

Avionics is the handy term for aviation electronics. And that is about as far as we can go in this book with any kind of assurance. Perhaps we dare suggest that electronics is the science (or art) of putting electrons to use in the service of humans. But what is an electron?

There are plenty of slick definitions. In *Jane's Aerospace Dictionary* this author offers 'Subatomic particle that possesses smallest negative charge, and which is so-called fundamental particle assumed to be building block of the Universe; mass at rest 9.107 $\times$ 10^{-28} g, negative charge 1.63×10^{-19} C.' Apart from the fact that I do not believe we can be so certain about either the rest mass or the charge, this still sidesteps the basic problem of what the electron actually is. Engineers think in pictures, but so far nobody can picture the electron. The childish description is that electrons are the things that orbit round the nucleus of an atom. The nucleus contains at least one proton, and so has a positive charge. A normal or electrically neutral atom has zero overall charge, so if its nucleus contains, say, 16 protons, then it must have 16 electrons around it to cancel out the 16 positive charges.

Fine, but whereas when I was a boy physicists were quite happy to think of the electrons as little planets — let's say, spheres of vanishingly small size — orbiting round the nucleus like a miniature Solar System, today we know better. The electrons are arranged in 'shells' at different radii from the nucleus. If there are 16 of them, there are 2 in the closest shell, 8 in the next, and 6 (of a maximum of 18) in the next, and so on. The trouble is, at any instant in time each electron is everywhere in the shell; there are ways in which you can prove it has to be everywhere all at once. Just to make things harder, electrons are associated with waves, called electromagnetic (EM) waves. It is possible to add energy to an electron and make it jump up to the next shell, a higher-energy state. When it 'falls' back to its original shell it emits a small parcel, or quantum, of EM energy, called a photon.

Electronics is partly concerned with beams of electrons rushing through air or a vacuum, partly with electrons rushing through a conductor, partly with electrons rushing (or crawling) through a semiconductor, and very much with EM radiation. A beam of electrons travelling through space is not difficult to understand, at least in broad-brush theory. The very first electronic devices were what the British call thermionic valves (or just 'valves') and the Americans call vacuum tubes. In these a heated cathode such as a metal wire emits a stream of electrons which are attracted towards a second electrode called the anode. As each electron has a negative charge it is attracted to the anode if the latter is strongly positive with respect to the cathode. In between the electrodes the electrons are free. They travel through space, the tube being evacuated free of air, at a speed which depends on the potential gradient between the two electrodes, and while they are forming this free beam they can be manipulated in various ways. A CRT (cathode-ray tube) has an electron gun at one end which projects a beam of electrons on to a glass screen coated with a phosphor. As each electron hits an atom of phosphor it stimulates the emission of a photon of visible light. Arrangements of magnets are used to focus the electron beam on the screen, while other magnets can be fed with variable voltages to deflect the beam in any way we wish. By applying a perfectly regular alternating current to one set of deflecting plates or coils the tiny spot of light where the beam hits the screen can be converted into a line. If we then apply another set of varying voltages to a second set of plates or coils at right-angles to the first we can make the spot move across the whole face of the screen in a saw-tooth pattern, filling the

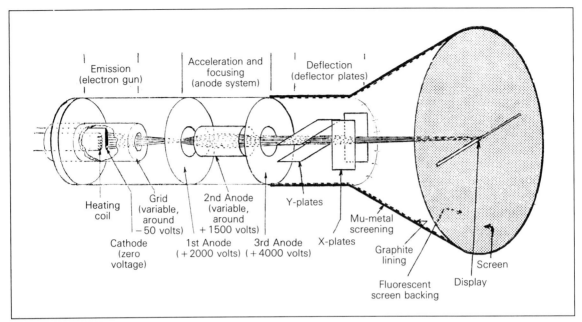

Above *Schematic diagram of a simple electrostatic CRT.* (Oxford Air Training School)

Right *An electric current is the name given to a flow of negatively charged electrons through a conductor, such as a wire. Whenever such a current flows it creates a magnetic field (note direction). If we keep varying the current, we send out electromagnetic waves. We call this broadcasting.* (Hughes Aircraft)

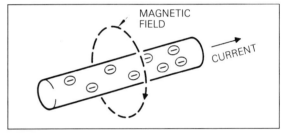

screen with bright parallel lines.

Early TV receivers used a CRT in which the parallel lines were all too visible, but today the CRTs used in avionics can give the appearance of a perfectly uniform overall colour, or a picture, or anything else we wish. The CRT is the commonest form of display, as described in Chapter 13. Some are no larger than a cigarette, and can be mounted on a pilot's helmet to give a display on a transparent screen in front of the pilot's eye(s). And there are many other ways in which electrons can be manipulated as they pour in a flood through space.

If electrons move through a conductor, such as a metal wire, we call this an electric current. As the electrons convey negative charges we say the current flows in the opposite direction to that taken by the electrons (which, as we have seen, always move from the negative to the positive terminal). If we connect up an electric circuit everything seems to happen at the speed of light, because the effect is

noticed immediately. The actual 'speed' of the current is less simple to determine. If we pass a tiny current, such as 1 microampere, through a length of railway line the electrons will mostly be staying with their original atoms. Every now and then one will jump to an adjacent atom, to replace another.

When I was a boy there were electrons rigidly bound to atoms, in what are called insulators, and electrons which readily hop from one atom to the next, in metals and other conductors. But over the past forty years a totally different kind of electron flow has formed the starting point for millions of devices and billions of electronic circuits all over the world. This revolution, without which avionics would be much, much less attractive, is based on the semiconductor. This now giant class of materials is the basis of solid-state electronics.

As the name suggests, the resistivity of a semiconductor lies somewhere between that of an insulator and that of a conductor. At room temperature (it varies with temperature) it is likely to be between 10^{-2} and 10^9 ohm-cm. Obviously, the resistivity (current-carrying ability) of a material depends on how many charge-carriers there are in unit volume of the material. Physicists imagine two kinds of charge-carrier migrating through any mass of semiconductor: our friends the electrons, which convey unit negative charges, and carriers of units of positive charge which are simply called 'holes'. Semiconductors are essentially crystalline solids (one or two are liquids). Silicon, for example, comprises countless atoms of silicon all arranged in their exact positions within a 3-D lattice; germanium likewise comprises rigidly arranged atoms of germanium. Usually the objective is to create perfect crystals, without the dislocations or 'defects' caused by having even single atoms out of place.

If we apply an electric field across a perfect crystal of silicon, the four 'valence electrons' which are available in the outer shell of each atom almost all remain bonded to their own atoms, and so no current flows; thus, pure silicon is an insulator. The trick is to 'dope' the silicon with an 'impurity', for example by heating it almost white-hot to about 1,100°C in an atmosphere rich in the impurity, whose atoms then diffuse into the crystal. If we choose phosphorus (valency 5), when each atom finds an Si atom only four of the impurity electrons can link with the four Si electrons. The fifth, unable to find a partner, wanders off and is free to carry a negative charge through the lattice when any electric field is applied. Alternatively, if we dope the silicon with boron (valency 3), the impurity atoms will each link with three of an Si atom's electrons, leaving the fourth with nothing to link with. The result is a 'hole' which again can migrate through the lattice, but this time carrying a positive charge. Thus we can create n-type or p-type semiconductor, depending on whether the free charge-carriers are negative electrons or positive holes. We can accurately control the resistivity by varying the concentration of the doped impurity.

This may all sound rather academic, but it is the basis of the revolution that has swept electronics (and incidentally resulted in an industrial situation where if you make a billion circuits a week you may still go to the wall because your output is not enough for the lowest unit price). We will return to the semiconductor later, but we can note that the first device to use this technology was an n-p-n junction transistor, created in 1948. Of course, the 1948

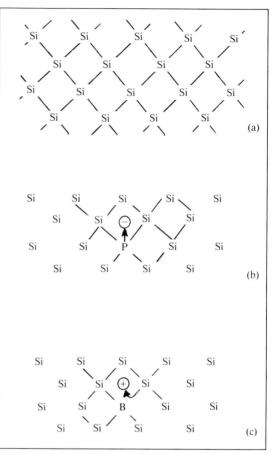

Almost all avionics involves semiconductors, such as a perfect crystal of silicon (a). If we replace some of the atoms by phosphorus (valency 5), free electrons will be available to carry negative charges through the 'n-type' material (b). If we replace some of the atoms by boron (valency 3), free 'holes' will be available to carry positive charges through 'p-type' material (c).

device was cumbersome and tricky, like the 1903 Wright Flyer, but some electronic engineers could see a long way beyond it.

Like the old 'tube' or 'valve', the main function of the transistor is to amplify weak currents. This is the basis of radio, the oldest type of avionics as described in the next chapter. Radio was historically preceded by the telegraph, in which, by translating messages from everyday language into a binary 'on/off' code (Samuel Morse's), information can be sent along electrically conductive wires. What followed needed a much bigger mental leap. Such workers as Tesla and Hertz investigated mysterious electric waves that could travel without wires; today the frequency of such waves, or of anything else, is measured in Hertz (Hz). Thus, the international distress frequency of 121.5 MHz means 121.5 million cycles per second. In the 19th Century workers investigated these waves, which are today called EM waves, as explained earlier. Gradually in this century we have filled in the gaps in an overall spectrum of EM waves of breathtaking compass. These waves are the most widespread and fundamental things in the Universe. Like the electron itself, we have only the most rudimentary knowledge of them. It is easy to say that EM radiation comprises alternating electric and magnetic fields which, though in phase, are at right angles to each other and to the direction of propagation. What we cannot comprehend is how they can travel at the speed of light not only through the atmosphere of our planet but also through the vacuum of space. Anyone want a Nobel Prize?

Though we find great difficulty in picturing EM radiation, we can at least be sure that the electrical field E and magnetic field H are always exactly at 90° to each other. But their actual directions can vary; in many modern radars the radiation is

We cannot draw an EM wave. Seen from the side it is often drawn as a sine wave (there are lots in Chapter 4). This sketch emphasizes that the electric field (E) is always at exactly 90° to the magnetic field (H), and the direction of travel is at 90° to both. (Hughes Aircraft)

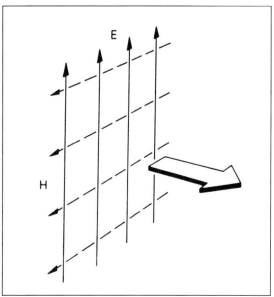

designed to rotate, rather like a propeller screwing itself along. When the electric field is vertical (pointing either up or down) we say the radiation at that point is vertically polarized. If the waves happen to encounter a receiver antenna in the form of a vertical dipole, that antenna can extract maximum energy from the vertically polarized radiation. If the radiation is rotated through an angle, θ, the antenna can extract only the energy multiplied by Cos θ; thus, if the plane of polarization is rotated through 60° the input to the antenna is halved. If the electric field meets the antenna at 90° the antenna cannot extract any energy and might as well not be there. This is important in the antennas of European fighter radars (Chapter 5).

Prehistoric people were surrounded by EM radiation. Life-giving light and heat from the Sun was always evident, but our ancestors could hardly have known that they are the same thing, differing only in wavelength. Another name for heat is infra-red (IR), because its band of wavelengths are longer than the red end of the spectrum of visible light. At the other end of the visible spectrum is ultraviolet (UV), though this is nothing like as important as IR in avionics. Well over a century ago James Clerk Maxwell showed that light and radio waves are identical apart from wavelength, and today we can play with EM wavelengths ranging from very short gamma rays, down to about 10^{-14} m at one end, up to 10^5 m (about 60 miles) at the other; the complete spectrum appears on p.8. Avionics cannot handle gamma or X-rays, for obvious reasons, and confines itself to devices operating at wavelengths from about 3×10^{-7} m (UV lasers) up to VLF radio and the Omega navaid at 3×10^4 m (19 miles).

EM radiation everywhere travels at, or very close to, the speed of light — in other words at just under 3×10^8 m/s (the exact figure in a vacuum is 2.997925). It therefore follows that for each wavelength we can assign an exact frequency. Pilots do not tune in to a wavelength but to a frequency, while radar engineers have usually found wavelength the more useful parameter to work with. Whichever you want, the nearness of 2.997925 to 3 makes the conversion simple. For example we can say we are emitting or receiving on 100 MHz or 3 m, because they are two ways of describing the same waves.

Early radio sets operated in what we now call the HF (high frequency) band at wavelengths of 50–100 m. It so happened that this was the kind of radiation that could be generated and received at the time. To the delight of Marconi and other pioneers it was found that such radiation can be received after travelling round to the other side of the Earth. Research showed that this is because it can be repeatedly reflected between the Earth and a layer of charged (ionized) particles surrounding the planet at heights from 55 to 90 miles. First called the Kennelly-Heaviside layer, it is today the E-region of the ionosphere.

Successive inventions and discoveries enabled workers to use other parts of the EM spectrum. By the start of World War 2 some radios were being developed in the VHF region, and it was found that at these shorter wavelengths the ionized layers above the Earth let the radiation pass straight through. Accordingly, EM radiation at shorter wavelengths, for communications, radar or any other purpose, is normally assumed to be like light and to travel in straight lines. Thus, an infantryman with a radio in a trench or foxhole might find his useful radius of communication was measured in inches. From 30,000ft the figure is about 240 miles. But at much shorter wavelengths still, other problems arise. Long before World War 1 it was known that searchlights don't do well in fog or with 8/8ths low cloud. The invention of the laser, enabling attention to be focussed on precise individual frequencies, threw emphasis on the fact that our atmosphere is highly transparent to some wavelengths (we say it has 'windows') and virtually opaque to others. In the same way, once aircraft designers began encasing radar* and other antennas inside streamlined radomes and flush-fitting covers it became essential to use materials as transparent as possible to the radiation used. Put a sheet of clean glass in front of a fire and you will see, or rather feel, that, though it transmits the light, it cuts out almost all the IR. Often IR seekers are inside domes or fairings that look opaque.

Britain pioneered airborne radar, as narrated in this author's book *Night Fighters*, published by PSL in 1976. Radar is further explained in Chapter 4 of this book, which makes the point that in 1939 the only radars in existence operated at wavelengths of 1 m or more, anything under 10 m being extreme-

ly difficult to generate. There was a desperate need for very much shorter wavelengths, in the range (say) 1 to 10 cm. This 'centimetric' EM radiation is called microwaves. Today these are so important it is hard to recall that fifty years ago they were a rare laboratory curiosity, created only by complex apparatus with output power measured in milliwatts. What was wanted was kilowatts, or one million times more power, but this was impossible. High-power microwave radiation made everything red-hot (one lab rig melted) and was dissipated uselessly into the atmosphere. Ordinary valves could not be used because of a mixture of their dimensions (and hence transit-time effects), electrode inductance and capacitance, and other fundamental barriers. All sorts of other tubes were studied, as well as the promising klystron, a device with features resembling the valve and the CRT, as well as having either one or two cavity resonators. The idea of the klystron was that the original beam of electrons from the cathode should be acted on by standing (motionless) waves in the cavity so that they emerged in tight bunches, received at a catcher and returned by coaxial cable to the cathode. By adjusting the voltages, cavity dimensions and other factors, it was expected to make the klystron oscillate or amplify at previously unknown frequencies, giving powerful microwave output.

Today klystrons are important, but in the late 1930s they were an imperfect art. So in the first weeks of World War 2 the British workers, mainly physicists, sought other sources of high-power microwaves. For a while all results were negative. One of the least-successful teams was J.T. Randall and A.H. Boot, at the University of Birmingham, who were seeing what could be done with modified Barkhausen tubes and with plasma oscillations in mercury vapour. Plasma was almost a non-starter, and the Barkhausen would not even work as an oscillator to test other tubes of the same kind. So Randall and Boot decided to make a little magnetron to use as a test oscillator. They talked far into the night about the magnetron as a possible high-power generator in its own right, conscious of the fact that dozens or hundreds had been made since World War 1 without high-power success.

A magnetron is a resonant cavity, like a penny whistle. It has an anode in the middle, a surrounding cathode, a high-voltage electric field and a powerful magnetic field. The two fields result in a cloud of electrons being 'blown' round and round

---

* This was originally an acronym, from 'radio detection and ranging.' Unfortunately numerous important authorities say the d stood for 'direction'!

like a small whirlwind of fierce intensity. Just as in a whistle — a better analogy here is a siren — the 'whirlwind' can be made to give a steady 'note'; instead of sound, out comes EM energy in the form of microwaves. But nobody had been able to get any power. Randall and Boot looked at the way resonant cavities were used in earlier magnetrons, and in the rival klystron which had always been one of the apparent best bets. They happened to have the right blend of theoretical, practical and industrial experience to know what needed to be done and how it could be done. One afternoon in November 1939 Randall and Boot sat down and wrote out the whole story, ending with a detailed specification for a radically new kind of magnetron. There followed three frantic months of turning those vital sheets of paper into hardware. The work was different from any seen before in radar: it involved very accurate machining of a massive block of copper, coupling up water pipes to keep it cool, and arranging round it a very powerful electromagnet.

It was all put together and switched on on 21 February 1940. The result surpassed Randall's and Boot's wildest dreams. The fact that it worked was obvious. Indeed, if one brought one's hand near the output lead, that hand soon became uncomfortably hot! As power was increased, the output began to be seen and heard as a sizzling violet arc dissipated into the air of the lab. A nearby garage supplied a succession of 6 volt bulbs as each in turn was burned out, and soon the output was blazing forth from large neon floodlights. This was obviously not milliwatts but hundreds of watts. On the second day a crude measuring device, hastily rigged up for a totally new task, measured about 450 W at a wavelength of 98 cm; three months later a properly designed pre-production magnetron, engineered largely under C.C. Paterson at the GEC Hirst Research Labs at Wembley, was delivering 50 kW at 9.1 cm! It was a breakthrough that ranks alongside man's greatest technical accomplishments. It had a profound effect on the war and on man's subsequent ability to navigate the skies and oceans.

Today the magnetron is just one source of microwaves. Others include the klystron, as described, and the travelling-wave tube (TWT). The TWT is like a klystron in that a stream of electrons is aimed in a straight line and made to bunch by interaction with an electric field, or 'travelling

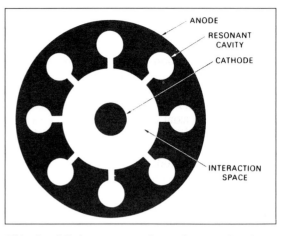

This simplified magnetron shows the central cathode, surrounded by a space in which an electron cloud with swirling spokes revolves at high speed. An aperture must be cut in the rim to bleed out the microwave energy.

wave'. In the original (1942) helix TWT the wave travels preferentially along a metal helix surrounding the electron beam. If the helix has a pitch of 1:13 then clearly the wave progresses along the tube at 1/13th the speed of light, which is about the same as that of an electron beam accelerated by a potential of 1.5 kV. The tube is so designed that the electrons travel faster than the wave. The latter's electric field slows the electrons, whose reduced kinetic energy therefore appears as increased energy conveyed by the field of the wave. From 1960 workers developed the slow-wave, or coupled-activity, TWT. This replaces the metal helix by a succession of up to twenty cavities arranged so that adjacent pairs are each coupled by an interconnecting hole through which the wave can pass, rather like a succession of klystrons.

These generators of high-power microwaves are discussed further in Chapter 5. They have made possible the majority of modern airborne radars, as well as many kinds of communication system. At most RFs (radio frequencies) it is possible to convey signals and other energy in the same way that we convey DC (direct current), by letting it travel along a conductor (wire) surrounded by an insulator. At the much higher frequencies of microwaves it is not only possible but essential to convey the energy by a waveguide which operates in the reverse sense, the microwaves travelling along a central insulator (usually air) surrounded by the conductor.

Waveguides can be of rectangular or (rarely) other cross-sectional shapes, and they usually look like squarish pipes or strips. They are made with extremely high precision, and the waves travel along them in a way chosen from many possibilities. Thus TE_{01} is a mode of propagation in which there is a TE (transverse electric) wave, the magnetic wave being aligned with the axial direction of the waveguide, and a simple single circular-section cylindrical surface (in the case of a circular tube waveguide). TM_{12} is a more complex mode in which all the transverse waves are magnetic (TM), the electric waves being in the pure axial direction, and there is one circular nodal surface and two radial nodal surfaces which separate the propagation into eight segments. In early airborne radars a single waveguide was arranged to feed on to a dish reflector producing the required almost parallel beam. Today there may be numerous waveguides with apertures cut in their sides to form a planar-array antenna or an electronically steered (mechanically fixed) antenna, as described later.

Since 1940 avionics has increasingly made use of ever-shorter wavelengths, moving into the field of opto-electronics, which is electronics at or near optical wavelengths. A remarkable feature of this process is how long it has taken. AEG in Germany produced the first Spanner I IR (infra-red) detector in 1939, and within six months it was flying on a Do 17Z-10 night fighter. This was an active device, emitting IR radiation and looking for returns from an aerial target. In 1940–41 Spanner II, III and IV were produced. These were passive; they emitted nothing, but searched for hot targets. After the war various teams pioneered IR homing for AAMs (air-to-air missiles), but it was not until 1960 — a gap of twenty years from Spanner — that IR sensors reappeared on fighters, the F-102 and F-4B. Even today these highly desirable passive sensors are absent from almost all modern fighters, notably excepting the MiG-29 and Su-27.

To the author this is almost unbelievable. It has been obvious for fifty years that an aircraft sending out radar signals, of whatever kind, is doing its best to broadcast its presence and location. This is especially the case if it is armed with SARH (semi-active radar homing) AAMs, because then, as elaborated in Chapter 5, it has to aim its give-away emissions directly at the enemy. In contrast, IR can be passive (non-emitting), and one might have expected the colossal tactical advantage of this fact to have made IR at least as important and widespread as radar in all kinds of combat aircraft. As it is, they are very seldom seen except as the FLIR (forward-looking infra-red) for use against surface targets, and the IRLS (IR linescan) for giving a reconnaissance picture of surface targets.

How do IR devices work? An active one is virtually a radar, but working at much shorter

A typical TWT, probably the most important source of microwaves and still unbeatable for broadband applications. Some have power gains exceeding 10 million (70 dB). Electron gun at left. (Ferranti)

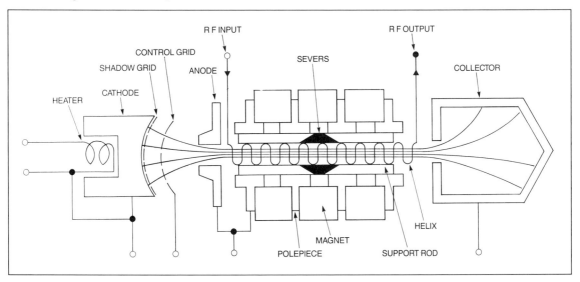

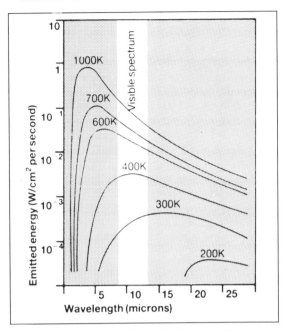

As an object gets hotter its radiation not only increases in intensity but it also extends to shorter wavelengths. The curve of 300K is what we might call room temperature, while 1,000K is a bright-red heat.

wavelength; except in IRCM (Chapter 9) such things are hardly ever encountered. Passive (non-emitting) IR devices rely upon the fact that, even on the darkest night or in the coldest places on Earth, every atom of every object, including clouds and rain, is continuously sending out EM radiation at an IR wavelength which broadcasts its exact temperature. We tend to think of IR emitters as being confined to hot jetpipes, cigarette ends, and so forth. We overlook the snow background beyond the jetpipe, or the fingers holding the cigarette. Part of the trouble is that we seldom think in terms of absolute temperature, where 0°K (minus 273.16°C) means total absence of thermal (gross molecular) motion. Once we relate to the absolute scale we can see the value of IR sensors. An iceberg surface at once becomes something between 230K and 280K. Any normal Earth scene is almost certain to contain a spread of temperatures, each of which will fall on a different point on the diagram of spectral emittance. Thus, even on a monochrome IR display, which looks like a black/white TV picture, we shall get sufficient contrast to learn not only what is present but exactly how hot it is.

This is more useful than most radar pictures, which usually only tell us the strength of the echoes from the target — a very variable and uncertain thing. In contrast, an IR picture can tell us such things as which aircraft in a line-up on the ramp has just landed, with wings containing fuel at the temperature of the stratosphere, which aircraft has one or more engines running, and even where a recently departed aircraft was parked. A truck or even a single soldier in a forest can stand out like a sore thumb, and traditional camouflage paint or nets are useless (a very few modern ones are cleverer). Usually the IR sensor depicts hot things as white and colder things as shades of grey or black, but the polarity can be reversed to give (for example) a black ship on a whitish ocean.

The typical IR sensor is packaged inside the aircraft or in a streamlined pod, from where it can see out in the direction(s) of interest through a window. This is usually optically flat, but hardly ever of glass (remember the way glass cut out the fire's heat?) For transmission over the most important range of IR wavelengths nothing can equal CaF (calcium fluoride). Trouble is, we have to use windows that can stand up to hail and birdstrikes at Mach 0.9, which makes life harder. No point in having thin CaF and then putting a slab of armour-glass in front of it!

Behind the window there is almost always an 'optical' system — I put the word in quotes because most dictionaries define it as relating to the wavelengths of visible light — which magnifies the incoming radiation and focusses it on the detector. One of the commonest arrangements is the Cassegrain telescope, but there are many variations. Just as the astronomer's telescope focusses faint starlight on a film, so do the IR 'optics' concentrate faint incoming radiation on the detector.

The detector can function in various ways, but virtually all those in modern avionics are of the photoconductive type. We have already met semiconductors, and also the fact that electrons can be either bound into the shell of an atom or lifted by the impact of an energetic wave or particle up to a higher-energy level at which they can move to an adjacent atom: in other words they can carry a current. Most semiconductors therefore become more conductive when they are irradiated with EM radiation. Photons, packets of EM radiation, hit the semiconductor atoms and, transferring energy in a manner rather like an impact of billiard balls, knock an electron up to the conduction band, causing a current to flow. There is a difference of at least a million to one between the photoconductive performance of one semiconductor material and another, and each material shows a spectral response curve which starts at a lower level of wavelength (below which it does not work), climbs to a peak and then falls again to become useless at some longer wavelength. To design an IR device we thus have to consider: the band of wavelengths emitted by the targets, and the likely wavelength of peak intensity; the way these wavelengths are transmitted or absorbed by the atmosphere; and the character of the likely background radiation, because we want to detect where the contrast is greatest.

We also have to achieve the highest possible S/N (signal to noise) ratio. Anyone interested in amateur radio will know that most electronic devices suffer from some kind of noise, or unwanted signal. Hi-fi systems, and certainly CDs, reduce this to very low levels, but if you switch on some car radios the background noise is all too evident (as explained in the next chapter). Now consider a piece of photodetector sensitive material inside the nose of a FLIR pod doing 700 knots at low level over an Arctic battlefield. The pod nose is likely to be at about 290K, a nice warm temperature and enough to raise plenty of semiconductor electrons to the conduction band. In front the optics focus incoming target IR at maybe 260K, which won't do us much good; our S/N ratio would be negative! The answer, of course, is to refrigerate our detector material, not just to domestic refrigerator level but to as near absolute zero as we can get. The colder the material is, the fewer electrons will be in the conduction band. We aim to reduce the background noise — ie, current in the absence of a target — almost to zero.

Some early IR devices were put inside a dewar (Thermos flask) and cooled by pouring in liquid nitrogen. This was even used in some early AAMs. Unfortunately the LN_2 boils off rapidly, and a FLIR in a P-3C may have to fly a twenty-hour mission. Accordingly most airborne IR devices are cooled by some form of cryogenic (very low temperature) heat engine running on a continuous basis. A few rely on the intense cooling resulting from letting gas under extremely high pressure escape through a fine orifice. Some of these systems use dry nitrogen, but British Aerospace is a leader in the production of Hippags (high-pressure pure-air

generators). These are common in missiles, but for aircraft IR systems the closed-cycle machine is more usual because it can run for as long as electric power is supplied. These are small but highly rated pumps, and almost all run on the Stirling cycle because of its greater efficiency.

Clearly, there is little point in using a super detector if its performance peaks somewhere where the atmosphere is opaque to the radiation! Against high-temperature targets silicon performs brilliantly, even without being cooled below ambient temperature (say, 300K), but a lot of the short-wavelength IR can't get through to be detected. By short we mean in the region of 1 micron, one-millionth of a metre, which is abbreviated 1μ. In any case, typical targets may be at around ambient temperature, and so their IR radiation peaks at a wavelength of about 10 microns. By great good fortune, this is right in the middle of the best IR 'window' in our atmosphere, which extends from around 8-13 microns. Accordingly, almost all today's FLIRs and other IR devices operate in this range of wavelengths, where the obvious detector material to use is CMT (cadmium mercury telluride, HgCdTe). It will be seen that it is normally cooled to about 77K (minus 196°C) because this is the boiling temperature of nitrogen at sea level, and cold enough to get a good S/N ratio.

Further design choices are possible in the overall sensor configuration. Increasingly the focal-plane array is becoming the norm. Even this can be arranged in many ways, but one choice is to use gimballed (pivoted) optics to focus the incoming radiation on each detector in turn in a large group. This group, the array (which of course has to be in the focal plane of the optics), may be made up of dozens, hundreds or thousands of individual detectors, each comprising a small refrigerated chip. Chips are faced with a thin film of detector material, such as CMT, and this can be deposited on a structural substrate by MBE (molecular-beam epitaxy), MOCVD (metal/organic chemical vapour deposition), AMP (atomic materialization process) or other technique. The optics are gimballed in much the same way as the antenna of a radar (Chapter 4). The FOV (field of view) is the total solid angle, often expressed in terms of azimuth (horizontal plane) and elevation, of the sensor optics themselves; in other words, what you can see at any one moment. FOR (field of regard) is the total solid angle of the sensor, in other words it is

IR Detector Response

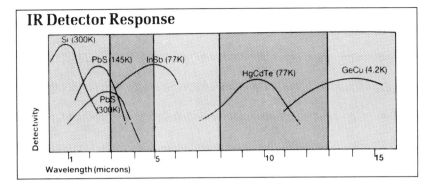

Some IR detectors work well at room temperature (300K), but the most useful is HgCdTe at 77K, because this covers the big atmospheric 'window' shown as a band at 8–13 microns (μ).

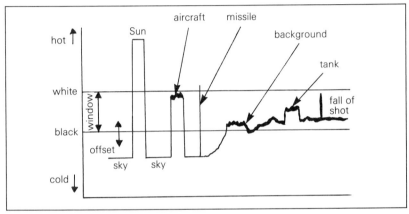

In IR imaging the sensor must be designed with a particular thermal window (gain) which determines the range of temperatures displayed, and an offset which dictates the temperature that will appear as black in the display.

FOV plus the sensor's own angular limits of left/right slewing and up/down tilting. Usually the sensor head is gyrostabilized, for example so that it can remain looking at a target no matter (within reason) how the aircraft on which it is mounted manoeuvres as it approaches the target. In addition, the sighting head has to be controllable, either automatically by a digitally controlled lock-on system or manually by a member of the crew using a pistol grip.

Depending on the detector array pattern the target is scanned at high speed, automatically, in one or two dimensions. The result is a rapidly varying output current or voltage containing all the acquired information about the target. Only since 1980 have sensors been clever enough to detect point targets. These are targets so small or distant that they subtend an angle smaller than one pixel (picture element) or detector element. The latest devices can not only 'see' and lock-on to such tiny targets, but they can also ensure they are detected correctly by each element in succession, which in a few seconds means a million or more correctly located detections. Moreover, some modern IR sen-

sors can 'see' at two different wavelengths, to provide so-called two-colour synergism for unfailing target discrimination. Two-colour sensors make life much harder for the designer of camouflage. However the sensor head works, its output is always fed to a digital processor. Often there is a separate computer for on-line tracking (gimbal) control. The processed data may be fed to an array of LEDs (Chapter 13) to create a visible picture, or it may be fed in to modulate a traditional raster (line-by-line) scan to build a monochrome TV picture. In combat aircraft the sensor is also required to output accurate boresight (pointing) information for a weapon-aiming system. One example of this is in aiming helicopter gun-turrets; another is in cueing the seeker heads of AAMs.

As the EM spectrum shows, IR is just one part of a broader waveband called EO (electro-optics). This extends from far or extreme IR down through ever-shorter wavelengths to visible light and on to extreme UV. Where visible light is concerned we can use various kinds of image intensifier. Whereas IR devices start at about 1μ (micron) and go on to around 13μ, image intensifiers (the common abbreviation II is misleading, looking like a Roman 2) operate entirely at wavelengths shorter than 1μ and extending into the visible region. They rely on the fact that even on the darkest night it is not strictly dark. Many millions of photons enter our eyes each

second, but nothing like at the rate needed for our brains to form a clear picture. Thus, to us the scene looks black.

The image intensifier simply multiplies the photon rate. The incoming photons fall on a screen which is the exact opposite of that in a CRT or TV: when light photons fall on it, it emits electrons. This screen, the photocathode, is often of GaAs (gallium arsenide). The electrons emitted by its inner face are then multiplied by an electrostatic field and microchannel plate to give a level which, when converted back into visible photons by a phosphor

In the first IR imaging systems the whole field was scanned across a single detector, in the parallel method (a). Later designs used serial scanning, in which a single detector (or an array, the diagram showing four) is scanned line-by-line, demanding scanning speeds up to 160,000 rpm and very wide bandwidths (b). The latest IR sensors tend to use serial/parallel (c).

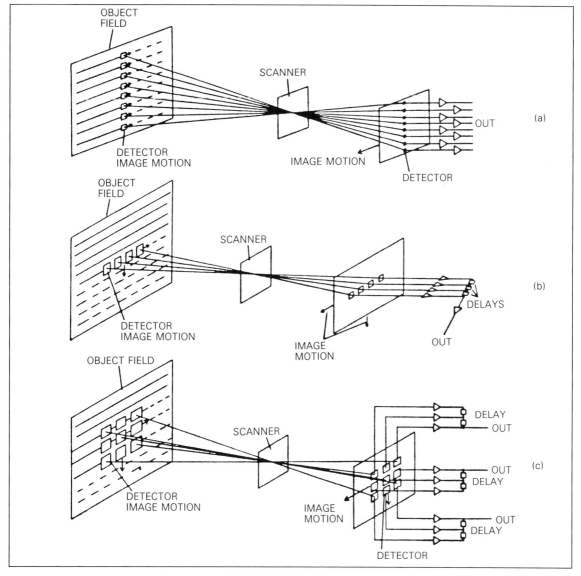

Image Intensifiers

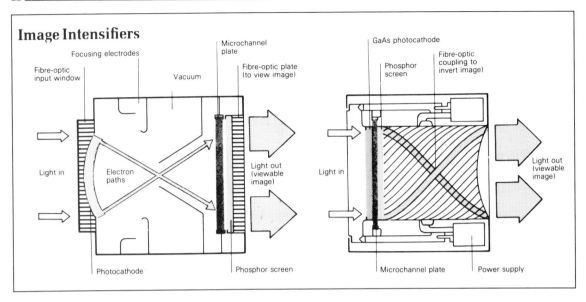

screen, produces a visible picture. Most output screens are coated with a phosphor which emits a blue-green light at about 0.5μ, which is the wavelength at which our night-adapted eyes (functioning mainly via the eye's rods, not the cones) have peak sensitivity. The latest, so-called Gen 3 (third generation), intensifiers operate almost wholly on incoming radiation in the IR region. This is not only because that is a fundamental characteristic of IR but mainly because starlight has far greater intensity in the IR bands than in the visible spectrum.

Intensifiers are used in NVGs (night-vision goggles, Chapter 7) and in many other avionic devices including LLTV (low-light TV) or LLLTV (low light level). These cover a range of packages, the simplest being a vidicon (TV camera tube) whose input is enhanced by an image intensifier, with fibre optics (Chapter 2) to link the two and often to turn the image 'the right way up'. More complicated are the intensified Ebsicons, in which a vacuum-sealed container houses the input/output optics, image intensifier, vidicon, a tailormade SIT (silicon intensified target) responsive to electrons, and the coupling optics and fibres. Future LLTVs will use solid-state silicon-based CCDs (charge-coupled devices) linked to Gen 3 intensifiers. Westinghouse even has things called ISITs (intensified silicon intensified targets).

The only devices that cover the whole EO spectrum are lasers. The name is an acronym: Light

Amplification by Stimulated Emission of Radiation, and Dr Theodore Maiman, a physicist at Hughes, got the first one working in May 1960. That primitive laser was based on a man-made crystal of ruby, aluminium oxide with a small fraction of the Al atoms replaced by Cr (chromium). The crystal was a cylinder with the ends cut precisely perpendicular to the axis. Around it was coiled a very powerful 'pumping source' in the form of a brilliant lamp. The flood of photons from this raised many Cr atoms to their upper-energy state. Before they could decay back to the ground state, emitting a photon, some of these atoms were hit by a second photon, forcing (stimulating) release of a second photon exactly in step with the one that triggered it. This stimulated emission swept along the crystal, triggering off other previously excited atoms, building up a wave with all the photons exactly 'in step' (in phase). At the end the wave was reflected back, surging to and fro at the speed of light and growing in strength almost like an A-bomb going off until it finally burst through one end (a semi-transparent mirror) as a flash of red light at 0.6943μ. This flash was not only of fantastic brilliance but it was coherent: all the wavefronts were in phase, like marching guardsmen. All previous light had been a confused jumble of different frequencies and phases.

Since then lasers have been made in amazing diversity. Some are crystal lasers, though not necessarily of ruby. Some are gas lasers, using for example carbon dioxide or a mixture of helium and neon. Others use liquids, while the smallest are tiny semiconductor lasers called LEDs (light-emitting diodes). The latter are really just FETs (field-effect transistors, described later in this chapter) in which a massive flow of electrons is injected across the junction into the 'holes' in the n-type material, which is usually GaAs or NdYAG, neodymium yttrium aluminium garnet. When each electron combines with a hole a photon is emitted, and the electron input is so great that the photons strike other electron/hole pairs to stimulate fresh in-step photons. The actual diode in such a laser is about the size, in area and thickness, of the smallest letter in this book, cut from the page.

Lasers are used for ranging purposes, in which their unrivalled short wavelength gives fantastic accuracy. They can be used like radar (lidar = light radar) to detect targets, such as wires in the path of a low-flying helicopter, or to 'designate' a target so that it emits scattered or reflected laser light on which a specially compatible missile can home. They can detect atmospheric dust, exactly measure relative velocities, or even the normally invisible CAT (clear-air turbulence), and huge lasers of awesome power are being studied as space weapons.

Today we can generate laser light at any of thousands of exact wavelengths; we can even have AM and FM (see next chapter), various forms of tuning or wavelength agility, phase-polarization and almost anything else you want.

In all these EO devices we can today have incredibly accurate pointing accuracy, instant computer control (if we want the fastest possible change of beam angle we can eliminate mechanical gimbals and use electronic beam steering), special techniques to preserve stealth capability (Chapter 9), and yet achieve an automatic locked-on target-data output bandwidth of about 150 Hz. We (especially the Soviet designers) can put several different kinds of sensor radiation through a common shared optical path whilst avoiding such problems as veiling glare and crosstalk.

One of the newest branches of EO is integrated optics (IO). This is the guiding of light in thin-film waveguides. Thus, it broadly resembles fibre optics (Chapter 2), with the difference that, instead of being conveyed over a distance, the light travels only a very short distance (perhaps 10–50 mm) whilst being split, filtered, modulated or in some other way processed. A typical example of IO is the fast frequency analyser. Suppose we wish to

Above left *A Gen 2 image intensifier receives photons at an FO input window backed by a photocathode which sends electrons to a multichannel plate. Today's Gen 3 uses wafer-type tubes incorporating very sensitive GaAs photocathodes which detect far into the IR region.*

Right *A simplifed IO (integrated optics) fast frequency analyser. Different input frequencies cause the surface acoustic wave to diffract light in different directions.*

measure the signal strength at every frequency from 100 MHz to 1,000 MHz; this would take anyone a long time, but in flight-control systems we may need to do this many times per second. The IO uses a transducer, a device which (for example by using a piezoelectric crystal) converts an electrical signal into mechanical stress. The transducer sends a surface acoustic wave travelling across the surface of a solid, rather like sea waves on a coast. This behaves like a diffraction grating which can diffract (turn) light of a particular frequency through an angle which varies with the frequency of the acoustic (sound) waves, which is the variable that we wish to measure. So we let the light fall on an array of photodiodes, and note which of the latter are excited in the time it takes the acoustic wave to cross the light beam. Thus we get our frequency analysis in a few microseconds. IO can also make extremely fast switches and do many other things, and in the 1990s this technology will become important in avionics.

Having outlined the EO devices, which were mostly non-existent before 1965 but now rival radar in diversity, we can return to the basic subject of microelectronics which is used in almost every modern avionic package, including the EO ones. There are, of course, countless types of microelectronic device and fabrication method, but here it helps to run quickly through the traditional (since 1958) way of making an IC (integrated circuit) or 'silicon chip'. The chief pioneer of this process thirty years back was J.S. Kilby, who catapulted Texas Instruments into the No 1 spot in solid-state device production.

No single worker invented solid-state microelectronics. Indeed we still have not fully realised the vision of G.W.A. Dummer, of the Royal Radar Establishment at Malvern in 1952, who predicted 'electronic equipment in a solid block with no connecting wires. The block may consist of layers of insulating, conducting, rectifying and amplifying materials, the electrical functions being connected by cutting out areas of the layers'. This great vision, tantamount in principle to duplicating the human brain, is very much a current objective in many laboratories. At present most circuits, gates, flip/flops and other electronic building blocks are epitaxial, created in a very thin surface layer.

The traditional manufacturing process begins by growing an ingot of semiconductor, such as silicon, looking like a giant dark silver-grey sausage. The objective is to make the whole monolithic ingot a perfect crystal, without a single atom out of place. Some of the atoms are not Si but a deliberately introduced impurity so that instead of being an insulator the crystal becomes a semiconductor, usually p-type, with its resistivity precisely controlled at a value which is usually from 2 to 10 ohm-cm. A diamond-impregnated saw then slices the sausage into wafers about half a millimetre thick. Each slice is lapped on one side with extremely fine abrasive and then acid-etched to leave a perfect strain-free mirror surface.

Meanwhile, circuit designers have been creating sets of masks. These used to be drawn, mainly by hand, the originals being perhaps a metre across. Today the whole job is done using computer graphics, light pens and the amazing ability of powerful computers to study many thousands of possibilities and pick the best choice. Each mask exactly defines areas of the eventual circuit that will be acted upon in the manufacturing process. Some masks are networks of lines, others patterns of thousands of small rectangles or dots, while some resemble a detailed map of a city. When each pattern has been checked and rechecked it is photographically reduced and repeated so that perhaps 1,000 will fit on to the small circular area of each wafer. Of course, by this time no human eye could see any of the fine detail of each mask, even with a magnifying glass. The individual dots and lines are similar in dimensions to the wavelengths of light, often smaller than 0.5μ.

Each wafer is coated with a thin passivation (blocking) layer of silicon dioxide and then with a layer of photo emulsion. The first mask is placed on top, and exposure to UV light develops and hardens the emulsion except those areas protected by the mask. These parts remain soft and are washed away, exposing the passivating dioxide which is then etched away by hydrofluoric acid. This exposes the underlying Si crystal, so that when the wafer is heated in a furnace in an atmosphere containing phosphorus atoms (for example) these diffuse into the exposed portions, replacing a proportion of the Si atoms and creating free electrons to form a pattern of n-type material. The rest of the passivation layer is then etched off and a fresh layer of epitaxial n-type silicon grown on top. This is then given a second passivation layer, and further masks, UV exposure, etching and doping (diffusing in impurity atoms) gradually builds up the final circuit, which

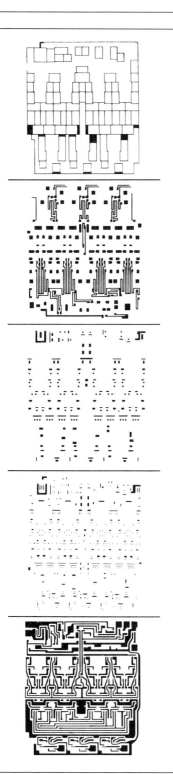

may be incredibly complex. Probably the last stage is to put the wafer in a furnace with aluminium vapour. It comes out topped by a layer of aluminium, which is then masked and etched to leave the required network of interconnections.

Each completed wafer is visually inspected, often by computerized pattern-recognition techniques, and tested by probes which delicately place current-carrying needle points on particular spots to check that performance is within specification. Any defective circuit is marked. Then the wafer is scribed with a diamond, like cutting glass, and broken into the hundred or more chips. Each chip, or IC, then has to be packaged, typically by bonding fine gold wires to the electrode pads around its periphery and then sealing the whole device in one of many ways.

This is only a broad outline of techniques. In LSI (large-scale integration) the wafer is used to construct a single giant device. This may be made up of thousands of separate circuits (which may be identical or totally different) interlinked in the optimum manner by deposited interconnections, or it may be a single device created by using masks of amazing complexity to give up to one million different active circuit elements on the one chip.

In the past the completed chips have usually been mounted on a PCB (printed-circuit board), a strong plate of thin insulating material on which is deposited the required network of metal conductive paths. The traditional PCB is the THP (through hole plated) kind: hundreds of extremely accurate holes are drilled through the board, which are then 'through plated' in an electroplating tank. The usual metal deposited is copper, and for various reasons it has been more an art than a science. Recently Hughes announced the Optrode, a device for automatically measuring the amount of light at specific wavelengths absorbed by the electroplating solution and hence the concentration of copper, or other material. In any case, there have also been problems in soldering the leads from each device into the copper-plated holes. For these and other

Masks for a typical monolithic IC. The first defines particular regions which will be changed by doping and in which devices will be constructed. The next three masks are used in forming the diodes, gates, transistors and other parts. The fifth mask is that for a metal interconnecting network. In practice more than five masks would be used, each duplicated photographically 500 or 1,000 times like postage stamps in a sheet (but much, much smaller).

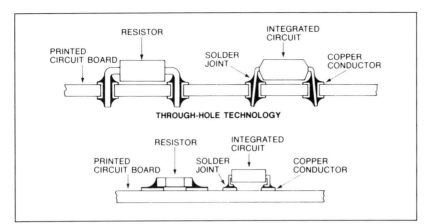

Today most avionics is based on through-hole technology. Surface-mounted devices (lower drawing) offer such advantages as up to six times greater packing density and enhanced reliability.

reasons surface mounting has been rapidly gaining ground. More devices can be packed on each board, weight and cost are reduced and if necessary devices can be soldered on both sides of the board. Computer-positioned lasers can make 100 soldered joints per second.

There are many other possibilities. British Aerospace has perfected COC (copper on ceramic), a technique in which ICs packaged in leadless ceramic carriers are attached by reflow soldering to multilayer ceramic boards as large as 165 mm × 150 mm. Each board may have up to six layers, with fine-line (0.018 mm) circuits in copper. The ceramic, aluminium oxide, is a good conductor of heat, and boards can be mounted in pairs on each side of an aluminium heat sink. Another BAe product is the Mynapak, a ceramic substrate with up to three conductive layers with gold wire connections to the uppermost gold circuit layer, which can include screen-printed resistors trimmed by laser to within 0.5% of design resistance. The Mynapak is enclosed by a Kovar or ceramic cover, and nitrogen filled. External magnetic signature is near zero.

As related in the final chapter, the demands of computers, more than anything else, have driven circuit designers to reach higher and higher speeds. The first digital computers used vacuum tubes connected by lengths of wire and did very well to achieve rates of a few hundred operations (such as multiplications) per second. To make electronics go faster you clearly have to reduce the distances the signals have to travel. If you can convey the data at the speed of light and reduce the distances between logic gates to about 1μ then you can make very fast circuits indeed. In early 1989 commercial silicon chips could divide by two — a basic processing

function — up to about 1.6 billion times a second. Commercial GaAs ICs can run at double this speed, nudging 4 billion per second. The record at present seems to be held by Hughes Research Labs at Malibu, where a GaAs chip has demonstrated stable operation at all frequencies from DC (direct current) up to an amazing 18 GHz, or 18,000,000,000 multiplications or divisions per second. The circuit incorporates capacitatively enhanced logic (logic whose performance is enhanced by incorporating capacitors into the circuit), which reached 17.8 GHz with a fivefold reduction in power consumption. A feature of this example of a VHSIC (very high speed IC) is its use of airbridges, metal interconnections raised off the chip surface by etching away underneath. These minimize the capacitative loading of the metal links, and keep losses to a minimum.

This VHSIC uses buffered FET logic. An FET (field-effect transistor) can be created in various ways. In the silicon epitaxial planar junction type the electrons flow from a source to a drain through a narrow epitaxial channel of n-type. This makes the channel increasingly reverse-biased towards the drain end, widening the space-charge or depletion region (the region near the p/n junction from which holes and electrons are collected) until the electrons can hardly get through. Beyond this level the current (which of course travels from drain to source, opposite to the electrons) cannot be increased in value. The MOS (metal oxide semiconductor) FET is another common, and rapidly growing family. The n-type applies a positive voltage to the drain, building a big space-charge region and severely restricting the current. But the silicon below the gate behaves like one plate of a capacitor; when positive

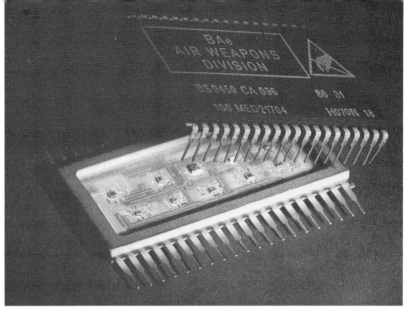

Right *BAe's Mynapaks are thick-film hybrid packages. They were chosen for the three-axes magnetometer in the JAS39 Gripen's standby heading system.*

Below *A microphotograph, magnified almost 900 times, of part of the Hughes GaAs chip believed to be the world's fastest. Note the flyover-like airbridges which interconnect the logic gates.*

voltage is applied to the gate an n-layer is induced near the surface in which free electrons can be swept along to the drain. Yet another FET is the TFT (thin-film transistor). This is constructed on an insulating substrate of silicon oxide (glass), and the channel, gate and electrodes are deposited from vapour and are extremely thin. All these transistors form building blocks for microscopic ICs, serving the roles of switches, amplifiers and anything else the bulky, power-consuming thermionic valve used to do.

These devices can process analog (varying voltage) signals, just like the valves. For a while circuit design changed but little, merely replacing

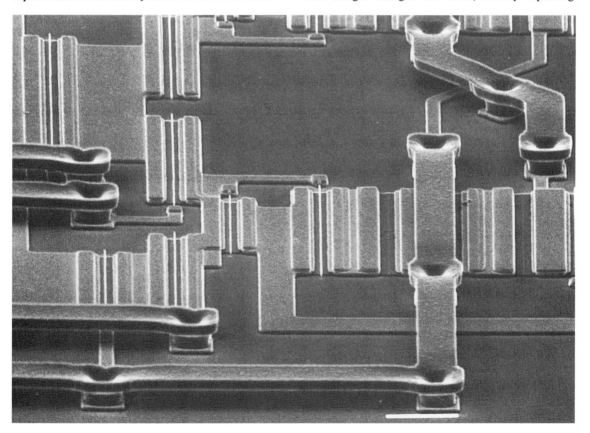

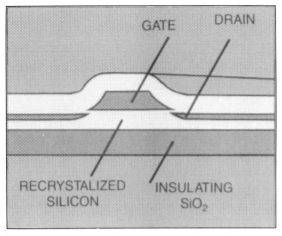

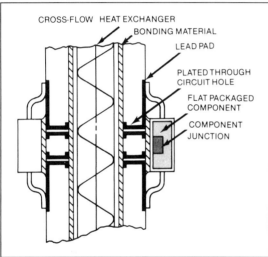

Top *An MOS transistor in a silicon film crystallized on silicon dioxide SiO₂. SOI (silicon on insulator) is a new technology, giving gates as small as 1 micron (1 μ) and reliable up to 350°C. (Bendix)*

Above *All avionics generates heat, which often must be removed by powered air or liquid cooling. A typical construction method is to sandwich a cross-flow heat exchanger between multilayer circuit boards. The plated through-holes help carry away the heat.*

valves by transistors. It was rather like the way, when the RAF switched to metal aircraft, the wooden structures were merely replaced by metal ones and the same fabric was sewn on top; only later was the revolution of stressed skin introduced. In the same way it was only later, after 1960, that electronics engineers (many reluctantly, because instead of being world experts they had to learn again from

scratch) gradually made the transition to digital technology. Instead of using variations in a continuous parameter, such as voltage or current, digital processing uses successions of discrete values or 'bits'. One way to picture the difference is to say that a simple analog computer is the slide-rule and a simple digital computer is the abacus, where you slide beads on wires. The subject is dealt with again in Chapter 15, but we can bear in mind that, except for the simplest General Aviation aircraft, almost everything that flies today has to make up its mind whether it is to be analog or digital. For at least a decade hardly anyone has designed a clean-sheet-of-paper jet, civil or military, with analog avionics. Upgrading older analog aircraft is a very big task. For example Grumman quickly put new engines into the F-14A Tomcat, to produce the F-14A(Plus), but needed three years longer to convert most of the avionics to digital technology in the F-14D, the first of which was to reach the US Navy in March 1990.

There are various kinds of A/D (analog to digital) and D/A convertor. One A/D method samples the varying analog voltages and 'freezes' each value in a capacitor in a track/store unit while the convertor compares it with a succession of voltages generated inside it, controlled by switches with binary '1' or '0' signals. These signals form the output, the time required being a few millionths of a second. This can all be done by a single IC costing a few cents. Conversion the other way is simple. The binary signal, so called because it can only have one of two states, being made up of 1s and 0s, is fed in parallel to a set of D/A switches each supplying a given voltage to an analog amplifier, the sum being the required voltage. Where the input is a sinusoidal waveform a digital output is obtained by PCM (pulse code modulation), in which the amplitude of the wave is measured at frequent regular intervals and the measures converted to binary form. Binary notation is merely a way of expressing numbers in terms of 1s and 0s, so that they can be processed by digital logic gates (switches) having just two states, on or off. It is based on powers of 2. Thus the number 618 becomes 0101011001 ($0 \times 2^0 + 1 \times 2^1 + 0 \times 2^2 + 1 \times 2^3 + 0 \times 2^4 + 1 \times 2^5 + 1 \times 2^6 + 0 \times 2^7 + 0 \times 2^8 + 1 \times 2^9$).

Today, wherever possible, avionics equipment is packaged into boxes of standard sizes. What is fast becoming the world standard are the ATR (US Air Transport Radio) sizes, which are boxes 7.63 in high, 12.6 in (so-called 'short') or 19.6 in ('long') in

Right *Analog systems deal with continuous signals, which may be continuously varying. Digital systems deal with streams of 'bits' which may be written as 0s and 1s but are actually 'current off' and 'current on'.*

Below *All avionics systems generate unwanted heat, sometimes enough to heat a small town. This diagram shows how both air and liquid can be used to remove it.*

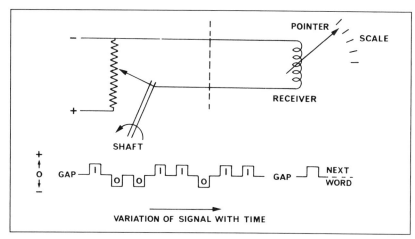

POINTER
SCALE
RECEIVER
SHAFT

GAP   GAP   NEXT WORD

VARIATION OF SIGNAL WITH TIME

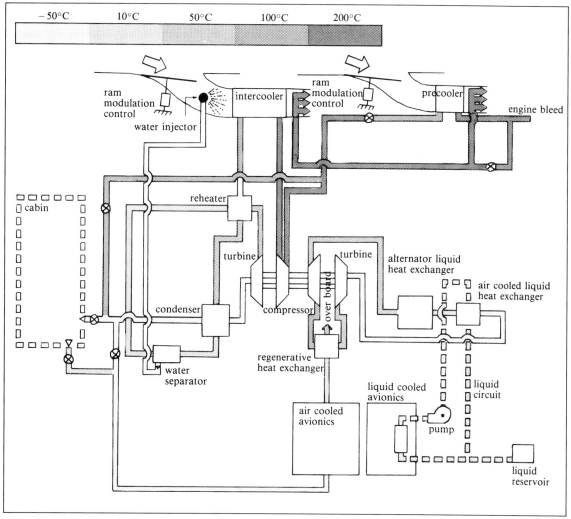

−50°C   10°C   50°C   100°C   200°C

ram modulation control
water injector
intercooler
ram modulation control
precooler
engine bleed

cabin
reheater
turbine
turbine
alternator liquid heat exchanger
air cooled liquid heat exchanger
condenser
compressor
over board
regenerative heat exchanger
liquid cooled avionics
liquid circuit
water separator
air cooled avionics
pump
liquid reservoir

front/back depth, and 2.25, 3.56, 4.88, 7.5 or 10.13 in wide. For greater reliability some equipments are duplicated, though with modern equipment and proper forced-air cooling the reliability should be virtually perfect and, except in flight-control systems, duplication is becoming rarer. Sometimes a single item is arranged to be everlastingly switched rapidly to a repeated cycle of inputs, in TDM (time-division multiplex). For example a flight recorder may be switched so that each channel records up to fifty or more different parameters in rapid succession. Today integrated avionic installations are connected to data highways (Chapter 15) so that 'any box can talk to any other box'.

As all subsequent chapters deal with particular classes of avionics, this is the place to study a single integrated system for a complete aircraft. A good choice is that for the Beechcraft Starship 1. In 1986 this was a totally new and very advanced General Aviation aircraft, and when it was being designed Collins (Rockwell) was awarded a contract for an integrated avionics system. This was an unusual opportunity. Even large passenger jets seldom present such opportunities to start from scratch, and the result is obviously instructive in exemplifying mid-1980s avionics architectures.

This integrated system comprises more than 70 LRUs. An LRU is a line-replaceable unit, a single box capable of being quickly unplugged electrically and unlatched mechanically and replaced by another of the same kind on the flightline. As far as possible every box in modern avionics systems is an LRU. It may be too much to claim the Starship system to be a blueprint for the future, but in the author's view it not only represents the best current practice but will be used as a model by other designers. It is especially remarkable that this comprehensive system should have been created for an aircraft financially within the reach of many private owners. One of the author's colleagues (Mike Hirst) has drawn attention to the way solid-state microelectronics has brought down the price of avionics. About twenty years ago a DME (Chapter 3), for example, 'cost about as much as a typical light twin; today it costs about as much as a typical light twin's paint job'. When I was a boy it was by no means taken for granted that a private or club aircraft would have a compass or artificial horizon. Today it is taken for granted that any serious light aircraft (excluding micros and hang gliders, that is) will have a pretty good suite of avionics.

The term architecture is self-explanatory. It means the overall design of the avionics and the subsystem inter-relationships. The Starship architecture is based on two buses (main highways), one

Block diagram of the avionics system of the Beech Starship. This not only gives an overview, showing the 'left/right mirror image' type of duplication, but also explains many of the acronyms found throughout this book. (Collins)

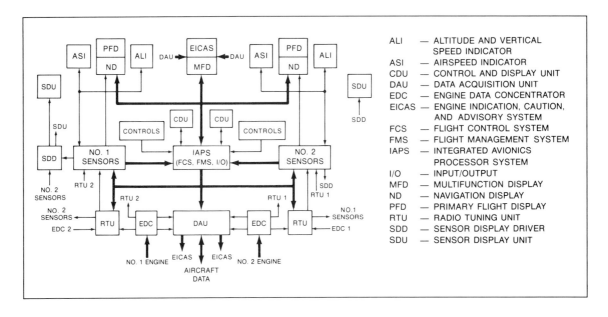

ALI	— ALTITUDE AND VERTICAL SPEED INDICATOR
ASI	— AIRSPEED INDICATOR
CDU	— CONTROL AND DISPLAY UNIT
DAU	— DATA ACQUISITION UNIT
EDC	— ENGINE DATA CONCENTRATOR
EICAS	— ENGINE INDICATION, CAUTION, AND ADVISORY SYSTEM
FCS	— FLIGHT CONTROL SYSTEM
FMS	— FLIGHT MANAGEMENT SYSTEM
IAPS	— INTEGRATED AVIONICS PROCESSOR SYSTEM
I/O	— INPUT/OUTPUT
MFD	— MULTIFUNCTION DISPLAY
ND	— NAVIGATION DISPLAY
PFD	— PRIMARY FLIGHT DISPLAY
RTU	— RADIO TUNING UNIT
SDD	— SENSOR DISPLAY DRIVER
SDU	— SENSOR DISPLAY UNIT

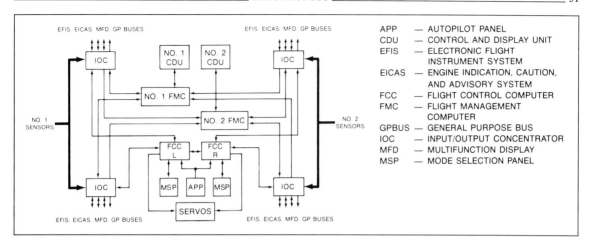

APP — AUTOPILOT PANEL
CDU — CONTROL AND DISPLAY UNIT
EFIS — ELECTRONIC FLIGHT INSTRUMENT SYSTEM
EICAS — ENGINE INDICATION, CAUTION, AND ADVISORY SYSTEM
FCC — FLIGHT CONTROL COMPUTER
FMC — FLIGHT MANAGEMENT COMPUTER
GPBUS — GENERAL PURPOSE BUS
IOC — INPUT/OUTPUT CONCENTRATOR
MFD — MULTIFUNCTION DISPLAY
MSP — MODE SELECTION PANEL

Above *Block diagram of the Starship IAPS (integrated avionics processor system). It provides for: flight guidance computation; autopilot computations and servo amplifiers; flight management computations; database memory; redundant I/O (input/output) concentration; power supplies; and provision for growth. It is about the size of a large atlas.* (Collins)

Right *The Starship's two IOCs (input/output concentrators) receive data from all senders in either the left or right halves of the network and provide output buses for an affinity group of data users.* (Collins)

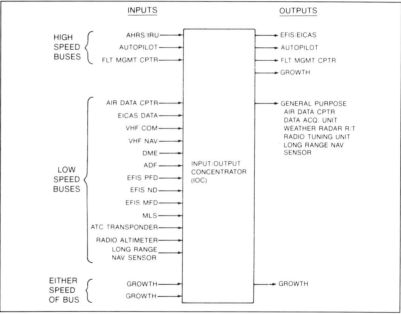

handling the left half of the aircraft and the other the right. What is called asynchronous broadcast bussing is used throughout. Arinc (Aeronautical Radio Inc) lays down standards for all avionics to ensure perfect compatibility, no matter who makes the equipment. The standards used are Arinc 429 for intersubsystem communication of parametric data (basically, all measurements) and Arinc 453 for the weather-radar data link to the displays (both, Ch. 15). The six large colour displays (Chapter 13), out of 14 CRT displays in the cockpit, all use software programmed in Ada, the US Defense Department language which is fast becoming an industry standard. The central IAPS, divided electrically into 'left half' and 'right half' shelves, contains twenty modules each about the size of a video cassette. The box is carefully air-cooled, measures 19.7 in × 11.4 in by 6 in and is located in the lower part of the coat-closet wall behind the copilot's seat. Four of the module cards are the IOCs, which input from up to eighteen sources and feed the data users. This is clearly the way to go.

2

COMMUNICATIONS

The first form of electronic communication was radio, and it still dominates all others. Many English-speakers originally called it 'wireless', because instead of needing telegraph wires it communicates by means of EM waves propagated through the atmosphere and through space. There are various species of radio. One form is radio telegraphy (also called wireless telegraphy, W/T), in which Morse-coded signals are sent by making and breaking a monotone signal. A British Army balloon received Morse in 1907. For many years this was important in air navigation (Chapter 3) and bad-weather landing (Chapter 11), using just two letters, A and N. Ability to modulate audio-frequency (AF) on to or out of the EM waves resulted in the radio telephone (R/T) and broadcasting. At higher frequencies, and with much wider bandwidth to carry the vastly greater flow of information, a similar process resulted in TV, made up of audio plus a mix of luminance and chrominance picture signals.

If DC is passed along a wire it creates a surrounding magnetic field, but no emission of EM radiation. If AC is substituted then EM waves are emitted, with a strength which varies with the square of the frequency. Thus, the radio emission from a wire carrying domestic 50 or 60 Hz current is for most purposes negligible. But if the frequency were to be increased to, say, 5 kHz (5,000 Hz), the radiated power would be multiplied by 10,000. Thus, no matter what signal may be carried, radio calls for high frequencies. It also calls for a suitable transmitter, with an antenna*, and a receiver, again with a suitable antenna. Some antennas are strongly directional, while others radiate in all directions and receive from all directions.

The fundamental component of the transmitter is some kind of oscillator to generate the required AC at a very high frequency. By 'very high' we mean in comparison with domestic AC; in fact VHF (very high frequency) today denotes just one specific waveband, 30–100 MHz or a wavelength from about 10 m down to 3 m. Other EM frequencies are listed in the spectrum diagram at the front of the book. To be of practical use the transmitter frequency must be controlled very precisely; so must every receiver, so that after each receiver has 'tuned in' it receives the desired transmission and not any of the thousands of others on frequencies very close to it.

The simplest oscillator is a circuit containing a self-induction coil and a capacitor (condenser). Obviously, sending out EM radiation consumes energy which has to come from the oscillating circuit. To replace this, exactly synchronized current is supplied from a feedback circuit containing transistors (in the old days it was taken from the grid of a triode valve). Thus, as long as the transmitter is switched on, raw AC fed into it comes out as precisely controlled oscillating current which, after being greatly increased by amplifiers, can be fed to the antenna. But to transmit intelligence we must impress coding onto this current.

In traditional W/T all we had to do was keep interrupting the current with a switch, such as a Morse key. For almost all modern avionic com systems the basic EM emission is used as the continuous carrier wave on which is impressed the speech or other information to be sent out. This calls for the basic waveform to be modulated. EM radiation can be modulated in various ways, but the two most basic are amplitude modulation (AM) and frequency modulation (FM). Each of these can become quite complex, but for the present purpose

---

* I hope I will offend nobody by preferring this term to the traditional British word 'aerial' which is ambiguous and is falling into disuse.

we can say that AM merely varies the amplitude (strength) of the waves while FM varies their frequency. Suppose we were to increase the frequency of the EM radiation until it becomes visible light of a yellow colour near that of a sodium lamp. If we then impressed FM upon it, we should find the intensity was held constant whilst the colour continuously varied, sometimes through orange towards red (longer wavelengths) and at other times towards green and blue (shorter wavelengths). If we impressed AM upon it the colour — exactly 5.896 μ — would never vary in the slightest, but the light would alternately grow dimmer and brighter.

When transmitting material such as TV or IR pictures we have to send data at a tremendous rate, and this calls for very high frequencies and rapid modulation. By comparison, speech is simple; audio frequencies are extremely low compared with those of EM waves, so it is not difficult to impress their modulation on the carrier wave. All we need is a microphone, a form of transducer which converts the physical air displacements of sound waves into electrical signals modulated at the corresponding audio frequencies. Ordinary speech outputs a continuous band of frequencies, and when this is impressed on the carrier wave the result (in either amplitude change or frequency change) is a waveform which varies in a seemingly very irregular fashion between the carrier minus the highest audio

Amplitude modulation (a) varies the strength of a broadcast signal in order to convey information, leaving frequency unchanged. Frequency modulation (b) continuously varies the frequency, leaving amplitude unchanged.

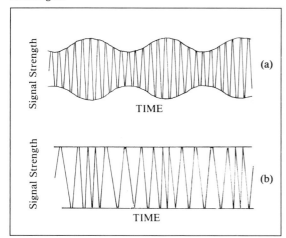

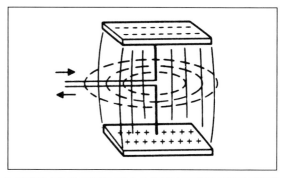

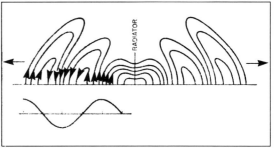

Top *The simplest antenna is a Hertz dipole, a vertical wire. This antenna is fed at the centre, top half negative, bottom positive. The broadcast magnetic waves are like ripples on a pond; the corresponding electric waves are seen as slightly curved nearly vertical lines (actually they are almost cylindrical wavefronts).* (Hughes)

Above *EM waves radiated from a short vertical antenna. The sketch shows a cross section through the electric field waves; the magnetic waves would be identical but at 90° to the paper. Note the small inset showing the sine-wave output, passing through zero each time the direction of the wave is reversed.*

and the carrier plus the highest audio. It is this which is amplified and sent out by the transmitter antenna.

The simplest antenna is a straight piece of wire. Ideally this should have a length somewhere near to the wavelength of the transmission, or to an exact multiple of it, either smaller or greater. If one could imagine a vertical wire or rod antenna suspended in space — it forms what is called a Hertz dipole — its emissions are rather like the ripples from a stone dropped into still water. The magnetic waves resemble rings spreading away from the antenna at the centre, while the electric waves resemble curved, almost spherical, wavefronts. An accompanying sketch shows how we imagine one set of waves might look if 'frozen' at one instant in time, together with the associated sine-wave plot. The associated magnetic waves would be sets of rings at 90° to the plane of the paper, centred on the radiating antenna. As EM waves need no medium to transmit them they can be broadcast equally well in space, but those sent out from Earth can suffer various kinds of external influence.

The process of modulation, either AM or FM, inevitably produces unwanted additional emitted frequencies spaced equally above and below the carrier. These are called the upper and lower sidebands. With the sky crowded with transmissions it is not uncommon for adjacent sidebands to interfere with each other. Another cause of interference is 'static', received noise caused by unwanted broadband radiation from electrical discharges in the atmosphere and ionosphere. Throughout flight every aircraft not only flies through atmospheric regions of widely varying electrical potential but can itself build up large electrostatic charges. Accordingly all aircraft, especially those whose structure is mainly or partly non-metallic, are carefully bonded, with all parts electrically linked. This is partly to avoid dangerous electrostatic buildups and consequent sparks jumping gaps, and partly to provide the biggest possible earth (US = ground) for any avionic installation. Any potential buildup is continuously emitted back to atmosphere via static wicks, which are usually provided behind the tips of the wings and tail. These contain minute conductive wires or graphite particles with such a small radius that the emission never reaches a level causing communications interference.

Very severe com interference would be caused by some on-board electrical systems if these were not 'screened'. The problem was noticed as early as 1912, in the first experiments with radio aboard aeroplanes. The HT (high-tension) circuit of the piston-engine ignition system, comprising magneto secondary coils, distributor, plug leads (cables) and plugs, was found to be the cause of intense crackling interference. The answer was to encase the cables in tight braided metal wires on an adhesive cambric covering, and to make the magneto, distributor and plugs so that they could not emit RF interference. Of course, every avionic item is itself designed to prohibit any interference with any other.

Apart from pioneer experiments the earliest aircraft voice radios were massive sets, little changed from those for ground use, carried in recon-

naissance aeroplanes and airships from 1915. They needed a supply of electricity, provided by lead/acid batteries which in any aircraft capable of long endurance were recharged by a windmill-driven generator. All these early 'wireless sets' were what we today call MF or HF, with wavelengths around 50–1,000 m. The point was made earlier that the length of a dipole antenna should be more or less related to the wavelength, and it is often found that good results with HF can be obtained with a quarterwave (0.25λ) or half-wave antenna. This means that the wire may be similar in size to the aeroplane, and so in early installations an insulated wire might be slung between a fuselage mast or the wingtips and fin.

An advantage of HF is that such wavelengths are reflected back to the ground by the charged regions of the ionosphere, as mentioned in Chapter 1, so with a powerful set and good conditions one can receive on the far side of the globe. A drawback is the strong interference to HF caused by solar activity such as Sun prominences, but despite this HF plays a very important role even today. You can, for example, fly a Phantom from the Falklands to Lossiemouth, taxi to the ramp, park and then call back and tell them you've arrived.

Of course, any practical radio com system must include a receiver. After travelling from Lossie to the Falklands the original broadcast radiation will have become greatly attenuated (much, much weaker), but the signals ought not to have changed significantly in character. The aircraft invariably receives via the same antenna it uses to transmit. Obviously the receiver has to be capable of being tuned to the desired radiation, and as noted earlier this is always done on a basis of frequency, not wavelength. The tuning has to be precise, to maximize the strength of the desired signal whilst as far as possible eliminating others. The weak received signal then has to be amplified, in one, two or more stages of RF amplification. Then comes detection, the process of separating out the signal from the carrier, and this is invariably done by rectification, or converting the AC into variable DC. This is also known as demodulation. Finally, the AF (audio frequency) voice current, or other desired output, is again amplified and fed to an output device such as headphones, a loudspeaker, recorder or other device.

Almost all modern radio receivers, and radar receivers as well, are of the superheterodyne type.

Block diagram of a very simple superhet receiver. Today the tuning knob does not drive variable condensers but selects precise frequencies by means of crystals.

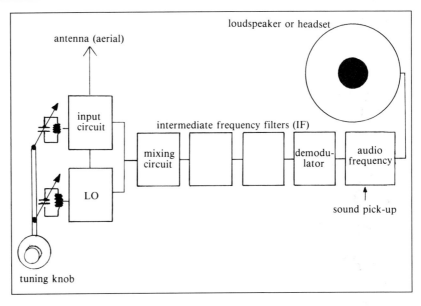

The incoming signal, or weak radar echo, is mixed with the (usually fixed) output of an LO (local oscillator), and it is the difference between the two, a much lower frequency than the one originally received, that is subsequently filtered and amplified. This difference frequency, called the IF (intermediate frequency), is then passed through the IF amplifier where it is magnified and as far as possible cleansed of interference or background noise. The resulting amplified and filtered IF is then passed to the demodulator where the original signal is separated out from the carrier. The demodulator is sometimes called a detector.

At the end of World War 2 the author was familiar with HF transceivers (transmitter/receivers) which used wire antennas and were tuned by the rotation of multi-bank variable capacitors in the form of intermeshing plates. Some used knobs whilst others used handles we called 'coffee grinders'. Suddenly VHF appeared (see EM spectrum). The earliest VHF aircraft radios had been produced before the war, but were slow to be introduced. In Britain their first use was in RAF fighters, just prior to the outbreak of war, and in the Battle of Britain the new clarity of VHF went hand-in-hand with the new ability of radar and ground controllers to convey precise information on the enemy. VHF meant that antennas could be smaller, initially a springy 'whip aerial' and later, with higher frequencies still, a streamlined flat blade only a few inches long. It also made available far

more frequencies. Allowing about 10 kHz between transmitter stations to avoid interference, MF can be broadcast on about 50 different channels in any one area, and HF on about 150. In contrast, with VHF one can select a channel from thousands of frequencies without bothering any adjacent station.

This called for a more accurate kind of tuning, using piezoelectric crystals. Such crystals, often of quartz, change shape when subjected to an electric field; conversely they generate a potential difference when subjected to mechanical stress. Each crystal has its own precise resonant frequency, and almost all modern radios use such crystals as unvarying stabilizers of oscillator or receiver frequency. Forty or more years ago the 'wireless operator' or fighter pilot had to remember to have the correct crystals on board for the desired frequencies. Today most radios are quite small boxes which, either on the box or on a remote panel-mounted controller, have several (usually four) small knobs. The operator, today virtually always the pilot, merely turns these knobs until the 'windows' above them give the correct MHz numerical readout. The picture of the standard VHF set of the US Air Force shows it tuned to 122.375 MHz. This compact set, which weighs 7.25 lb, provides 1,760 channels of AM voice and 2,320 channels of FM. You just twiddle the little knobs to get any of them!

Today private owners and commercial transports use VHF, whilst the military also (often exclusively) use UHF. These UHF (ultra-high) sets operate mainly in the band 250–400 MHz, with wavelengths of around 1 m. There is no intrinsic difference between VHF and UHF, which are purely arbitrary divisions of the EM spectrum. In the author's view UHF is even clearer than VHF, in other words offers better S/N ratios. Like VHF, UHF travels in straight lines, so effective range is limited by the Earth's curvature. Today there are other more serious limitations, because when in hostile airspace aircraft tend to fly at the lowest possible level, and this means the LOS (line of sight) to or from the aircraft may be blocked by a hillock or even the buildings of a small town. Of course, most pilots penetrating hostile airspace tend to fly the mission and not chat to their friends, but the battlefield helicopter is a special case. This may spend all day hiding in wooded country, part of the time on the ground and the rest hovering or moving fairly slowly. The pilot may wish to tell base what the enemy ground forces are doing, and he may have to receive

Left The ARC-186(V) is the standard VHF com radio for the USAF and US Army. It is a solid-state 10W package which can be connected to a 1553B digital bus. (Collins)

Below The Narco Mk 12D is a typical nav/com for private owners. The big knobs select channels for Com (left) or Nav (right). The small white pushbuttons transfer from standby to active, while the small white blob at left is a photocell which automatically dims the alphanumeric LED displays as dusk falls. The whole package weighs 4.1 lb, or 4.4 lb with glide-slope receiver.

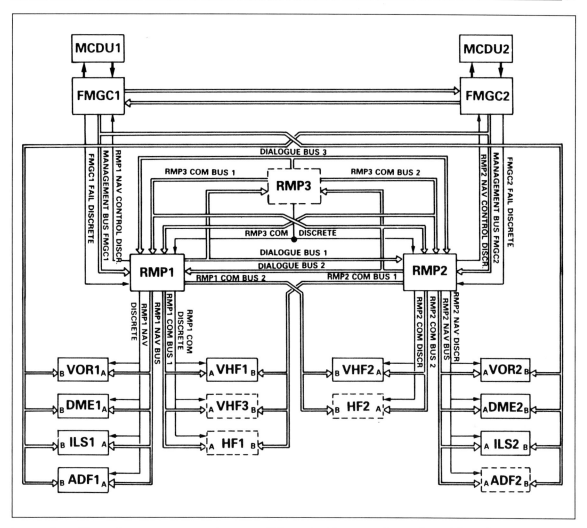

Architecture of a modern airliner Com system, actually for the A320. RMP is radio management panel, FMGC flight management guidance computer and MCDU multicolour display unit. Most items are duplexed but there are three VHFs. (Airbus)

instructions. The only answer seems to be to use HF sent almost straight up, reflected from a suitable ionospheric region and reflected almost straight down again. GEC Avionics has pretty well solved the problem with sets using Navis (near vertical-incidence skywave) propagation. This sends transmissions about 80 km upwards and 80 km downwards to reach a helicopter maybe a few hundred metres away!

It is unusual to find HF being used by tactical air units, but they remain essential for aircraft flying thousands of kilometres from ground stations, such as long-haul widebodies. Today's HF sets no longer use coffee grinders. A typical box, the Collins HFS-700, operating in the band 2.0–30 MHz, provides 28,000 precisely preset channels, with frequency stability within 20 Hz. Though it weighs less than 26 lb, complete with its cooling blower, it provides RF power of 400 W, and like rival equipments can offer 'USB/LSB/AME/CW'. This means that it can operate in selected modes: upper sideband, lower sideband, AM equivalent data or in continuous-wave. It works just as well at 40,000 ft, resists high temperatures, vibration and impacts, and hardly ever goes wrong. We take it all for granted.

Though the general trend in com avionics over the period 1920-60 was towards ever-shorter frequencies, the ability of HF to travel round the world has kept it in a position of importance in airlines and major air forces. Moreover, since the late 1960s the crucial need of the US President to retain immediate interference-proof communications with the missile-firing submarines of the US Navy led to a remarkable system in the VLF band called Tacamo (take charge and move out). Originally deployed in EC-130Q aircraft and now also the central installation in the E-6A, fifteen of which will be delivered by 1993, this VLF set forms the downward link in the com network. The upward link uses secure voice, relaying orders via the Presidential E-4B and other airborne national command posts via satellites and the ERCS (emergency rocket communications system). These links reach the E-6A via wingtip pods for HF and Satcom (satellite communications) UHF. The downlink is the remarkable VLF, which feeds the command signals at a power of 200 kW to an STWA (short trailing wire antenna) almost 5,000 ft (1,500 m) long reeled out from

under the tail (where the boomer lies in a tanker). This energy is then re-radiated from an LTWA (long trailing wire antenna) reeled out from the belly. On the end of the LTWA is a 90 lb drogue. As the LTWA is reeled out eventually the drogue stalls, so that when the full 28,000 ft (8.5 km) has been deployed the E-6A can go into a tight orbit and keep about four-fifths of the LTWA absolutely vertical. A verticality of 70 per cent is needed to convey the vertically polarized signals to the submerged submarine, which picks them up via a very small towed buoyant wire antenna.

There are many other special-purpose com systems, some civil and others military. Among the latter are new systems at both ends of the frequency spectrum. Westinghouse has developed a VLF/LF system which can be stored for fifteen years and then quickly brought into service at a time when existing com networks are destroyed, to give LOS

Racal Avionics pioneered satellite communications with 747s of British Airways. The transmit and receive antennas are mounted above the rear fuselage.

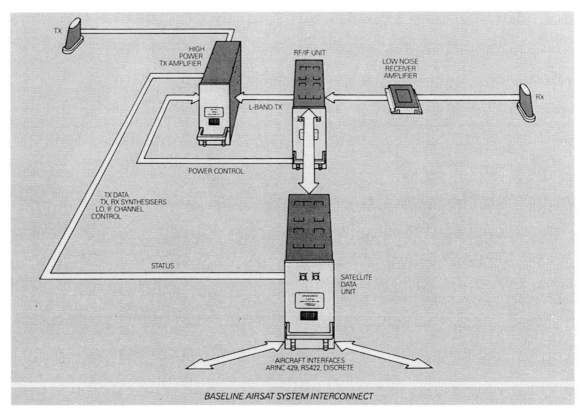

BASELINE AIRSAT SYSTEM INTERCONNECT

and ground-wave links with strategic forces. The required vertical antenna is deployed by an aerostat, such as an airship. At the other end of the scale is a classified com system fitted to the USAF E-4B national command post operating in the SHF band. To minimize hostile jamming and eavesdropping it is a satellite link, clearly using a large steerable dish antenna because of the need for a dorsal 'doghouse' fairing to cover it.

There are bound to be similarities between the USAF equipment and the Satcom systems now available to the airlines. The advantages of Satcoms to air traffic are enormous, especially from the ATC (air traffic control) viewpoint, but the capital outlays are large and the advantages cannot be realized until all major commercial transports, and business jets, are Satcom-equipped. What has spurred the cautious operators to get equipped has been the instant revenue they can get from providing on-board passenger telephones, a development of the late 1980s. Every 747-400 has provision for a Satcom installation, and it is unlikely that any will enter service without the equipment being fitted. The three industry leaders are Racal Avionics of the UK and Ball Aerospace and E-Systems of the USA. Ball make only the antennas, and Boeing has picked this as standard (though at extra cost customers can choose otherwise). Ball fit a flush electronically steered phased-array antenna measuring 32 in × 16 in on each upper side of the fuselage facing diagonally upwards at about 45°. A computer steers the beams 'through at least 60° in any direction', though of course the gain coverage is poor to nose and tail. E-Systems picked a steerable dish, similar to that for the E-4B but much smaller, the diameter being 9.8 in. It can point anywhere in azimuth and from 90° up to 30° down. Racal have also gone for phased arrays, but mounted inside an external blade with a small aerofoil on top. At the cost of slightly higher drag this gives outstanding upper-hemisphere coverage, and also facilitates retrofitting existing aircraft. In early 1986 Marconi Defence Systems began testing a steerable dish in the fin-top fairing of a Nimrod for tests with the purely military Skynet 4.

This book is not concerned with ground electronics and thus does not have much to say about ATC (air traffic control), but Satcoms clearly make possible the long-time dream of close real-time surveillance of the position of every airborne aircraft, even over the South Pole or central Pacific.

The option of CIS (cooperative independent surveillance) will probably not become effective until 2005 at the earliest; each aircraft transmits a signal via satellite from which ground stations determine its position. Much closer is ADS (automatic dependent surveillance) in which every aircraft automatically (ie, with no crew action) keeps transmitting its own position as outputted by its INS and other navigation systems. To be useful a totally reliable Satcom system is needed, and this can now be provided. ADS would make possible a reduction in separation between aircraft on busy oceanic routes, leading to greater flexibility, reduced journey times and lower fuel and crew costs. The present small inaccuracies in air navigation should soon be virtually eliminated by GPS (Chapter 3), and by 1996 or so separations — even in mid-ocean — might be able to be reduced to very close values which today's captains would consider totally unacceptable.

Basic elements of an IFF system. The key to IFF lies in the complexity, security and precision of the transmitted codes. (Cossor)

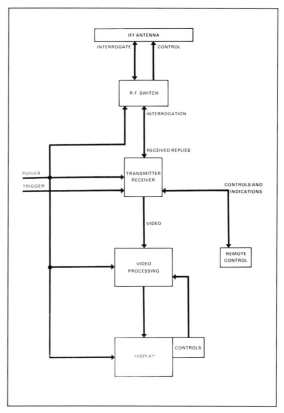

ADS works by the automatic periodic polling (interrogation) of the FMS (flight management system) of every aircraft in the oceanic airspace. The ground ATC controllers could then extend their coverage everywhere that commercial transports fly, each blip looking like an actual radar blip and being accompanied by its FL (flight level), track and speed.

This is the latest in a succession of forms of automatic interrogation which began in 1939 with the first IFF (identification friend or foe). IFF has always been an exact electronic equivalent of the sentry's challenge 'Who goes there?' The airborne portion of IFF is a transponder, sometimes abbreviated to xpdr, which is a transmitter-responder. In other words, upon interrogation it instantly transmits a reply. Modern IFF interrogators may be on the ground or in an intercepting fighter, and they normally send out precise streams of pulses on the known bearing of the target (and not in other directions). The pulses are coded in various ways, a common civil and military code being 3/A, a 1 microsecond (μs) pulse followed by a 1 μs gap followed by a 1 μs pulse followed by a 5 μs gap, the pair of pulses then being repeated, the frequency being 1,030 MHz. The airborne xpdr instantly sends back a pulse train on 1,090 MHz. Civil traffic sends its unique four-figure code, made up by adding the

NATO has spent years trying to replace old IFFs, unable to interrogate each other, with a standard form, called Mk XII. The Cossor 4740 is one of the new sets, designed as a plug-in replacement for the IFF at present fitted to Tornados.

subscript numbers of the pulse positions in a train of 12 pulses lasting 20.3 μs. Military xpdrs send more complex codes, generated cryptographically and automatically changed each day (in time of war perhaps each hour).

The preferred civil name for this kind of interrogation is SSR (secondary surveillance radar) in Britain and ATCRBS (ATC radar beacon system) in the USA. The four-digit code automatically sent back by an interrogated aircraft is called a squawk. In many national ATC centres the squawk is automatically translated into the flight number — thus, 2995 might become AF501 — and throughout the design of the whole system the accent has to be on reliability, to avoid conflicts in civil traffic and 'own goals' in wartime. Not really relevant to this book is the fact that, while the Warsaw Pact has (of course) always enjoyed total standardization of IFF systems, NATO has (of course) been in a mess which is a disgrace to all the decision-takers. With luck, some time in the 1990s the various NATO air forces will actually be able to interrogate each other as well as potential enemies.

Another thing military forces like to do is enjoy secure communications, in other words com links with which the enemy cannot interfere and into which he cannot break in order to hear the messages. There are several ways of attempting to achieve this, but by far the most important fall within SS (spread-spectrum) technology, a very broad field which uses various techniques to modulate a signal whose bandwidth is much wider than that needed for the plain message. The latter may be PDM (pulse-duration modulation) analog, but is increasingly likely to be a biphase (0s and 1s) digital stream. This is then merged digitally with SS modulation. Perhaps the simplest SS technique to understand is FH, frequency hopping. The transmitted signal is sent out on a carrier whose frequency hops extremely rapidly (for example, after every few waveforms, or perhaps a thousand times a second) and randomly, the receiver alone being able to decipher by reversing the process. Another is PN, pseudonoise; a PN generator emits what sounds like pure noise (what you get when you turn up your TV volume with the antenna disconnected), but which actually serves as the very complex carrier. Spread-spectrum com has very great anti-jam capability, high security (in the present state of the art), multiple access and numerous other advantages.

Right *On board a NATO E-3A Sentry a US com operator 'talks' securely with an Aegis command centre via JTIDS. The Canadian computer operator is reviewing the digital text, while in the rear a West German technician monitors the JTIDS control panels.* (Hughes)

Below *Class 2 JTIDS transmitter/receiver made by Collins for Singer Kearfott. This is for an F-15, but most tactical aircraft installations are similar.*

At a cost of many billions, the biggest of several US programmes for secure C^3I (command, control, communications and intelligence) is JTIDS. Strictly the Joint Tactical Info Distribution System is not an across-the-board C^3I provider, but it does enable users in every kind of air and ground platform to receive accurate information on who is where and what they are doing, in real time (ie, without even a thousandth of a second's delay). It has to be a very large theatre-wide system, with architecture tailored to interoperability between data-collection elements, combat elements and C^2 (command and control) centres.

JTIDS achieves its security and resistance to jamming by using SS and FH techniques over a frequency band of several hundred MHz. Additional protection against jamming is provided by use of a forward error correction code (Reed-Solomon was chosen), which enables the message's information content to be reconstructed in real time even if half the data pulses keep on being lost. Each JTIDS transmitter can broadcast in all directions at rates of 59 kbit/s (59,000 bits per second), or 119 kbit or 238 kbit (the higher rates are for future growth). To enable large numbers of transmitters and receivers to link into the one network on a real-time basis one

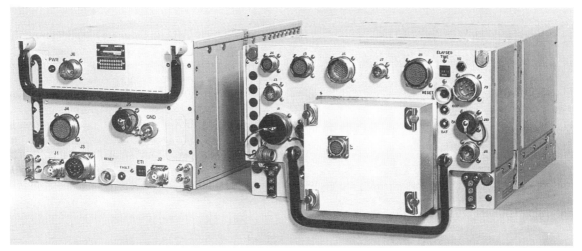

of the basic com techniques is used: TDMA. Time-division multiple access means that each transmitter sends out its message in short bursts lasting a very small fraction of a second. Computers synchronize from dozens to hundreds of messages from different sources so that all can use the same network, perhaps all of them transmitting a different message in a single second. Each message may be repeated up to fifty or more times, each time on a different spread of frequencies to make jamming of each transmission almost impossible. Each terminal can select or reject any message, depending on its need for the information. One might concern fuel stocks, another local weather, another a hostile aircraft formation, and another the location of a particular commander. JTIDS includes Class 1 terminals supplied by Hughes and installed in E-3 Sentry aircraft and certain major ground centres (such as Nadge and Aegis sites). Smaller Class 2 terminals by Singer-Kearfott and Collins go into USAF and some other F-15s, and RAF Harrier IIs and Tornado F.3s.

For ordinary folk who cannot afford JTIDS, various alternatives are becoming available. Almost the only proven one on the market is GEC Avionics' AD.950 low-cost anti-jam com system. It does not use wide-band SS/FH techniques but transmits on ordinary speech bandwidth on HF, VHF or UHF, with various means of enhancing S/N ratio in noisy environments. Security of the link rests on the fact that messages can be repeated three times in a total time of 0.5 s, and each message is protected by encription with a code 10^{15} bits long with eight variable keys. The ground operator has a tiny keyboard from which, using a Selcal (selective calling) facility, he can independently transfer data to up to sixteen receiver stations, which would be in fighters or helicopters. Each brief, correctly-coded transmission passes target range, bearing, height, speed and various basic commands. It is simple enough to be quite useful, at an overall programme cost certainly less than one-thousandth that of JTIDS.

In World War 2 the desperate need of the Luftwaffe to provide secure anti-jam ground direction of its night fighters led to the use by mid-1944 of FuG 120 Bernhard/Bernhardine, a supposedly secure link. It included a teleprinter giving a hard-copy coded printout in the cockpit. Today very few aircraft carry a teleprinter, and even the terminology is undecided; some are called a 'fast

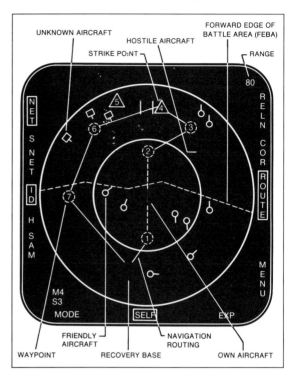

All this information on an F-15 cockpit colour display can be provided by JTIDS. Thus, it is much more than a traditional com system. (Singer Kearfott)

printer', some a 'radio teletype' and some a 'hard copy printer'. Most are to be found in long-range maritime patrol aircraft. Teleprinters are just another facet of the vast and ill-defined group of subjects called C^2, C^3, CNI (com, nav, identification), ICNI (integrated CNI), CNIA (CNI avionics) and by many other acronyms, which confuse rather than help because very few people know, for example, how CNI, ICNI and CNIA differ. Avionics has suffered terribly from the contagious spread of acronyms, which are threatening to make the whole subject unintelligible even to avionics engineers.

Selcal, selective calling, is a relatively simple ground-based method of broadcasting messages to particular aircraft. As each airborne transponder has its own address code, the ground ATC computers inhibit calling that code until the ground SSR is aimed at that particular azimuth (direction). This cuts out about 99 per cent of the interrogations, and thus avoids saturation. The UK calls this Adsel (address selective) and the US term is Dabs (discrete address beacon system). Auto height reporting is achieved by linking the aircraft's ADS or DADS (digital air data system) to the transponder.

Probably the simplest forms of airborne communications are the intercom, between members of a flight crew, and the PA (passenger address) system in a commercial transport. Among traditional forms one of the most complex is the Hughes 1150 ACIS (advanced cabin interphone system) for the 747. In a typical version it has a central microprocessor, cockpit control unit, chime light sensor and handsets for the pilots and nineteen attendants. The attendant handsets are distributed all over the above-floor area. Any station can call any other, or can call 'all attendants' or 'all' (flight crew as well) or 'all passengers' or three separate passenger groups. The pilot station can override all others, but not vice versa. If any handset is not properly seated it howls loudly but does not affect system operation. There are various other checks and overrides.

Airbus Industrie pioneered the use of standardized digital buses running the full length of the passenger cabin with the ability to link up with PSUs (passenger service units) in any position. Each PSU can have three or more reading lights, attendant chime-buttons, fresh-air outlets and possibly other services such as drop-down oxygen masks and audio headset plugs. Previously any change in cabin configuration was a major problem, requiring dozens of PSUs to be disconnected and rewired in a new position. Now Airbuses can have seat pitch changed, or have a section changed from cargo to passenger, all in a matter of minutes.

Satcom facilities have today resulted in telephones appearing in passenger cabins, but Airbus are again leading in recognizing the need for a proper on-board com centre. The A340 will have a 'flying office' for the purser or chief stewardess, providing a sensible work station for such tasks as maintaining pax manifests, using computer spreadsheets to record galley status, bar stocks, duty-free sales and future catering requirements, inflight positioning, and other clerical duties. For the passenger the com centre will provide not only telephone but also telex, computer and word-processor facilities, plus telexed hotel booking and car hire, and issue of onward air tickets.

The com centre will also have five video monitors (one First, two Business and two Tourist) with centralized control. Though only peripherally 'communications', inflight entertainment is very much

avionics. It started in 1952 with piped radio. Today the IFE installation can be complex, with wide choice of audio outputs and various arrangements of video. In the mid-1970s actual projectors were used, with Super-8 film, but today it is all remote videotape. Operators have a choice between projectors and screens or retractable monitors. The latter are compact but each serves a smaller section of cabin. Traditional dual projection gives a generally better picture, but the projectors and screens swing down above the aisles causing obstructions.

Chapter 1 briefly outlined the fundamentals of lasers. Their coherent light opened up something that for generations had been science fiction: communicating with light. Purists could say we have done this for some time: Red Indian smoke signals, semaphores and Aldis lamps are examples. In the modern world we mean something different. The bit rate of smoke signals might be 0.2/s, and a good Aldis signaller might get near 1/s. This does not compare well with the few thousand per second of modulated radio waves, which have served us well throughout this century. But today, like Oliver Twist, we are asking for more. Lasercom is coming out of the lab at last, raising the available frequencies from 10^9–10^{11} Hz to around 10^{15} Hz. The USAF launched Project 405B in 1969, and by 1972 the detailed spec was issued for a lasercom system

Mock-up of the A340 com centre, as envisaged by MBB. This would be used by passengers and by the cabin crew, as explained in the text. (Airbus)

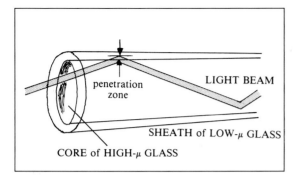

penetration zone

LIGHT BEAM

SHEATH of LOW-μ GLASS

CORE of HIGH-μ GLASS

with HDR (high data rate). HDR meant 1 Gbit/s (1 gigabit, 1 billion bits, is roughly the content of the *Encyclopedia Britannica*).

We tend to think of impressive high-power lasers. Lasercom needs mere milliwatts, but very clever design. The first of several Lasercom systems, built by McDonnell Douglas at St Louis and tested on the ground in 1978 and aboard an EC-135 in 1979, used an Nd YAG laser modulated by an LiTaO$_3$ (lithium tantalate) crystal. This pioneer device used pulse quaternary modulation, combining exact pulse position with vertical and horizontal polarization. The beam was previously split and folded back on itself to double the data rate, with two bits impressed on each pulse. The receiver, on the ground or in an aircraft or satellite, then depolarizes and decodes the light.

Difficulties are obvious, and centre mainly on the unprecedented beam pointing accuracy required.

This is thousands of times more accurate than anything dreamed of with sniper rifles or searchlights. The link began with a 70 mrad (milliradian, about one-twentieth of a degree) beam from the transmitter aimed at the receiver, and a 12.5 mrad beam in the opposite direction. The airborne transmitter MAR (multiple access receiver) senses the receiver beacon beam, and refines the transmit beam to 3.5 and then to 1.5 mrad. The latter, the 'green beam', triggers the receiver to correct its own line of sight and transmit a narrow beacon beam, increasing pulse rate to 3 kHz. This in turn is sensed by the aircraft, triggering further reduced tracking error, narrowing the green beam to only 100 microrad for lasercom, which in turn readies the receiver. It is difficult to imagine a link with a 100 microrad beam at a range of seventy miles or more; it is rather like aiming from London to hit one particular pinhead in Bristol. The whole uplink/downlink time was about 10.5 s, and after studying atmospheric distortion the bit loss was brought down to one in a million, whilst 'transmitting each second more information than the US Postal Service carries in a week'.

If that isn't impressive I don't know what is. Since then the USAF has taken the process very much further, and the US Navy has developed lasercom with blue-green light to punch through space, atmosphere and seawater. When these highly classified stories can be told they will make a lot of people take degrees in physics and join the team.

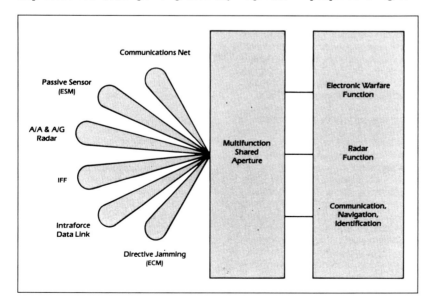

Communications Net

Passive Sensor (ESM)

A/A & A/G Radar

IFF

Intraforce Data Link

Directive Jamming (ECM)

Multifunction Shared Aperture

Electronic Warfare Function

Radar Function

Communication, Navigation, Identification

Above left *Optical fibres comprise a core and sheath of glasses of different μ (refractive index). The light penetrates a little way into the sheath.*

Left *Several companies are investigating the use of a single shared (possibly conformal) aperture for virtually all emissive avionics functions. This is the scheme proposed by Westinghouse for the GD/McDD A–12A attack aircraft, though Harris has won the antenna contract.*

All these are very long-range systems. Optical communications are also becoming important over short ranges. Tiny LEDs can be used to power various kinds of lasercom system. For example in March 1989 Ferranti announced the ACQUIRE system for secure communications over ranges around 1,700 ft (500 m); it was first tested in a helicopter. ACQUIRE conveys digital voice or data at 10 kbits/s, using GaAs diodes so small the system is 'eye safe'. An alternative, for fixed networks (for example, inside aircraft) is to use FO (fibre optics).

FO is being used over ranges from centimetres to a few dozen kilometres. Fantastic data rates can be channelled along optical fibres or 'light pipes'. These behave like common coax cables, but are typically made of two kinds of glass. Each fibre, which is usually finer than a human hair, comprises a core of glass of high refractive index surrounded by a sheath of low refractive index. If light can be fed in at one end it has to travel along the core, being repeatedly reflected from the core/sheath interface, or very slightly beyond it, until it emerges at the other end. Fibres are made in two main ways, one by drawing off the core and sheath from concentric compartments in a crucible and the other by vapour deposition (for example of germania) inside a tube (for example of silica) which is then collapsed inwards to force the germania into a solid core, the fibre then being pulled out in a furnace. In any case, the objective is to get perfect transmission with the lowest possible loss, measured in decibels per kilometre.

The obvious source for fibre-optic com is the semiconductor laser, such as the GaAs chip, which has microscopic physical dimensions compatible with the fibres. Again, in order to achieve near-perfect transmission without loss of intelligence, digital techniques are clearly preferred. FO com can be used in ground networks, and are coming in for anti-tank missile guidance, but in avionics their main applications so far have been to carry intelligence around the aircraft. Optical fibres are used in several new aircraft to convey information from one 'black box' or other functioning item to another. They offer all the advantages of multiwire flat electric cables with the additions of thousands of times higher potential data rate, probably higher resistance to difficulties caused by lightning strike or nuclear EMP (electromagnetic pulse) and potentially even greater resistance to combat damage. Fibre optics are a big growth area in avionics. FBL (fly by light) is discussed in Chapter 14.

Yet another incoming com technology is speech recognition and DVI (direct voice input). Today's combat pilot is increasingly having to look down into his cockpit to hit edgekeys which reprogram his MPDs (multipurpose displays). This is bad enough, but the result of any particular keystroke (pressing one button) depends on a previous series of inputs. Thus, though multifunction controls and displays reduce visual scanning and tactile actions, they add to the pilot's memory task. For the helo pilot doing 70 knots at an altitude of 5 ft in duff weather the situation is getting out of hand, and the only answer seems to be to allow the pilot to issue spoken commands.

There are obviously problems, the most basic being getting the hardware and software to understand and obey the input without fail. Smiths Industries (Lear Siegler) has long been a leader in this field, working with RAE Bedford and many other groups and using such test aircraft as the RAE One-Eleven and the AFTI/F-16. The first flight using isolated-word speech recognition took place with an Armée de l'Air Mirage IIIR on 5 July 1982, and it was followed by the AFTI/F-16 using 34 words organized in rigid syntax structures. This was enough for changing com frequencies and nav waypoints, but tests with Farnborough's Buccaneer S.2B went on to the use of connected-word speech in a noisy environment. By matching the command with stored word patterns, and outputting a display or synthesized voice prior to implementation, the error rate is being brought to acceptable levels. By 1995 DVI will probably be a routine part of the pilot's interface in military and perhaps big civil cockpits.

Another exciting development is the possibility of using a single antenna for every avionic function in the aircraft. This is a real challenge because there may be 10,000 totally dissimilar signals going out or coming in each second, and everything has to be precisely separated. It seems clear that the only way to do this is to use thousands of individual phased-array modules in an aperture of substantial size. Westinghouse pioneered the concept of the shared-aperture antenna, and proposed to use this for the first time in the very important GD/McDonnell Douglas A-12A. In the event the award of the very advanced antenna system for this aircraft went to Harris. Unfortunately details will remain classified for several years.

3

NAVIGATION

For at least 3,000 years mariners have been guided by the EM radiation of lighthouses. In 1919 scheduled commercial flying began in Europe, but the favoured method of navigation was to follow railways (this was called 'the iron compass') and some of the aircraft did not even carry 'wireless'. On 1 July 1924 the first transcontinental mail route was opened across the USA, but in bad weather it often made demands on the pilots that no human could meet. The only navaids were visual beacons, and for the first two years these were mainly bonfires, lit when aircraft were expected. Of course, all this time pilots had had simple magnetic compasses, and were trained in how to maintain a graphical plot on a chart. A few were skilled in astronav, taking shots with a sextant, but if you are by yourself struggling in rough air with a heavy DH-4 mailplane you can't do much except look at your ASI, wrist or pocket watch and compass (and any identifiable heavenly bodies that might be visible), and 'smell your way' with a lot of luck.

The first overt avionic navaid was the D/F (direction finding) loop antenna, though the same idea in reverse had been tested with Imperial German Navy Zeppelins in 1913 and used routinely in subsequent raids over Britain. The airship would transmit Morse signals, and three or more ground stations would send back the direction of their arrival, by rotating a large loop antenna until received signal strength was a maximum. By plotting the bearings on a chart the crew would obtain a (hopefully small) area, called a cocked hat from its shape, within which they were probably flying

In 1821 Faraday showed that a current is induced in a wire, part of a conductive circuit, moving through a magnetic field. From 1919 experiments took place with airborne antennas capable of indicating the direction of received radio waves, but it took until 1928 before practical types were on the

market. The first were clumsy rectangular frames on which wires were wound, but soon smaller circular loops were devised, these being made so small by 1935 that they could fit inside a streamlined 'acorn' fairing. Suppose a radio wave travels horizontally past two vertical wires. It will induce an alternating voltage in each in turn. If the wires are joined at top and bottom to form a loop, the loop will carry a current, first in one direction, then in the other, with frequency depending on the 'peaks and troughs' of the passing waves. If we now turn the loop until it is aligned with the oncoming waves, in other words at 90° to the direction from which they are coming, no current will flow. This null position shows the direction from which the waves are coming, but we have two possible answers 180° apart. If we connect the loop and the aircraft's fixed antenna (adjusted to equal the peak loop output) to the receiver we will get a much less precise null direction but only one in each 360°. Sometimes a separate, 'sense' antenna is used to give the single output, with no ambiguity. Then, going back to the loop alone, we rotate it until we have a precise zero output. This gives a clear position line (line on which we are at that particular moment). As radio waves follow great-circle paths, which except along the Equator cut meridians at constantly changing angles, the null position has to be corrected to give us an accurate position line. To get a 'fix', by obtaining several position lines in rapid succession, we tune in to a succession of known ground stations.

The only real problem with this form of early D/F was that of night effect. At night a much greater proportion of the radio waves would be reflected from the ionosphere, and, arriving at the aircraft from above, these would generate a loop output when there should be a null. A complex form of Adcock antenna was in use for ground stations, but it was not until late in World War 2 that night effect was virtually eliminated from airborne D/F by improved designs of antenna. With the D.H.106 Comet jetliner the need to minimize drag resulted in twin loops being mounted flush with the skin on top of the fuselage, the skin being cut away above each loop and replaced by dielectric (insulator) to allow the waves to be received. The fact that these cutouts were not round but square was to cost the lives of everyone aboard two Comets and throw away Britain's massive lead in jet airliners. Today almost all the D/F loops still in use are suppressed flush with the skin, either on the top or bottom of the fuselage. They are tuned to any of the 3,000-plus NDBs (non-directional beacons) still in use. Most continuously send out a clear tone interspersed every thirty seconds by a Morse three-letter ident code. A few (called voiceless) require the pilot to tune a BFO (beat-frequency oscillator) to obtain the tone. The onboard receiver normally outputs an unambiguous direction which drives a needle on a cockpit instrument. These instruments vary slightly, having been called a radio compass, RMI (radio magnetic indicator) or ADF (automatic D/F).

Radio D/F was the earliest radio navaid. It was virtually all-weather, and one of its advantages was that it enabled the pilot to home on the ground station, in other words to fly directly towards it. If necessary he could then tune in to another beacon and proceed towards that. This established the idea of following fixed 'airways'. Common sense shows that it was stupid to take what Sir George Cayley

almost 200 years ago called 'the ocean of the air, which comes to every man's door' and then make aircraft keep to overcrowded pathways. We will return to this later; meanwhile, the rotating loop antenna was hardly the best way to home on a ground station. The nearer you got to the station, the more the waves approached not horizontally but from below, and this meant that the null position progressively disappeared, unless you were at very low level. For this and other reasons a better method was sought of flying the fixed network of 'airways', which in the late 1920s were fast being linked up across the United States. In 1925 work began on the radio range, and parts of this came into use from 1928.

Each range station comprised a transmitter feeding two pairs of antenna towers, each pair at opposite corners of a roughly square plot. One pair of towers continuously broadcast Morse A ($\cdot$-) and the other Morse N (-$\cdot$). The result was a set of four narrow beams radiating out like thin vertical walls to a distance of about 100 miles along which a continuous monotone note would be heard. A very short distance to one side either an A or an N would

P9249, *a Wellington IC, was delivered from Weybridge in 1939. Apart from a drift sight and compass, its only navaid was the DF loop, housed in the streamlined pod above the fuselage. The only other avionics was the TR.1154/1155 radio, whose wire antenna joined the mast to the fin. It also had a transparent astrodome, but sextants are not considered avionics.*

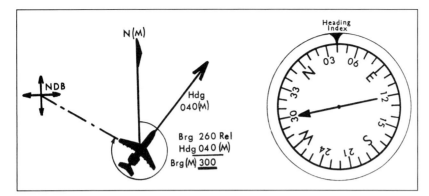

The RMI (radio magnetic indicator) automatically adds the aircraft's heading to the apparent relative bearing of an NDB to give a true readout, in this case 30 (= 300°). (Oxford Air Training School)

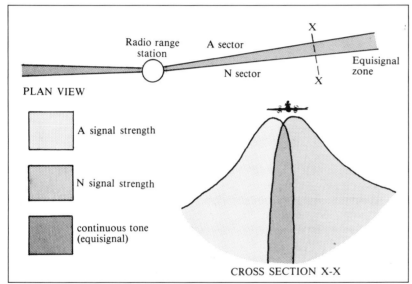

CROSS SECTION X-X

A schematic plan view of a radio range station and cross section through one of its beams. The continuous note along the centre is produced by the intermeshing of the As and Ns. In the position shown, an aircraft would hear strong Ns with a faint background tone.

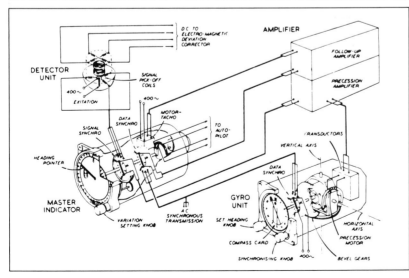

More than 35 years ago the Sperry C.L.2 Gyrosyn compass was probably the most advanced item of avionics to be found on any ordinary production aircraft. It was a contemporary artist who misspelt 'exitation'.

be heard above the tone. Further to that side only the Morse would be heard, the tone (produced by the interlocked As and Ns) disappearing. The radial directions could be adjusted by varying tower output powers until each range beam pointed at the range stations adjacent to it. Thus, the pilot would fly until his headphones heard a continuous note and then fly the beam to the range station, where transmission would fade to zero. He could then follow the same station's back beam on the far side, or tune in to the next station. In many ways the range was a great all-weather system, but it forced traffic to follow narrow overcrowded routes, forced traffic to dogleg instead of going straight to its destination, and forced pilots to spend the entire day with As, Ns and monotones singing in their ears.

By 1930 there were fifty range stations in the US, and this total grew to about 270 by 1940. By this time there were also some radio range stations in Europe. A modification, partly overcoming the stress of continuously flying according to headphone monotones, was the aural range in which the left/right signals were used to feed vibrating reeds in a panel instrument. By 1938 this had been further refined in the VAR (visual aural range) to give left/right needle indication, the pilot steering to drive the needle to the central position. Such improvements could do little to prolong the life of what had always been a very limited system. The radio range, though extremely valuable when first introduced, was also the first time that the political and financial power of the USA made an intrinsically imperfect system so much the world standard that it was difficult to replace.

What was clearly needed was a global electronic system that would permit aircraft to fly great-circle routes from take-off to landing. Many workers took out patents but, tragically, did not have the right political connections to get anywhere. Two examples picked from many were H.A. Affel, who worked for AT&T in the USA, who in 1923 described in detail a radio navaid based on phase measurement giving both relative positions and velocities, and a second scheme using two fixed ground stations sending out synchronized pulses giving crossed hyperbolic fields in exactly the way used eighteen years later for Gee and all that followed it. In 1929 and 1931 W. Albersheim and C.R. Englund, respectively, took out patents using the beat frequencies generated by fixed stations broadcasting

common frequencies to give a doppler effect. The doppler effect is the apparent increase in frequency of a signal received by an observer with relative motion towards the source, and the decrease in frequency as the two move apart. It does not matter whether it is the transmitter or the receiver that moves, or both. One is familiar with this effect from the sound of a close beat-up by a jet, or the passage of a racing car or of a train (especially one sounding its whistle or siren). Again, nothing much was to happen for a further 21 years.

Meanwhile, a lot was being done to remove some of the numerous inaccuracies of the traditional magnetic compass, some of them being cured by electronics. In the 1930s the pilot had the choice of using either the compass, which erred whenever the aircraft turned or changed its speed, and the directional gyro which progressively drifted away from the true heading. The answer was to steer on the DG, especially when changing headings, and use the compass periodically to correct it. In 1937 Sperry linked the two, while in the same year Farnborough tested the first DR (distant reading) master compass, which overcame almost all the inaccuracies and also avoided the interference caused by cockpit armour. The master comprised a very accurate gyro driven electrically at 12,000 rpm, located far from disturbing influences (in Lancasters it was in the rear fuselage). Any change in course (heading) fed current to a motor driving a transmitter system fed to cockpit repeaters. The US answer, perfected by 1944, was the Sperry Gyrosyn, which was identical in principle, except that the magnetic detector was called the flux valve. In recent years this traditional two-axis 'valve' has been replaced in some aircraft by British Aerospace three-axis magnetometers. These compact units (you could almost close your fist on them) sense the Earth's field in three orthogonal axes. The outputs, plus data from the flight control system, are processed in a 1st-order integration to give desired heading. The three-axis mag is a simple strapdown unit with no moving parts, and could well replace all other compass systems. Turns and acceleration have no effect on accuracy.

From the 1930s workers strove to improve the radio range and also to devise area-coverage systems, which would obviously be intrinsically superior. In Germany the Lorenz blind landing system (Chapter 11) was cleverly modified as a guidance system for bombers. With a landing aid the aircraft flies down the beam towards the transmitter, so the accuracy gets progressively better. A bomber would be flying away from the transmitter, so the beam had to be very powerful and extremely narrow in azimuth (directional angular measure), and the receiver had to be highly sensitive. British intelligence knew nothing of this work in 1934-38, but then British intelligence was unaware of such German fighter and bomber prototypes as the Do 217 and Fw 190, flown in public places before the war, German radar or German jet engines! Therefore, Dr R.V. Jones of the Air Ministry had to start from scratch when, from scraps of paper and interrogation of prisoners, there seemed to be evidence that Luftwaffe He 111s were being guided by a beam called Knickebein (crooked leg). After thrilling detective work, and scouring London's Soho district to buy American VHF receivers (the RAF having nothing able to receive on 30-35 MHz), Jones had an Avro Anson rigged up as the first Elint (electronic intelligence, Chapter 8) aircraft. It was ready to go on 21 June 1940, but after the top expert on VHF propagation had said beams couldn't travel from the Continent to the Midlands, Jones was told to cancel the flight. Jones fought back, and that night the Anson clattered aloft from Wyton. Flight Lieutenant Bufton and ham radio fanatic Corporal Mackie had been told nothing except to listen out on 30 or 31.5 MHz. In cloud and darkness Mackie eventually heard Morse on 31.5, found it was a beam and Bufton followed it. It passed over the Rolls-Royce works at Derby, and what's more a second beam was found which intersected with the first to give an offset fix for bomb release!

Subsequently other beams, called X-Gerät, were set up on different sites. They used even higher frequencies, over 70 MHz, and sent out a coarse beam with an extremely fine and precise one down the centre. RAF No 80 Wing searched for the beams but miscalibrated its receivers. Far worse, Jones got everything set up to jam the beams, and someone inexcusably set the false modulation frequency at 1.5 kHz when it was easily measurable at 2 kHz (as a result on 14 November 1940 Coventry was almost destroyed). Even more outrageous, Dr Cockburn (later Sir Robert Cockburn, one of our most eminent scientists) set up a complete apparatus for 'bending the beams' by detecting them on the south coast, sending them by telephone line to Beacon Hill near Salisbury, and re-radiating them exactly in phase but from the wrong place. On the very night operations were to start, the telephone line was *commandeered by someone else*! The belief that Britain could bend the beams was to endure until 1976.

While the Americans remained hooked on their nationwide system of beams, and developed this into VOR as described later, the British, with no nationwide system to influence their ideas, worked from the proverbial clean sheet of paper. The European airlines of the 1930s used a hodge-podge of LF and MF systems, primitive blind landing aids (Chapter 11) and a single microwave link beamed from Lympne in Kent to towers at St Inglevert in France. The only universal aid was the D/F loop, and each bearing supplied by the ground took about one minute, so the cocked hats were inclined to be large even cruising at only 90 knots. Once World War 2 had started, the position was even worse. The RAF bombers had to rely entirely upon their full-time navigators, who laboriously plotted their course*/airspeed, wind velocity and resulting track/groundspeed (the classic triangle of velocities) on charts, using pencils and rulers. This is called dead-reckoning (DR). When possible they stood under the transparent astrodome and took sightings on heavenly bodies using the Mk IX sextant, or looked down the drift sight (not helpful on a dark night) to try to measure drift (angular difference between course and track, due to wind). The results were worse than anyone had imagined. For example, on 19 March 1940, out of fifty crews who took part, 41 reported *they had found and bombed the seaplane base on Sylt*, but subsequent reconnaissance showed not a single bomb crater on this large and distinctive island! On 15 May 1940 Bomber Command was at last allowed to bomb Germany itself, and an attack was mounted on specific industrial targets in the Ruhr. A little later a bomber captain visited the Telecommunications Research Establishment and asked if anything could be done. He reported 'we were told to bomb the Krupps works, but we were completely lost as soon as we left the aerodrome'.

In fact a very great deal had been done already. Back in 1937 one of the talented 'boffins' at Bawdsey (Chapter 4), R.J. Dippy, invented and wrote a detailed report on a bad-weather landing

---

* Course (British) is being replaced by heading (US); I have used both in this book.

aid, pointing out that its coverage could also be wide enough for precision navigation over typical RAF bomber distances. He showed that if synchronized pulses were broadcast from two stations about ten miles apart, then any aircraft receiving them simultaneously was clearly on a position line that was everywhere equidistant from the two stations. By suitably siting the stations this PL could be made to pass along the centre of the landing runway. For use as a navaid, the navigator would read the time-differences between the pulses on a CRT. For any one time-difference the aircraft would follow a curving hyperbolic path passing between the stations (thus Dippy's invention was the first of what were to become known as hyperbolic navaids). With three stations spaced further apart it would be possible to navigate with an accuracy measured in a few tens of metres, on the darkest night. It was such a brilliant idea for 1937 that the Air Ministry decided to do nothing about it.

When the lost RAF bomber captain visited TRE, Dippy was appalled. He reminded his boss, A.P. Rowe, about his hyperbolic navaid of three years earlier. The dusty report was found, and things began to move. Called Gee (G from grid), a Master station and three Slave stations were built, with transmissions precisely keyed together, and airborne receivers designed and constructed. The first Gee mission was flown on 26 June 1941, and to say it transformed the effectiveness of Bomber Command is an understatement. All the navigator had to do was get the right (hyperbolic) chart, tune in to the Gee chain (a VHF system on 30 or 80 MHz), align the bright pulse spikes on his CRT, note the coordinate readings and then read off the position from the chart, the whole task taking maybe fifteen seconds for each fix.

By March 1942 every RAF heavy bomber had Gee Mk II. Eventually 50,000 of these receivers were delivered, many going to the USAAF, ships of the Allied navies and other moving platforms. Without it the first '1,000-bomber raid', on Cologne on 31 May 1942, would have been a shambles. As it was, all but the most inexperienced navigators could use Gee to navigate blind back to their own airfield. In 1943 selected heavies were equipped with Gee-H, a more precise navaid in which the aircraft's known Gee position was then refined by briefly interrogating two beacons in England. Gee-H aircraft had two horizontal yellow bars on their fins.

The range of Gee proved in practice to be con-

siderably greater than LOS (line of sight) limits, especially at low level. Gee, in its greatly improved Mk III form, remained important in northern Europe until the 1960s. In 1948 a Scottish Gee chain was built for civil use, and this was invaluable to BEA and the RAF until its closure in 1969.

The next RAF Bomber Command navaid, chronologically, could hardly have been more different. Oboe, the brainchild of TRE's A.H. Reeves and F.E. Jones, had features in common with X-Gerät. A 'cat station' near Dover and a 'mouse station' at Cromer broadcast streams of VHF pulses which could be received by a high-flying bomber up to about 280 miles away — far enough to cover many important German targets. Each night the Oboe aircraft would navigate near to the target on Gee and then listen to the Oboe signals. If they kept dashes on the left and dots on the right they flew along a circular arc centred on the cat station and passing over the target. Eight minutes from the target the crew would hear a B in Morse. Five minutes out they would hear a C, and three minutes out a D. Finally there would be five dots at 0.5 s spacing followed by a 2.5 s dash. The bombs or target markers were released at the end of the dash. The whole concept struck at the roots of established training and dogma, and many people in authority were so ignorant that they considered Oboe to be nonsense and campaigned against it, whilst actively promoting H_2S (Chapter 6) which in many respects caused more trouble than it was worth. In fact, Oboe probably quadrupled the damage caused by all the RAF's major night attacks on Germany. Fitted to Pathfinders and Master Bomber aircraft, either Mosquitoes or heavies, it was so accurate that the transmissons were adjusted according to the stores that were being dropped, to give 50% error radius within 500 ft and usually much less. In the first raid on Krupps, as noted earlier, the percentage of bombs hitting the factory was less than 3%; in a massive attack on 25 July 1943 marked by Oboe the percentage was not less than 99%.

The pressures of World War 2 spurred development of new radio navaids in many countries, especially systems which could be used over enemy territory without requiring emissions by one's own aircraft. Some had an active life extending to the present day. One of the less-attractive methods was developed in Germany as Sonne, and taken up postwar by the Allies as Consol. Operating in the MF band, it was one of the pioneer long-range devices,

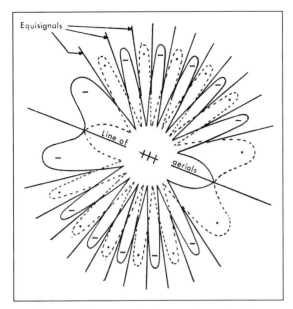

For historical interest, this is a typical polar diagram of the radiation from the three transmitters, a few miles apart, of a Consol station. Aircraft would hear complex streams of dots, equisignal notes and dashes. Consol's main advantages were long range and reliability. (Oxford Air Training School)

able to be received after ionospheric reflection. It sent out a CW (continuous-wave) transmission, comprising a repeated sequence made up of a station identification code, a steady note and then a sequence of signals made up of dots and dashes. These dots and dashes were sent out at a speed at which they could easily be counted, and the numbers varied depending on the azimuth direction. Thus, the Consol station might send out on 089° a stream of 35 dots followed by 25 dashes, while on 090° the broadcast might be 36 dots and 24 dashes. The airborne navigator counted and then corrected the dashes and dots, and then read the station bearing off a chart, remembering that the great-circle path taken by radio signals means that a big correction has to be applied at long ranges to get the rhumb-line bearing of the station. Consol was used by civil and military traffic over remote oceanic areas.

Gee sparked off two more advanced hyperbolic systems which are still used today. Britain produced Decca, which resembled Gee except that it used CW instead of pulses. When one considers that in 1959 the political pressure of the United States prevented

Decca from becoming the basis of a worldwide area-coverage navaid it is ironic to recall that its inventor, William O'Brien, was born in Chicago. In August 1939 O'Brien wrote to his friend Harvey Schwarz, who worked for the Decca Gramophone Co. Nobody in the USA had shown much interest, but in April 1942 the British Admiralty ordered a demo. Deeply impressed, it quickly built the first Decca chain (master and three slaves spaced about eighty miles apart) and receivers for ships. The night before D-day (ie, 5 June 1944) Decca enabled minesweepers to follow exact routes clearing paths through the minefields to the invasion beaches. Decca has been No 1 electronic navaid at sea ever since.

In the air things were tougher, but Decca began flying on the airlines in 1946. At first the crew had to interpret the needle indications of three dial instruments called Deccometers. By 1952 the Decca Flight Log was in use, automatically plotting with a pen on a roller-blind chart the track followed by the aircraft. The author did a lot of flying at this time, and soon had confidence that the inked line really did record aircraft position with sufficient accuracy to do a blind letdown and, with luck, an almost blind landing (though it could not have been certificated for such use). By the 1960s Decca had developed the Omnitrac, a computer able to accept inputs from Decca, VOR/DME (described later), doppler or inertial sensors, plus a DR backup driven only by the air-data system. Omnitrac provides an automatic pictorial display with undistorted charts, can be coupled to an autopilot or flight director, and provides not only time/distance readouts to a waypoint (going direct and not doglegging via overcrowded airways) but also vertical guidance. Decca Omnitrac was the pioneer 3-D R-Nav (area navigation) system, and it was outstanding in the context of this time. In 1969-70 it was evaluated by Eastern, TWA, United and Mohawk for use in congested traffic areas, and in 1970 Eastern bought thirteen Omnitracs for DC-9s working the Washington-NY-Boston shuttle. A particular advantage of Omnitrac, proved in long trials, was that the 3-D guidance made it possible to make 'instrument' bad-weather approaches to any runway, instead of having to join the queue for the active ILS-equipped runway.

In the late 1960s Decca developed the Roller Map Mk 5 as a neat and simple pictorial display for tactical and local-service aircraft, especially

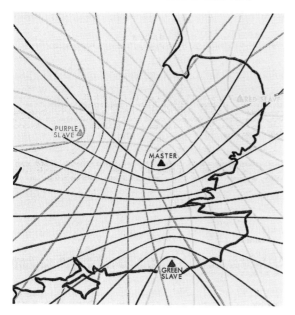

helicopters, able to portray up to 737,000 sq miles from a single cassette. The display could receive data from doppler or inertial sensors, accuracy

being 1.5% of distance flown. In a very different development Decca teamed with Ambac Industries to develop Mona (modular navigation). This was not so much a navaid as a package for receiving inputs from on-board sensors and to display and manage the flight, the associated computer being able to store practically the entire world's airways, including SIDs (standard instrument departures), lat/long of waypoints and VORs, VOR frequencies and all published STARs (standard terminal arrivals). Mona was fitted to the first TriStars.

Quite unrelated was another Decca product, Dectra. This was a long-range hyperbolic aid with a range of rather more than 2,000 miles. It used pairs of stations at each end of the route being covered.

In the USA the success of Gee prompted development of Loran (long-range navigation). This was a pulse system, but aimed at achieving greater ranges by using longer wavelengths reflected from the ionosphere. No navaid has ever been developed through so many variations, with wavelengths, PRFs (pulse repetition frequencies), formats and cockpit interpretation all going through numerous major changes. One of the four early forms was

Above *The first Decca chain, broadcast by four interlinked stations in southern England. Decca was not only CW but also LF, so it was usable down to ground level. (Oxford Air Training School)*

Right *Part of a Loran-C hyperbolic pattern, sent out by master M and secondary station S. The numbers represent microseconds. At point P on 53000 an inaccuracy of 1 microsecond in the time difference would represent a position-line error of about 1,640 ft (500 m).*

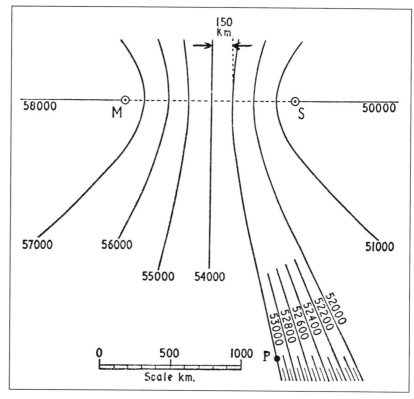

Standard Loran, with fourteen different PRFs on 1.75, 1.85 and 1.95 MHz and a blip display on a CRT. Most of the seventy Loran stations at the end of World War 2 were of this type. In 1951 Loran-C became important, and today this is the standard form, but the hardware has changed out of all recognition. Until the 1960s airborne Loran-C was invariably a receiver tuned to the Loran networks, especially those covering North America and the oceanic areas, installed in such aircraft as 707s and DC-8s. Today airborne Loran is usually a tiny panel-mounted solid-state package for GA aircraft, and absent from modern jetliners. It has multiple key input, alphanumeric output and, whilst still being able to accept Loran inputs, it also processes magnetic (compass type) input, fuel (quantity and burn rate), waypoints (storing up to 200) and air-data inputs. Outputs can interface with the autopilot or various panel instruments or displays. Somewhat different forms of Loran were the main (often the only) precision electronic navaid in the Vietnam war, used for blind bombing and (as Pave Nail) to guide OV-10 FAC platforms.

The various forms of Decca and Loran were the pioneer area-navigation (R-Nav) systems, but to the lasting detriment of aviation a totally different navaid has been the world standard for 30 years and so now covers the globe. This is VOR (VHF omnidirectional range), and it is our old friend the 1920s radio range updated to be a bit more useful. Each VOR station on the ground continuously broadcasts CW on a frequency between 108 and 118 MHz. Thus, it has LOS limitations, which rule it out for low-level operations (in any case it would be useless in a modern fighter or helicopter cockpit in combat). The transmission incorporates Morse ident letters, and a method of modulation which varies through the 360° of each revolution in azimuth. First, a reference frequency of 9.96 kHz is superimposed; then an amplitude-modulated variable signal is added which in each 360° revolution starts from a minimum, steadily builds to a maximum and then after 360° instantly starts again at the minimum amplitude. Each revolution takes 2 s, in other words the beacon frequency is 30 Hz. This means that the signal sent out will vary throughout the 360°, each direction having its own unique phase-difference between the reference and bearing modulations. Though of course the signals are sent out in all directions, not just 360 discrete ones like spokes on a wheel, it became customary to think of the broadcast from each beacon as being made up of 360 'spokes' called radials.

It was sensible to set up each station with the reference modulation aligned with local magnetic north. Thus, the phase-difference is a minimum at 000/360° and a maximum on 180°. This makes VOR more useful than ADF from an NDB (non-directional beacon). To recap, the latter broadcasts the same signal in all directions, so the best we can do is obtain a reading on our RMI or HSI (horizontal situation indicator) of the station's bearing relative to north as seen from our own aircraft. If we have duplicated ADF receivers and a two-needle RMI we can get the two bearings of a pair of NDBs simultaneously, but we still have some work to do to navigate, especially bearing in mind that wind causes drift, so our track is not the same as the aircraft's heading from which the radio bearings were measured. In contrast, as the VOR signal received at the aircraft contains information telling us the true bearing of that station, we do not need to allow for our own heading. If we have a simple ADF or RMI indicator, or a complex HSI, the needle will always swing to the actual direction of the VOR station to which we are tuned. In other words we get the QDM (one of the sixty-year-old three-letter Q-codes, in this case meaning 'In zero wind what course should I steer to reach you?') based on the magnetic meridian at the VOR. But we may still need a 'to/from' indication, depending on what display we have on the instrument panel.

There is no VOR instrument. Today most aircraft of over 12,500 lb gross weight have an RMI or HSI which, among other things, can give an instant dial readout to a VOR, or to an NDB. Light aircraft usually lack such expensive instruments but may have a simple ILS (Chapter 11). This will include a localizer needle which, on the landing approach, swings left or right to indicate which way we should steer to get on the glide-path centreline. Many ILS receivers, and every one made since about 1960, can also be used to present VOR left/right steering information. Simpler indicators, having the left/right needle only (in other words, no glide-path up/down needle) are called a VOR/LOC, meaning VOR plus localizer. The VOR is colloquially called an Omni, and the pilot often tunes in to a VOR station with a knob called an omni bearing selector (OBS), with which, having tuned in to the selected VOR, he can pick the bearing he wants either to go TO the station or FROM it. With most cockpit

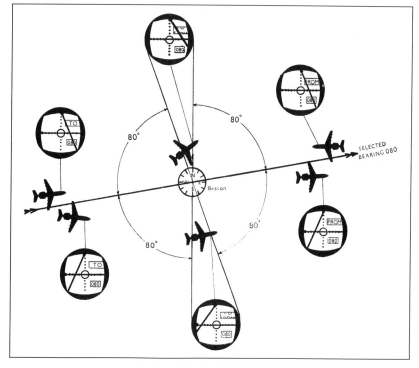

Some Omni (VOR/ILS deviation indicator) indications that would be seen in a One-Eleven near a VOR with 080° set on the OBS. Note that they are independent of the aircraft's heading (one is flying reciprocal). No clear TO/FROM is obtainable within about a 20° sector abeam the station on each side. (Oxford Air Training School)

instruments, certainly a simple VOR/LOC, a TO or FROM flag appears in a window. Then all you have to do is fly left or right until the needle is centred. As you fly over or past the station the flag changes from TO to FROM, and normally one would switch the OBS to the outbound radial. Of course, with commercial transports and other well-equipped aircraft the autopilot or flight system can itself interpret the phase-difference of a VOR signal, and steer the aircraft automatically towards or away from any VOR station.

In the early 1950s the VOR navaid seemed in the United States to be the best system available around which to construct the US air routes. Nevertheless, it was recognized as far from perfect, but it was to take time for its faults to be fully appreciated. Only today, when we can enjoy essentially perfect navaids, can it be seen that VOR was the last chapter in the horse-and-buggy era of aviation. The list of its shortcomings is awesome. Each VOR, broadcasting VHF from ground level, can be received only within its line of sight. In practice 200W stations, which are almost universal (except for TVORs, terminal VORs, which are of only 100W power) cannot reliably be received beyond 200 nm even from 50,000 ft. Only 80 spot frequencies are

allocated for the many thousands of VOR stations around the world. Stations using the same frequency are separated geographically, but for every station a protection range (typically 80 nm) and protection altitude (typically 25,000 ft) are published. Outside these limits the Earth's curvature no longer gives reliable protection from interference, so pilots can no longer rely on the bearing information received from the station concerned.

With almost all VORs there is varying interference around the 360° of radials, including interference from other stations. More serious are site errors. The signals sent out around the different radials ought to travel straight to the aircraft, but in almost every VOR in practice there is a greater or lesser proportion of the radiated signal that reaches the aircraft via an indirect path, reflected by hills, large buildings or various other disturbing factors. Thus the received signal will be a mix with an electrical phase different from that of the direct signal, and the aircraft receiver has no way of allowing for this. Even at a distance of many miles from the VOR irregular terrain always exerts a distorting effect, and this can be serious enough (causing errors called scalloping or bends) to require promulgation in the literature (in the UK, *The Air*

Pilot). These aberrations are especially serious when the receiver is a low level. There are also the errors in the airborne equipment, which are generally in the region of plus or minus 2° to 3°. ICAO (the International Civil Aviation Organization) adopted a total system error for planning purposes of 5°, but in practice VOR was soon found to be liable to errors of plus or minus 7° 30′. This means that its steering information can put you outside the 10-mile width of an airway within 90 nm.

On top of all these shortcomings, VOR could never be anything but a highly imperfect system which continued the philosophy of the old radio range in carving up our planet's sky and forcing traffic into overcrowded channels. In the 1950s air traffic of all kinds was growing, and there was every reason to expect the trend to continue. Anyone with the ability to imagine the most probable future could see that by its very nature VOR would have to be replaced as soon as possible by an area-coverage, or so-called R-nav, system. And I have left until last the fact that, like an NDB, a VOR merely gives a bearing. It provides no information on distance. To fix one's position using VOR requires plotting on a map, or some kind of computer display, using the bearings from two or three VORs. Even back in the 1950s this seemed archaic, especially to a 707's crew.

As you stand on the apron at an airfield the sky seems a very open and big place. The airlines might be thought fortunate in that their vehicles just ride on the air, unlike the railways which need track on a ballasted foundation, bridges, tunnels, junctions, level crossings and much other infrastructure. It so happens that two steel rails 56.5 in apart are a marvellous system, which can go on into the 300 mph era in the next century; but supposing such track had stuck at, say, 60 mph? The world's railways would spend half their energy trying to find billions for a new system and the rest of their energy arguing about it. And to a considerable degree this is what the world's aviation community has been doing, because though less visible than steel rails the world's air traffic *does* need worldwide infrastructure. In 1958 ICAO decided there had to be an international standard navigation aid, so a giant conference was held in Montreal in 1959 to take the decision. It was attended by delegates from 37 countries, but it had been obvious for eighteen months beforehand that it would be a two-horse race, the two candidates being point-source VOR and area-coverage Decca.

Had both been American systems Decca would unquestionably have been chosen, but Decca had the great misfortune to be British. So from the very outset the whole meeting became not technical but political, and where technicalities could not be avoided they were shaped and bent for political ends. ICAO decided there should be two committees, called A and B. Committee A was told to list all the operational problems and requirements and specify what a navaid should do, and the committee took extreme care to avoid even thinking in terms of area coverage and polarized its requirements on point sources. Committee B was told to look at what was actually available and evaluate how well each met the requirements. Instead of waiting to see what Committee A's requirements might turn out to be, Committee B immediately launched into an evaluation of VOR against Decca which was quite astonishing in the openness of its one-sidedness. To cut a very long story short, VOR, being American, could not fail to win. Decca, being British, could not fail to lose. Nearly all the 37 countries, which were in receipt of US technical and financial aid, never even thought that the almost universal choice might just possibly have been wrong.

Clearly, I still smart at this monumental wrong decision. Obviously, in 1959 Decca was by no means a perfect navaid, but it would have been a thousand times better than VOR. The published record of the 1959 ICAO meeting stands for all time as a monument to political power winning over both common sense and a genuine global requirement. If there was any merit at all in the choice it was that horse-and-buggy VOR was, at least in the United States, a known system, which could with assurance be duplicated (at vast expense, bringing good business to the US electronics industry) all over the world. Decca seemed, except to the few people who were familiar with it, to be rather new and unproven, to the extent that US evaluators felt they could describe it as 'inaccurate and unreliable'. In fact its reliability in 1959 was virtually 100 per cent, and its accuracy approximately fifteen times better than several of the existing VORs, and perhaps five times better than the average.

Having been stuck with VOR ever since, the world's aircraft then had to be fitted with an extra black box in order to find out how far they were from the VORs. The result is DME (distance measuring equipment). This is similar to secondary radar, or IFF. The aircraft's DME transmitter is first tuned to the UHF frequency of the DME station the pilot wishes to interrogate. A total of 252 frequencies are available, from 962 to 1,213 MHz at 1 MHz spacing, and these provide 126 channels, each comprising two frequencies 63 MHz apart. Thus Channel 1 uses 1,025 MHz air/ground and 962 MHz ground/air, while Channel 64 uses 1,088 MHz air/ground and 1,151 MHz ground/air, and so on. When tuned and switched on, the airborne DME broadcasts a stream of pulses. When these reach the DME station they trigger a transponder which, 1 μs (microsecond) later, sends back a stream of response pulses picked up by the aircraft's DME receiver. Older DMEs needed perhaps 20 s to carry out a range search and lock-on, but modern DMEs take about 0.25 s, and stay locked on for about 10 s during loss of signal, such as when a wing blocks the line of sight during a steep turn. The DME display is normally on the HSI, but in older aircraft it may be a separate instrument, either with odometer (veeder counter) windows of nm and time to go, or a dial/pointer presentation. Many DMEs have a knob for setting the readout to show distance, time or ground speed. Of course, DME ranges are slant ranges. Should Concorde ever wish to use DME, the readout when overhead the DME station would still be 11 miles, and the ground speed would be zero, so DME has its problems too!

It was sensible to try to site DMEs as near as possible to VORs. The DME antenna looks like a vertical pole, whereas a VOR is a giant horizontal ring of antennas rather like a miniature Stonehenge, on top of a metal mesh disc about 200 ft in diameter, called the counterpoise, to remove the worst of the site errors due to terrain. A co-located station is called a VOR/DME, and tuning in to its facilities (VOR on one channel, DME on another) gives a so-called ϱ-θ (Greek rho-theta) or polar coordinate output of range (rho) and bearing (theta).

Thanks to modern microelectronics DMEs are now small and cheap enough to be found in many private aircraft, but their sheer numbers, especially in the United States, means that DME ground stations are becoming overloaded. Despite the fact that the response follows in microseconds this overloading is having a serious effect, resulting in delayed responses and a general reduction in reliable interrogation range.

By the late 1940s a closely related rho-theta navaid, Tacan (tactical air navigation) was in production for military aircraft. In principle Tacan is a

UHF VOR/DME, though with numerous mostly minor differences. Airborne Tacan transceivers were originally bulky, often weighing 100 lb, and could be tuned to Tacan ground stations within a range of 200 nm. Today microtacans often weigh less than 10 lb, and can interrogate out to a range of 300 nm. The normal system has 252 channels, 126 in Mode X and 126 in Mode Y, and each ground station can be interrogated by 100 aircraft simultaneously without overloading. Output range and bearing can be analog or Arinc 429 digital, accuracies today invariably being better than 0.1 nm and 0.7°. Until the 1980s civil aircraft could obtain only range from a Tacan, bearings being unobtainable, but today numerous small Tacans are regular equipment in GA aircraft. Some Tacans can operate in inverse modes which (for example) enable a bearing to be obtained from a DME-only station. A specialized inverse mode for tankers gives immediate range and bearing of Tacan-equipped aircraft seeking fuel. Conversely, airborne Tacan beacons in tanker or mission-lead aircraft can be interrogated by friendly aircraft and get a bearing related to magnetic North, irrespective of the heading of the beacon aircraft.

In many countries Tacan stations are co-located with a VOR, the station then being called a Vortac. Where a plain VOR and a Tacan are far apart but both within range, the keen civil pilot can get a range from the Tacan and (mentally or with a pencil) picture how this range circle is cut at two places by the VOR radial. The ambiguity is usually immediately resolved by seeing whether the Tacan range is increasing or decreasing, showing which of the two possible fixes is correct (see page 58).

From 1971 the accuracy of some VORs was greatly improved by replacing them with DVORs (doppler VOR). These use a different waveform, broadcast by a wide-aperture antenna which significantly reduces distortions caused by the local terrain. The signal modulations are also exchanged, so that the reference signal is amplitude-modulated. Airborne equipment is unchanged.

Doppler is a common word in avionics, as mentioned earlier. Suppose a noise with a distinctive pitch — the common example is a train sounding its whistle — travels close past our ears at high speed. C.J. Doppler explained that, as the source comes towards us, we receive the wave fronts at an abnormally rapid rate, resulting in a falsely high note. As the source passes, the pitch quickly falls, passing

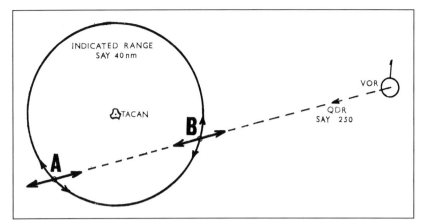

A pilot flying the 250° VOR radial interrogates a Tacan and gets a reading of 40 nm. This gives him two possible fixes, A or B. He can soon resolve the ambiguity by noting whether the DME range is increasing or decreasing. (Oxford Air Training School)

through the correct value at the point of minimum distance, where range rate, ie rate of change of range, is zero. The sound from the receding source is falsely low; subtracting the speed of the source from the speed of the waves could, with a fast jet, result in a received frequency below the ear's aural range, so we should hear nothing.

In DVOR the principle merely reduces errors in an existing ground station, but from the earliest days of radar (next chapter) it was obvious that the effect could have many useful applications. One such use was to form a self-contained navaid, strictly called a doppler radar or doppler navigator or DVS (doppler velocity sensor), but today often just called a doppler. This comprises a simple low-power radar sending out CW or FMCW (frequency modulated continuous wave) signals with an extremely high frequency. These signals are sent out in the form of either two, three or four narrow pencil beams, each similar to the visible beam from a searchlight, from the underside of the aircraft. The beams are inclined down at an oblique angle so that, even from 60,000 ft, the beams from the aircraft in level flight will all reach the ground much nearer than the visible horizon. The beams are symmetric left/right about the aircraft's centreline; there may be two pointing ahead and two behind (the Janus arrangement), or one pointing dead ahead and one diagonally to each side. With radar instead of sound the movement of the source is extremely slow compared with the speed of the waves, but with a very high wave frequency the doppler shift is significant and can be measured precisely, and the result gives an accurate measure of the aircraft's velocity (speed and direction).

The first doppler was code-named Green Satin,

developed for the British V-bombers by Marconi in 1949-54. Subsequently many companies have produced military and civil dopplers, Marconi's own team (as GEC Avionics) having in the AD660 the smallest, able to fit between frames and stringers in the belly and weighing 19 lb. Like nearly all modern dopplers it has a printed-circuit microstrip antenna behind a flush dielectric cover fitting the curvature of the skin. Any three of the four beams can be used, the fourth providing self-checking and enhancing accuracy at high altitudes. Modern dopplers separate out the received signal in each beam, and compare its frequency with that of a fixed reference in a local oscillator. The resulting doppler shift is fed to a microprocessor and used to display ground speed and drift, or TMG (track made good), or orthogonal velocities (Vx/Vy/Vz) or whatever measure may be required. A doppler plus a compass provides a complete autonomous navigation system. Alternatively it can operate in parallel with an AHRS (attitude/heading reference system) to give accuracy not far short of the best INS (described later) at much less cost. Today's big jets have a doppler integrated with four or five other navaids, all driving the same computers and displays.

At this point mention should be made of a host of 'area navigation' (R-Nav) systems which are merely various arrangements of computers and other devices able to process and display inputs from existing radio navaids. One of the first to be tested by US airlines, to try to overcome the congestion caused by VOR, was the Butler-National. This computer system enabled aircraft to fly direct, instead of having to dog-leg from VOR to VOR. It was tested in 2-D form in 1968 and in American's 727s in 3-D form in December 1969. Today another

US avionics firm, Foster, markets a range of 'area navigation systems' which simply help GA users to navigate by Vortac, VOR/DME and Loran C. In Britain Racal's RNav2 accepts inputs from VOR/DME, Decca, Loran, doppler, VLF/Omega and air data, and stores details of 100 waypoints and information on 300 routes, airports and other facilities. In France CEIS Espace has the Alpha-Nav for light aircraft which even includes a plotting table!

Before outlining two important global radio navaids, Omega and GPS, it is chronologically proper to turn to the INS (inertial navigation system). This is the only totally self-contained navaid, able to function on Earth or in deepest space, and requiring no emissions or external help. It is, in most respects except price, the ultimate perfect navaid.

An INS depends on the fundamental fact that any mass possesses inertia. As Newton postulated, it stays at rest unless acted upon by an external

All doppler navigators known to the author are self-contained packages mounted immediately above the antenna which is flush with the bottom of the fuselage. This was a Decca product of the 1960s.

force. Thus, a suspended mass can be used to measure acceleration. We could, for example, hang a weight on a thread inside a car. At rest, no matter what the attitude of the car, it would hang so that the thread pointed towards the centre of the Earth — or so nearly that we can ignore the error. If we now drive away, the pendulum will be displaced to the rear, by an amount proportional to how hard we 'put our foot down'. As we reach steady speed, the pendulum will return to the vertical. Sideways displacements will indicate bends, or corners. Braking will result in forwards displacement. If we add a system for continuously measuring the position of the mass we can obtain a continuous record of all the accelerations during our drive. Integrating these with respect to time would give velocity (speed and direction). Integrating again would give a continuous readout of position.

Aircraft INSs measure acceleration with accelerometers. In principle these consist of a free mass able to slide inside a tube, without friction, and restrained by springs to rest normally in a null or neutral position (in practice they are not like this, but are tiny straingauges based on piezoelectric crystals, which sense acceleration by measuring the

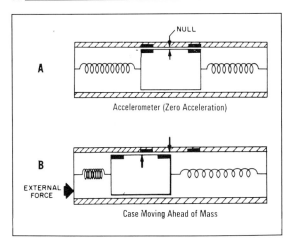

A purely schematic accelerometer, shown first at rest (A) with black bars showing magnetic transformers exactly aligned. When the vehicle in which it is mounted accelerates (B) the magnetic transformers induce an output voltage proportional to the displacement.

crystal's electrical output). To build an INS we first take one accelerometer and arrange it N/S or aligned with the aircraft's longitudinal axis, and then take a second and arrange it E/W or aligned with the lateral axis. Most advanced types of INS also have a third accelerometer, mounted vertically. The three accelerometers thus can measure accelerations in the three orthogonal planes with extraordinary precision. But, at least in early types of INS, they could not just be bolted on to the aircraft. No pilot could hold the wings precisely level for a single second, let alone for fifteen hours, and each unwanted rotation about any of the three axes would cause two of the accelerometers to give false output caused by a component of the Earth's gravitational field.

Accordingly, most INSs at present in use mount the accelerometers on a stabilized platform. This is a frame mounted on three sets of virtually frictionless gimbals (pivots) so that, no matter how the aircraft manoeuvres, the innermost platform can always remain precisely level. To ensure that it does stay level we mount on it three (sometimes two) gyros, similar to those used in aircraft instruments for sixty years but made to a totally new standard of accuracy. Arranged in the same three orthogonal axes, the gyros tend to maintain their axes fixed in space, thus holding the platform level. Errors caused by Earth rotation, Coriolis force and gravity tend

to precess each gyro, trying to rotate its axis at 90° to the applied error force, and these are automatically countered by pick-off voltages which drive small torque motors to hold the platform stable. The same motors are used to drive the platform level throughout any manoeuvres the aircraft may perform. Yet another requirement is Schuler tuning. A Schuler pendulum is a pendulum with a period of 84 minutes, which is that of a simple pendulum whose length is the same as the radius of the Earth. Obviously we cannot make such a pendulum physically, but it is simple to achieve Schuler tuning by suitably designing the software of the INS computer. Thus we effectively fasten the stable platform to a pendulum whose mass is at the centre of the Earth. This achieves two objectives: it avoids sudden swings and oscillations caused by (for example) an afterburner take-off, and it keeps the platform level (ie, aligned with local horizontal) even in a flight from the Equator to one of the poles, which would otherwise tilt the platform 90° and invalidate the whole idea.

The first INS, of a sort, was the guidance system of the German A4 'V-2' rocket of World War 2. It was a considerable achievement, but to modern eyes it was massive and clumsy. Following trials in several aircraft, a prototype INS weighing 2,600 lb steered a B-29 across the USA in 1953. In 1956 I visited North American Aviation's Autonetics division and was deeply impressed by their then-secret REINS (radar-equipped inertial navigation system) which later guided the A-5 Vigilante, its pioneer Verdan computer being described in Chapter 15. Convair would have liked to use an Autonetics INS

A schematic inertial platform (one gimbal omitted for clarity), with three accelerometers and three gyros, marked E, N and Z (aircraft vertical axis).

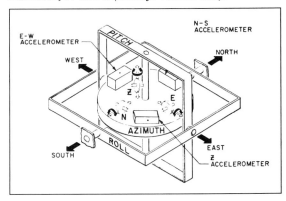

in the B-58, but for reasons of timing had to use Sperry's complex ASQ-42V which combined an early INS with doppler, astro tracker and much else!

All these pioneer systems demanded gyros and accelerometers much more accurately made than anything the metalworking industry had previously known, resulting in 'clean rooms' into which nobody may carry a pencil, indiarubber, cigarette or almost anything else, and where feet and hair must be encased in tight nylon bags. By 1958 a rising star in world avionics, Litton, had created the LN-3 system compact enough to fit the tight-packed F-104G Starfighter, and rather surprisingly this was allowed to be not only widely exported but also licensed to resurgent German industry. The LN-3 was true pioneering, and, starting with an MTBF (mean time between failures) of fifteen minutes in 1960, it swiftly matured to a figure of several hours.

In these military aircraft there was pressure for a fast spool-up. When you switch things on in the cockpit the little gyro wheels take time to run up to speed, typically driven electrically to 24,000 rpm. Some INSs use 'floated gyros' in which the spinning wheels or spheres are supported hydrostatically in a liquid. It took ten minutes for the LN-3 to warm up, which in a nuclear environment over central Germany was like being told to 'take the pills ten minutes before you feel the pain coming on'. Litton accordingly devised an alert-align mode which could be done during refuelling and rearming. Provided the aircraft was not thereafter moved, nor jolted by the pilot's frantic rush for the cockpit at

the next 'scramble', the platform could be regarded as pre-aligned, and the gyros would reach adequate speed in 90 s. To align the platform you have to use traditional gyrocompassing to insert the North reference. Then, unless this was already in the computer memory when the aircraft was parked, you tap out the latitude and longitude, not of the airfield but of the exact spot on the airfield. This is all fed into the software mathematical model (which also incorporates the Schuler tuning), together with the coordinates of each waypoint along the route.

Sperry pioneered civil INS in 1966 with the SGN-10. This taught the airlines almost 'everything they wanted to know but were afraid to ask'. It helped Boeing and the airlines draft Arinc-561 for civil INS systems, but when Boeing ran a competition for the INS for the 747 it was won not by Sperry but by AC Spark Plug (General Motors), later renamed Delco, with an INS called Carousel IV. AC were far from sure they would recoup their development costs with possibly only thirty or forty sales. Today Delco make this number in a week, with deliveries nudging 8,000! Many of these are military ASN-119s. The original Arinc-561 requirement included accuracy of 20 nm cross-track and 25 nm along track after a 10-h flight, INS errors being related to elapsed time and not to distance. This was good enough to put aircraft well within terminal

The Litton LW-33 (AN/AJQ-25) was a variant of the pioneer LN-3, fitted to the F-104G and the first inertial system to go into combat service. The stable platform is seen at left.

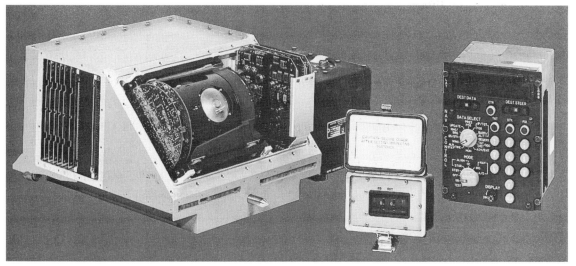

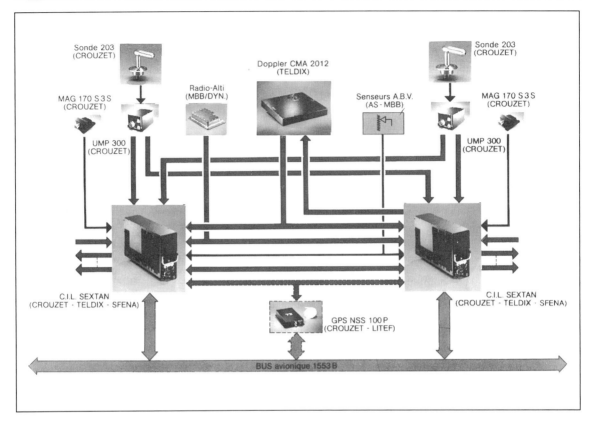

VHF and radar range. Today virtually all Carousel
IVs are linked with doppler and increasingly with
Omega, giving 10-h accuracy well within 1 nm. In
1968 AC, whose previous INS experience was
entirely in ICBM and space programmes, promised
Boeing an MTBF of 1,250 h; today the figure is
around 4,000 h.

There are numerous variations on the INS theme,
some leading to dramatic simplification. Ferranti
concocted the delightful name 2 Gins for the
2-gimbal INS (FIN 1110) which, fitted to non-
aerobatic aircraft such as transports and most
helicopters, manages with a single Oscillogyro (a
patented gyro able to measure angular displacements about two axes), a floated RIG (rate
integrating gyro) and three accelerometers. The
package weighs 15 lb, compared with 55 lb for
Carousel IV, and costs about 30 per cent as much.
Azimuth is strapdown, in other words fixed to the
aircraft. Another advantage of such a system is
that, without outside help, it can align within 0.1°
of true N within 2 to 5 min. FIN 1110 stabilizes the
antennas of the radars of Royal Navy AEW Sea

*The Franco-German Eurocopter PAH-2 will have a
complex Sextan navigation and air-data system. It
comprises two strapdown inertial units (CIL), two
magnetic sensors, two air-data units, a doppler, a
radio altimeter and a GPS. (Crouzet)*

Kings. Since 1985 Ferranti, like a very few other
companies, is marketing IRSs, (inertial reference
systems) of completely strapdown type, providing a
Schuler-tuned sensor of attitudes and accelerations
without needing a stable platform, the three gyros
and three accelerometers being fixed to the aircraft.

In 1964, long before any civil INS, testing
began on the first RLG (ring laser gyro), and the
first 'breadboard' airborne RLG flew in 1969.
Honeywell flew the first properly engineered RLG
in 1974, and began civil and military deliveries in
1981. The RLG is a new kind of 'gyro' entirely,
because nothing moves except photons! There are
two forms of laser gyro so far, the traditional one
being based on a block of quartz machined with
great accuracy to provide a four- or (much more
common) three-sided channel along which passes

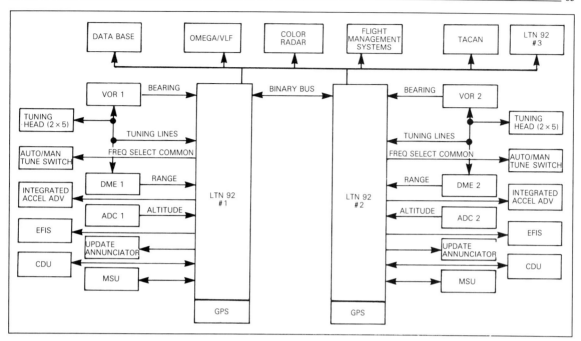

| DATA BASE | OMEGA/VLF | COLOR RADAR | FLIGHT MANAGEMENT SYSTEMS | TACAN | LTN 92 #3 |

light from lasers aimed in opposite directions. At two (or three) of the corners are mirrors, with the remaining corner arranged to provide an output. In most RLGs the light path is filled with He-Ne mix to give light at 0.633μ. In the absence of movement the light will travel round the circuit in either direction in exactly the same time, but if the optical path is rotated, no matter how slowly, there will be a detectable output. This normally takes the form of movement of the alternate light/dark fringe pattern

generated by the interference of the opposing sets of waves. The result is that the RLG behaves like a gyro in sensing rotation, but it is much more sensitive. Placing an RLG on a table gives an output caused by the Earth's rotation!

Litton flew their first RLG on an A300B in May 1979, and in November 1982 the LTN-90 series was the first laser IRS to be certificated. Using a square optical path with a length of 280 mm, the LTN-90 is standard on the A310, being the primary source of

Above *Block diagram of the Litton LTN-92, the first RLG INS to meet Arinc 561 (Ch. 15). It is 'pin for pin' compatible with older INSs using gimballed gyros. Most LTN-92s do not yet have the plug-in GPS module.*

Right *RLGs are often distinctively triangular. Here two of the strapdown Type 160 RLGs can be seen in the Ferranti FIN3020 INS for combat aircraft.*

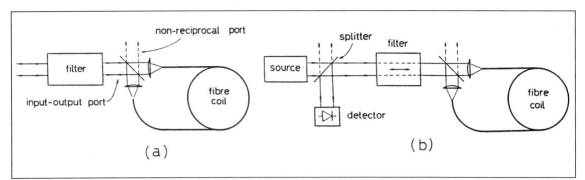

attitude and as the source of velocity and position for navigation, the actual nav computation being performed by the aircraft's flight management system. In contrast Ferranti's FIN 3000 series RLGs all use triple (three axes) arrays of triangular lasers, either an isosceles ring of 330 mm or an equilateral of 430 mm. The longer the optical path, the greater the accuracy. The FIN 3020 strapdown platform gives heading accuracy within 0.1° and V within 2 ft/s despite being designed for sustaining 12 g and a 400°/s roll rate in fighters.

The phase shift induced by rotating an optical closed circuit around which light travels in both directions simultaneously was described by Sagnac in 1924. There seems little doubt that it will become the almost universal method of measuring attitude and angular rotation of all except the simplest aircraft. A key factor in the wider acceptance of the RLG will be the perfection of the other kind, the FO (fibre optic) gyro. Here the gas-filled block of quartz is replaced by a coil of hundreds or, preferably, thousands of turns of a single optical fibre. There is only one light source, an LED. The output is passed through a beam splitter, and a single optical mode selected. The light then passes through a second beam splitter, and propagates both clockwise and anticlockwise around the coil. Without rotation of the coil the propagation times are identical, so when the light arrives back at the second beam splitter the waves are superimposed in perfect constructive interference, giving full brightness. The slightest rotation results in a difference in propagation times, causing a phase shift which reduces the light intensity as measured by a photodetector. Several companies have worked on the problems of producing fibres of suitable type at low cost, injecting the light, making the optical length long enough to get a substantial phase shift and, above all, using EO techniques to enhance the

Two forms of FOG (fibre-optic gyro); (a) with single-mode filter at the in/out port, (b) with an additional splitter to tap out the returning optical power and send it to the detector.

resolution. A major advantage, apart from eventual low cost, is small size. In 1988 British Aerospace delivered prototype FO gyros with a diameter of only 75 mm (under 3 in).

With such exciting developments in inertial systems it might seem odd even to mention radio aids again. In fact, they are fighting back in impressive new forms. Chronologically, it was to a large extent the inability of existing radio navaids to provide adequate accuracy midway between ground stations, such as in mid-Atlantic, that caused long-distance operators (military as well as civil) to rely increasingly on doppler from 1962 and INS from 1969. But this resulted in errors proportional to time spent in the air, so that old VOR/DME had to be used towards the destination. Thus, despite the doppler/INS option, long-distance aviators have never ceased to wish for some kind of external radio navaid that could provide high accuracy all over the world. Now they have not one but two.

The first to become operational was Omega, often called by the Greek letter of the same name Ω. This is almost an updated Decca, but with significant differences of which the greatest is that it operates at wavelengths of around fifteen miles in the VLF band. Such waves travel almost round the world before dying away, so they can form the basis for a global system with only a few stations, and still retain adequate accuracy for safe separation of traffic in busy mid-Atlantic corridors. A vast amount of research was needed on VLF propagation, and at least half this was done by RAE Comets. In true British style the resulting navaid was left to the US Navy to create, and this began to be implemented around 1960 for ships, using eight ground stations. These were later handed over to the host nations, opening the way to worldwide commercial use by aircraft as well as marine traffic. For aircraft a new receiver was needed, with a processor to correct potentially large propagation errors and give a near-instantaneous readout.

Today Omega is an important navaid for oceanic air routes. In principle it is a traditional CW hyperbolic phase-difference system. Before take-off the pilot inserts the date and GMT, because the propagation correction factors change every twenty min. He then punches in TO location and waypoints. The processor then starts working, and at any one time during the flight the aircraft receives the fundamental 10.2 kHz transmission from a single station, interspersed with signals at 13.6 and then 11.33 kHz. The resulting phase relationship is stored until signals are received from a second station. All eight stations are synchronized, but at any one instant only three transmit. Over a 10-s cycle each station transmits on the three frequencies, never two on the same frequency simultaneously. The phase relationship from the second station gives a hyperbolic position line, and when the third is heard the pilot has a fix, which can be refined as other stations are heard. Accuracy is seldom worse than 1 nm by day and 2 nm by night. There is a basic lane ambiguity at a distance of one-half wavelength, or about every 8 nm. The frequency changes resolve this: with the switch from 10.2 to 13.6 the lane width becomes three times wider, and the second switch to 11.33 makes it three times wider again (72 nm), which surely eliminates the problem. In any case, if you punch in the starting position there can be no ambiguity throughout the flight.

This leaves just one subject to be covered: use of satellites. The US Navy pioneered the technology with a series of satellites originally called Transits, to enable missile-firing submarines to know their position anywhere in the world within 528 ft, the first being launched in September 1959. Via other USN and USAF systems this led to the Navstar GPS (global positioning system), which completed concept validation in 1974. In 1979 Collins received a US Department of Defense contract for preproduction GPS receivers, which were subsequently tested on A-6E, B-52, F-16 and UH-60A aircraft, CV-63 aircraft carrier, an SSN-688 submarine, a utility truck and a manpack. The possibilities are endless, and today GPS is moving fast into the civil field.

Moreover, at an ICAO meeting in May 1988 the Soviet Union suddenly announced that its own Glonass system would be made available for worldwide civil use. At that meeting ICAO completed a major Fans (future air navigation systems) study covering the period up to 2015. Its report, approved in November 1988, states 'The exploitation of satellite technology to provide CNS (communications, navigation, surveillance) for civil aviation on a global basis is the only viable solution that will enable one to overcome the shortcomings of the present air navigation system and fulfil the needs and requirements of the foreseeable future'. Small wonder then that avionics companies all over the world are racing to market GPS receivers, and from 1989 they are also competing to produce receivers for the Glonass system.

In the original DoD requirement for GPS the stipulated position accuracy for aircraft was 50 m (164 ft) horizontally and vertically, with 50 per cent probability. In fact GPS will provide 3-D position information within 52 ft, irrespective of weather, time of day or the location of the receiver: you can be at the South Pole. It will also furnish the receiver's velocity within 0.1 m/s and local time within ten millionths of a second. This can be achieved by the original GPS plan to use a constellation of eighteen Navstar satellites, but as now defined there will be 24. Instead of three groups of six, each group orbiting the Earth in one plane, there will be three groups of eight. The satellites are built by Rockwell, of whom Collins is part, and the first was placed in orbit in 1978. Six were in position in 1981, but there was then a delay while the design of the final eighteen was upgraded. The 24 satellites will orbit the Earth with eight spaced evenly around each of three planes 120° apart. Each satellite will be in a semisynchronous circular prograde (going the same way as the Earth) orbit at 20,000 km (12,427 miles). Thus, it will make exactly two revolutions while the Earth makes one, and thus follow the same track over the Earth continuously.

Each satellite contains a precise atomic clock. Every 30 s it transmits its exact position, together with spread-spectrum coded signals. All transmit with different codes but on the same frequencies: L_1 at 1,575.42 MHz and L_2 on 1,227.6 MHz. L_1 carries a C/A (coarse/acquisition) code and both carry a P (precision) code at ten times the rate (10.23 megachips/s). In fact the C/A code has been found more accurate than P for outputting receiver veloci-

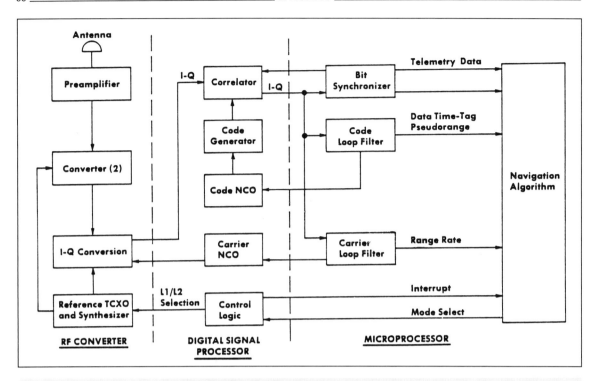

ty, and invariably adequate for position. The receiver picks up the signals from three satellites and, by measuring transit time and multiplying by the speed of light, obtains X/Y/H (east/west, north/south and height) position. By adding signals from a fourth satellite four equations are available to solve four unknowns, the fourth being T (local time). Major problems included the necessarily low satellite transmitter power and minimum distance of some 12,500 miles, so S/N ratio inevitably tends to be low. Accordingly, clever design was needed to achieve small receivers; indeed the US Defense Advanced Research Projects Agency is funding one no larger than a pack of cards.

The Soviet Glonass system is very similar, and has been developed from the outset for all kinds of

Left *Simplified block diagram of a GPS receiver using an NCO (numerically controlled oscillator) as carrier frequency generator. I and Q are in-phase and quadrature (tracking); L1, L2, see text.*

Below left *GPS receivers are often very similar. A typical installation is this Collins group for a Royal Australian Army S-70A-9 Black Hawk. Control/display unit left, two-channel receiver with fixed-pattern antenna in front, and antenna electronics right.*

Below *Typical production process for a digital map. The output at right means red/green/blue or monochrome (black/white). Tiles can be composite or divided into feature-plane layers to facilitate the declutter function and allow various forms of terrain data to be introduced in place of contours.*

civil use as well as military. It will be served by 21 satellites arranged seven in each of three orbital planes 120° apart. The orbits are circular at a height of 19,100 km, at an inclination of 64.8°, giving a period of 11 h 15 min, all extremely close to GPS values. Glonass receivers will provide for similar passive measurement of position and time, using signals in the 1,600 MHz band from a group of four satellites. Navigation signals will last 30 s, interspersed with satellite integrity information lasting 2.5 s. Satellites 1 to 11 were scheduled for launch in 1989-90 and 12-21 in 1995. It remains to be seen whether these two valuable global systems can be integrated.

There are other aspects of electronic navigation which at present are almost entirely military. One is the digital map. Hardly any fast-jet combat pilots today take a folded paper map on a mission. A few have a projected map display, as described in Chapter 13. These are fine, but a recent paper by GEC Avionics describes ten shortcomings of film-based projected maps. The same chapter describes modern multicolour displays, and these, combined with modern digital memories, have made possible the totally synthetic map. Several hundred megabytes of map data are stored in the Eprom (Chapter 15), and this vast amount — changed only slightly, at infrequent intervals — forms the map in the most flexible manner possible. The map is constructed from millions of 'tiles' which can be formatted with contour lines or alternative displays for terrain avoidance, threat avoidance and contour

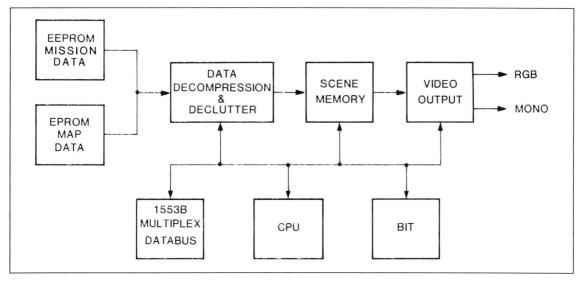

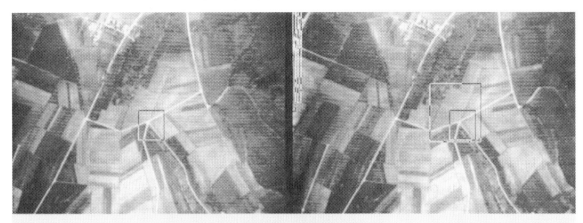

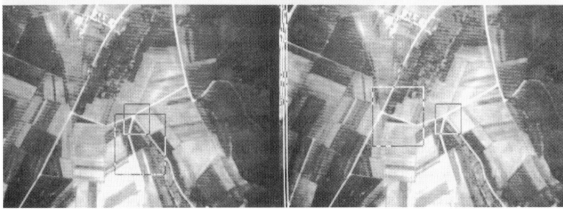

shadowing. Much smaller amounts of mission data are loaded immediately before take-off from an external port and ground support bus (or, if there is time, supplied as a cartridge inserted into a cockpit socket). These data are stored in an Eeprom (Chapter 15) and provide up to the minute details on the mission, targets, threats and other rapidly changing factors. An Eeprom is ideal, but as the data density is about 0.25 that of an Eeprom, at about four times the price per bit, it cannot be used for the huge memory that constructs the map.

Another military technique is recognition of features on the ground, to update the accuracy of an inertial system (and, in the case of cruise missiles, to ensure recognition of the target). This is the sort of thing humans can do very well, whereas computers have to store a formidable amount of digital data describing selected features, and then laboriously go

Near-vertical scenes showing pattern recognition: top left, pattern selected; top right, target in search window, similarity bar shorter than threshold value; bottom left, target not completely in search window, similarity bar longer than threshold; bottom right, target not in search window, bar longer than threshold. (Dornier)

through a comparison with what is seen by on-board sensors. For example, in the reference pattern of a road junction the left-hand outer bar indicates the threshold value for similarity. The second, inner bar indicates the reciprocal value of similarity. When the inner bar is smaller than the outer bar the target has been recognized. Of course the sensor must 'see' at a suitable wavelength and digitize the scene into at least 10^6 bits to get an adequate picture.

4

RADAR PRINCIPLES

Radar is a subject of awesome complexity. There is no way this book, or indeed any single book, can impart a complete understanding of the principles, let alone current hardware. In this chapter it is proposed to overview just the more basic fundamentals. Subsequent chapters say more about the major applications, the history of airborne radars and in broad outline how current radars work.

EM waves can be changed in direction by diffraction, refraction and reflection. Apart from mild and unwanted effects we can ignore the first two. Reflection from a mirror is obviously familiar. To make a mirror we construct a surface which is an electrical conductor and whose irregularities are small compared with the wavelength. As the wave strikes the surface its electric field is in effect short-circuited. At each point in the surface this causes an exactly corresponding movement of electrons along the surface, which is the same thing as a current. This immediately causes the energy to be reradiated from the surface, which is the same as reflecting the original wave. Radiation of the energy arrests the electrons, stopping the current, until arrival of the next wave. Clearly, the current and hence the emitted wave are exactly proportional to the

The basis of radar is that when an incident electric wave (E) strikes a conductive surface, such as an aircraft, it causes a small current to flow in the skin (time 2). This then re-radiates a similar wave (time 3). (Hughes)

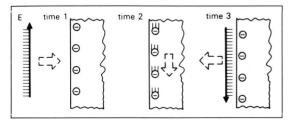

power of the incident wave.

Aircraft are not built like mirrors. Their conductive surfaces are highly irregular, and an incident wave strikes them at an infinite diversity of angles. Accordingly, instead of getting specular (mirror) reflection we get scattering of the incident energy. Parts of the aircraft are not conducting but are made of dielectric material. Such parts include radomes and antenna fairings, transparencies and parts made from composite material (the whole wing of a Harrier II and the whole tail of an A320, for example). With such parts the dielectric constant K_e (a measure of the electric capacitance of the material) determines the way the wave's energy is divided between the electric and magnetic fields. In a vacuum or high-altitude air K_e is taken as 1, so until it reaches the aircraft the wave's two fields are equal. To adjust the balance on entering the dielectric medium some of the incident energy is rejected. Thus, if we made an aircraft wholly from dielectric material we should get precisely the same pattern of scattering of the incident wave but perhaps only one-tenth or one-hundredth as strong.

It will be noted that the wave reflected at each point in the aircraft surface has its electric vector reversed. This is unimportant. What counts is that a fraction, usually an extremely small fraction, of the incident energy is received back where the wave was sent out. In general the reflected* waves faithfully duplicate those sent out, though much weaker and displaced in time by the round-trip distance divided by the speed of light.

To recap on a fundamental point, EM signals can be represented as sine waves. Suppose we send out a CW beam which hits an aerial target. In practice the

---

* I shall use this word for convenience, but what is really meant is the very small fraction of scattered energy that happens to go straight back to the original radar antenna.

cross-section of the beam is usually much bigger than the target. Thus, part of the beam will hit one area of the target, and another part of the beam will hit another area. Suppose we get back from these parts two strong returns (which we can also call reflections, echoes or, if seen on a display, blips). At one particular orientation (aspect or attitude) of the target the two reflected sets of waves will start at exactly the same distance away, so they will be additive. Each coherent wave will have its peaks in the same place as its partner, so the result will be a very bold and bright blip on our display, showing a nice juicy target. But aircraft move about and change their attitude, even when flying straight and level in bumpy air. Next moment the distances from our radar to the two big reflective areas of the target are no longer the same but differ by an inch or two. This can put the two reflected waves 180° out of phase. What happens? They cancel each other out, and our bright blip almost disappears. Of course in practice we get reflections from millions of different spots on our target, but the fact that the distances to each spot are constantly varying means that the received signal strength varies enormously, as the waves either add together or cancel out.

This is called scintillation. If we could see radar waves we should discover that every aircraft in the sky was sequentially bright, dark, rather brighter,

This gives a rough idea of how aircraft, or other targets, appear to a radar. The returns scintillate, fade and are mixed with variable noise. Apart from this, small differences in target aspect can make a big difference to the echo. (Hughes)

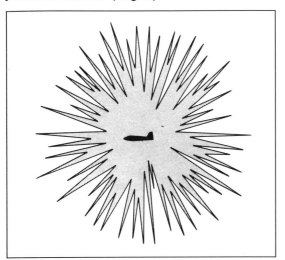

brilliant, dark, almost invisible and so on. What is the range of a radar? We often say something like '25 miles against a fighter, 70 on a 747'. This is far too slick. What we mean is 'The range is impossible to state. It depends on the target's apparent size, aspect, distance, method of construction and materials, our wavelength, atmospheric attenuation and many other factors, and the range also varies several times a second depending on whether the scintillating target is dim or bright'. I did say radar was complicated.

We could also get deeply involved with decibels (db). We think of these as being 'units of sound'. In fact a dB is not a unit but a ratio, and used properly it is a ratio of two powers which we can call P_2 and P_1. Specifically $10 \log_{10} P_2/P_1$ gives the answer in dB; thus if P_2 is 100 times as powerful as P_1 then the ratio is 20 (because $\log_{10} 100$ is 2). Decibels are convenient in such fields as radar powers and acoustic noise because the ratios of powers involved may be many billions, and a log scale avoids the need to use gigantic numbers. Thus instead of writing 0.00001 we can write -50 dB, and instead of 1,000,000 we can write 60 dB. If we are concerned with very small powers such as those of distant target echoes we can use dBm, which means dB referred to a power of 1 milliwatt (0.001 W). It is quite common for an airborne radar to have to handle an echo whose power is only $0.000,000,000,000,001$ W or 10^{-13} mW; instead we can just express the received signal strength as -130 dBm. In the same way the apparent size of a target as seen by radar, called its RCS (radar cross section), can vary by factors of tens of millions. A SRAM or F-117 from most aspects has an RCS about one-millionth that of a Tu-142 'Bear' or B-52, so RCS ratios are expressed by dBsm (decibels related to square metres). Anyone hooked on radar may know, or can calculate, that 0 dB means a power ratio of 1, 1 dB = 1.259, 2 = 1.585, 3 = 1.995 (say 2) and so on. You can look up the ratios from any antilog table.

If this seems boring, try to imagine what the sky would look like if our eyes were sensitive to radar wavelengths. Except perhaps in parts of the Pacific or over the Poles the entire sky would be filled with brilliant coloured light. Some would be giant fanlike beams sweeping round like lighthouses, or nodding up and down in different directions. Some would be beams like searchlights, in many varying colours. The military ones would seldom stay one colour, but might flash through many shades faster conclusion we could draw is that all the signals are sent out at the speed of light, and the echoes return at the same speed with unchanged characteristics, and that as the waves travel in what we can take to be straight lines (ignoring Einstein) they cannot see targets hiding behind mountains and other solid obstructions. What we could not readily deduce is that many targets seemingly in full view can be invisible to a radar, or at least can be (as far as the radar knows) in many different places or travelling at many different speeds. Radars have to be clever to resolve such ambiguities.

Let's start with the simplest radar possible. We need a supply of electricity, a transmitter, a transmitting antenna, a receiving antenna, a receiver and some kind of display. The transmitter sends out some kind of signal and the receiver tries to detect any echoes. If there are any, they give rise to a bright blip on the display, and we arrange the display so that the position of the blip tells us something about the target's position.

In practice we need a few more things, but we usually do not need two antennas. As the echoes are similar in wavelength and other variables to those we send out, we can make one antenna serve both the transmitter and the receiver. But whenever the antenna is being used for transmission we have to switch off, or blank, its connection to the receiver.

A computer-processed image of the radar scattering values of an aircraft seen from ahead and below. (MBB)

than the eye could follow. Some might stay locked on particular targets, which in turn would diffuse the energy away in all directions. Near a big city we might see 500 radars all working at once, some sending out fans, some pencil beams, some continuous waves, some sharp pulses, all seemingly with complex forms of transmission and following every imaginable kind of scanning pattern. So diverse would be the emissions that perhaps the only firm

The main parts needed for a simple pulsed fighter radar. The synch times the pulses, and the servo drives the (mechanically scanned) antenna. (Hughes)

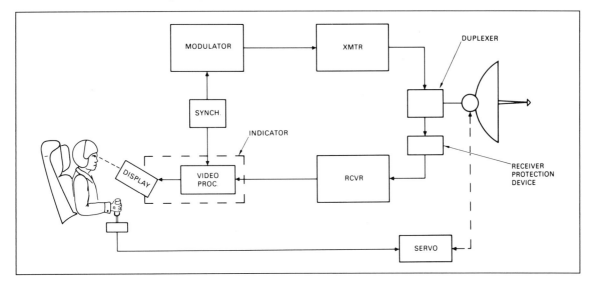

This is done by a ceaselessly oscillating switch called a duplexer. Moreover, the transmitter may pump out microwave power of 100 kW or more, whereas the delicate receiver has to be sensitive enough to notice echoes with a power less than one-billionth as great. So, to avoid damaging the receiver by power leaking past the duplexer, or by sudden massive echoes (helpful ground crew have been known to test a fighter radar parked facing the hangar wall), we add a receiver protection device (RPD). Like the duplexer, this is a very fast microwave switch, but in this case it is inserted in the waveguide carrying the incoming waves. Whereas the duplexer works all the time, and may be an active powered device such as a gas-discharge switch, the RPD has to be a passive switch triggered by arrival of any dangerously high energy heading for the receiver.

Apart from altimeters, doppler navigators and AAM missile guidance, which use CW (continuous wave) transmission, virtually all airborne radars use some form of pulsed transmission. In a simple pulsed radar the PRF (pulse repetition frequency) is determined and controlled by a synchronizer, which is really an electronic clock set to an exact frequency (which can often be altered, even many times per second). The synch sends out to the modulator and to the display indicator a continuous stream of very brief, evenly spaced pulses of low-power current. Upon receipt of each timing pulse the modulator sends out a powerful flow of DC electricity, switched on and off by the beginning and end of each pulse. These bursts of heavy current go straight to the oscillator (usually a magnetron) in the transmitter, to generate high-power signals of RF energy. These microwave pulses may each be of fixed frequency or tunable over a range of about 10%. The

succession of microwave pulses travel down the waveguide to the antenna, the duplexer opening to let each one through.

We often describe a radar as 'operating in [for example] the Ku band'. This refers to the frequency of the oscillator, and has no connection with PRF. The frequency selected for a radar tends to be related to the physical size of the antenna. Thus, airborne radars, which usually have to be compact, tend to operate at higher frequencies, ie, shorter wavelengths, than those used on the ground or on ships. Most airborne radars operate at frequencies from 400 MHz to 40,000 MHz (40 GHz). Active guidance radars for small missiles tend to be even smaller, and so may operate in the millimetric range at perhaps 94 GHz. Some typical waveforms are shown here actual size. To a very rough approximation, the sheer power of a radar can be greater, in the megawatt range, at longer wavelengths, and conversely must be lower in miniature multi-GHz radars, which are usually less than 1 kW. Clearly, more power tends to mean longer range and better ability to 'burn through' enemy jamming and other countermeasures. On the other hand, when it comes to range we have to remember the varying attenuation of the atmosphere, and especially of clouds and other moisture, at different wavelengths, which strongly favours wavelengths longer than about 6 cm, equivalent to 5 GHz. Extraneous noise tends to be minimal between 0.5-15 GHz. At lower frequencies galactic noise from sources throughout the Universe becomes severe, and at higher frequencies virtually all the noise is of atmospheric origin. A major factor is that, for any given size (eg, width or diameter) of antenna, the angular width of the beam of a fighter-

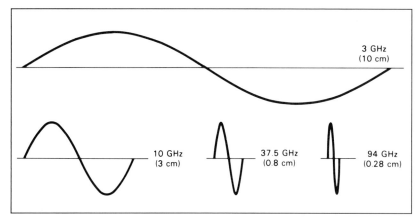

3 GHz
(10 cm)

10 GHz
(3 cm)

37.5 GHz
(0.8 cm)

94 GHz
(0.28 cm)

Some wavelengths used by airborne radars, shown actual size. (Hughes)

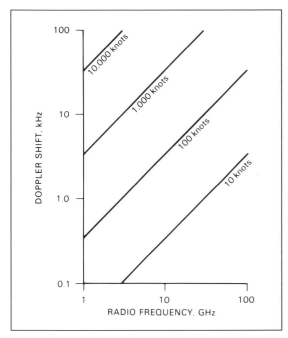

Doppler shifts are proportional not only to the closing rate — the relative velocity between radar and target — but also to the transmitter frequency. (Hughes)

way, and the actual profile is complex, but radar designers often assume the pulses are rectangular. In that case peak power is the power sent out during the transmission of each pulse. But most of the time a fighter type radar is not transmitting but listening. The ratio of pulse width to interpulse period is called the duty factor. It is often important to know the average power of a radar, and this is peak power multiplied by the duty factor. If peak power is 200 kW and duty factor is 0.5% then average power is only 1 kW. Often the duty factor may be even less, such as a 1 μs pulse followed by a 1,999 μs interpulse (listening) period.

It is important to remember that pulse width is a time, whereas pulse length is a distance, the actual length of the pulse of RF energy as it travels out from the antenna. EM waves travel at almost exactly 300,000km (186,000 miles) per second, so the pulse length is 300m (984ft) per μs of pulse width. It is not uncommon for non-Metric designers to use the round figure of 1,000 ft. Pulse length, which is not directly related to PRF, determines the radar's ability to discriminate between two closely spaced targets. In modern radars this discrimination is usually enhanced by varying the modulation within each pulse, but the basic rule still applies. With long pulses you cannot separate close targets. With unmodulated pulses you cannot see the two targets if, by the time the leading edge of the echo from the further target has reached the near target, the trailing edge of the same pulse has not passed the near target on its outward journey; in other words, the targets have to be separated in range by more than half the pulse length.

So far we have said nothing about the antenna. We could stick up a vertical dipole or use some other kind of antenna broadcasting our carefully designed pulses in all directions. In plan view our plot of radiated power would then be a circle centred on the aircraft. This is usually not what we want. We want to concentrate the energy into a narrow beam, either (in a fighter or commercial jet, for example) pointing somewhere ahead, and in an AWACS type platform scanning a large sector which usually goes round all 360° but which uses a narrow beam of vastly greater power than one broadcasting everywhere at once. We therefore use a directive antenna which focusses the energy into a narrow pencil beam or, in mapping and reconnaissance radars, into a vertical fan. The ideal beamwidth might be very narrow indeed, but any

type radar is directly proportional to the wavelength. Thus, the higher the frequency, the finer the beam will be, which means greater power concentrated at the target and better angular resolution. Yet another factor is that doppler shifts are always proportional to frequency (but large shifts can cause problems, as explained later).

PRF is a totally different, and much lower, frequency. As its name implies, it is the number of pulses sent out per second. Typical airborne radars use PRFs from a few hundred Hz to maybe 300 kHz. Different choices are called low, medium and high PRF; the factors affecting the choice are enormously complex, but are discussed superficially in the next chapter. Another important measure is the PRI, pulse repetition interval, which is also known as the interpulse period; it may be anything from 100 μs to 10,000 μs.

In theory a pulsed radar sends out perfectly rectangular pulses. This means pulses which instantly reach their full power (wave amplitude), hold this throughout the duration of the pulse and then are instantly cut off. In practice, pulse power builds over a small finite period and decays in the same

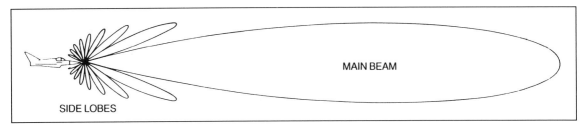

SIDE LOBES

MAIN BEAM

measure of beamwidth has to be qualified by where it is measured, because nobody has so far been clever enough to design an antenna that sends out only the single beam we want. Almost every airborne radar sends out a main beam, flanked by a long succession of progressively weaker concentric surrounding beams called sidelobes, which even extend round to the rear. Almost every radar designer strives to eliminate these sidelobes, which not only waste power but can cause problems. We want the power in the main beam. The basic measure of performance of a radar antenna is its gain, which is usually defined as the power (peak or average) radiated in the desired direction (which we hope is our main beam) divided by the power that the same radar would radiate with an isotropic (all directions) antenna.

Practical radars such as are used in today's fighters often reduce the illumination (radiated power) around the edges of the antenna. This technique, called tapering, slightly increases the beamwidth, which we do not want, but greatly reduces the strength of the sidelobes. This likewise puts more power into the main beam and reduces problems with, for example, ground clutter and enemy jamming. There are various rules-of-thumb for beamwidth and gain. What is the beamwidth? One measure of it is to measure the angle between the first null (point of zero radiated power between the main beam and the first sidelobe) on one side and the first null on the other side. A more common measure is the angle between the directions on each side of the boresight line at which the main beam power has dropped to half the boresight maximum. Expressed in decibels 0.5 is -3 dB, so this is called the -3 dB beamwidth. So one rough rule which applies in the X-band around 10 GHz is that beamwidth is 85° divided by antenna width in inches; thus, a 10 GHz radar with a 28 in antenna should put out a beam with a width of around 3°. A rough rule for gain with radars of this class is $G = 9d^2\eta$ where G is gain, d is antenna diameter or width measured in wavelengths and η is antenna efficien-

Above *Nobody has yet been clever enough to invent an antenna emitting just the beam we want. We always get sidelobes as well, and these are not just above and below, as this drawing suggests, but annular; they literally send energy out in all directions, except directly astern. Note: sidelobe radiation does not "stop short"; the sidelobe lengths are drawn to indicate power.* (Ferranti)

Below *This diagram is instantly recognized by any radar designer. It is typical of the plot of field strength of a pencil-beam radar. The main beam can be seen on the central boresight line. 1, 2 and 3 are sidelobes, and odd-numbered sidelobes are plotted as negative because their RF phase is reversed.* (Hughes)

Bottom *Beamwidth is commonly measured between the directions where power has fallen to half the maximum, in other words the -3 dB value. This beamwidth is roughly half the null-to-null beamwidth Θ_{nn}.* (Hughes)

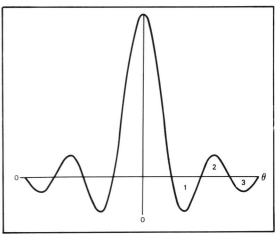

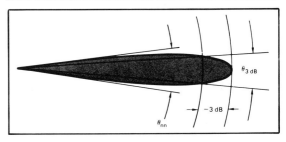

cy, which should be somewhere up towards 0.8.

Subsequent chapters will have more to say about hardware for specific applications, but here I will outline some factors affecting design of antennas in general. Today some radars are used to create detailed pictures of the Earth's surface or to measure the (doppler) velocity of the aircraft in which they are installed, but for most radars the basic objective has always been to detect some kind of target and to indicate where it is — and, more recently, to measure relative velocities. Measuring range is in theory simple: you multiply half the round-trip time (the time each wave takes to reach the target and come back) by the speed of light. Thus, if the round-trip time is $20\mu s$ the range is almost precisely 3 km or 9, 840 ft. There is more on this in the next chapter. But to find out where the target is we usually need to form our energy into a fine pencil beam, and then aim this in different directions and note where the beam is pointing when we detect a target. We call this scanning, and the number of ways this can be done is virtually limitless.

Early radars carried in fighters and large transports sometimes used various kinds of conical scan. Some, especially those in transports, had the boresight line of the antenna offset at a fixed angle less than half the beamwidth so that there was no blind spot dead ahead; then all the antenna — sometimes called a scanner — had to do was ceaselessly rotate so that the boresight line described a cone whose vertex was the projected longitudinal axis of the aircraft. At least one early fighter radar had a scan pattern which slowly oscillated between zero and a wide forward-facing cone (Chapter 5). Others set up a fine conical scan and then proceeded to sweep out horizontal left/right and right/left scans at different elevation angles. The pioneer H_2S mapping radar (Chapter 6) used a rotating fan to illuminate* a nearly circular area beneath and ahead of the aircraft. Most surveillance radars sweep a narrow beam round and round to all points of the compass, either with or without an up/down elevation scan. Anti-ship radars look ahead and sweep left/right through a limited azimuth whilst holding the elevation angle constant, or nodding through a very small arc, so that the beam sweeps along the horizon (but they have to be stabilized to keep doing

---

* The common word in this context, even though radar wavelengths are not visible to humans.

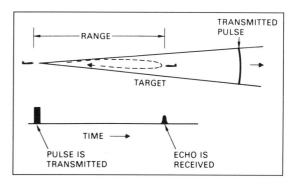

Top *The simplest way to measure target range is by measuring the time between transmitting a pulse and receiving its echo. Of course, nearly all the pulse carries on past the target.* (Hughes)

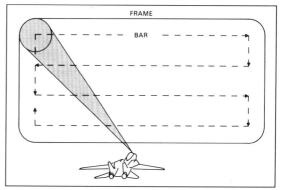

Above *A typical search scan pattern for a fighter radar. Almost always the operator can control the width and position of the frame, the number of bars, the scan sequence and other variables.* (Hughes)

this while the aircraft or helicopter dives, climbs or makes banked turns).

In virtually every modern fighter radar the scan pattern is an interleaved sequence of horizontal sweeps, alternately left/right and right/left. Added together these sweeps, which are called bars, cover a region ahead of the aircraft called the frame (rarely, the scan volume). The frame is usually rectangular, its angular width (azimuth) being greater than its angular height (elevation), but such factors can often be controlled, especially if there is a backseat operator able to concentrate on the radar. The operator can also usually control the scan pattern, the number of bars, the frame time (the time taken for the sequential scans to complete each frame) and other variables, as described in the next chapter.

It is helpful to overview antenna types here. In the earliest days of radar, powerful RF energy could not be generated at wavelengths less than a few metres; with great difficulty British workers devised an airborne set working on 1.5 m, about 5 ft. Suitable antennas for such wavelengths are dipoles, similar in principle to those on millions of rooftops. Separate antennas were used for transmission and reception. Such radars were used to detect enemy aircraft, ships and, it was hoped, submarine periscopes, the antenna configurations and scan patterns differing for each application.

Once the breakthrough into centimetric wavelengths had been achieved the antenna could be made much smaller, though of course it still had to be several times as big as the wavelength. The obvious answer was the parabolic reflector, used for decades in searchlights and car headlights. The microwave radiation was fed along a waveguide pointing straight ahead along the axis of the reflector. Then at the focus of the parabola it was turned back through 180°, either by simply turning the waveguide back on itself and leaving the end open or by putting a suitable reflector on the end. In an alternative arrangement the waveguide was taken up to the top (12 o'clock position) of the reflector and brought forward diagonally back to the axis

The simplest antenna for a forward-looking radar is the parabolic dish, with a central microwave feed. This emits the microwaves on to a small reflector at the focus of the parabola, which results in a narrow parallel beam. (Hughes)

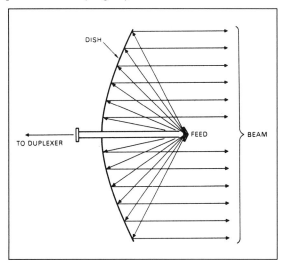

before being turned back to face the reflector. Usually the open end of the waveguide was in the form of a horn to funnel the received waves back into it. However it was arranged, the diminution in antenna size meant that the whole assembly could be mounted on gimbals and scanned mechanically, independent of movements of the aircraft.

One gimbal on a vertical axis provides for left/right pivoting in azimuth, another on a horizonal axis provides for up/down pivoting in elevation and, certainly in fighters, a third gimbal is added for rotation about the aircraft's longitudinal axis. This third gimbal allows the antenna to be stabilized in roll, slaved to a vertical gyro, so that the wide frame always remains aligned with the horizon ahead. The drive to the antenna may be electric or hydraulic. By the 1960s hydraulic drives were seemingly becoming universal, but work in the laboratories was resulting in improved balanced electric drives which are now found on all the very latest fighter radars. These save weight and rotational inertia, eliminate local hydraulics and the need for mechanical interlocks, and are likely to become the standard method, especially with the introduction of SmCo (samarium cobalt) magnets of many times the power of existing ones.

Antenna direction can be governed by the search scan circuit, or by an automatic tracking system (described later) or by a cockpit pistol-grip hand-control. These inputs supply control signals to the drives to the three gimbals. Each gimbal incorporates an angle-measuring transducer whose output voltage is subtracted from the input to produce an error signal proportional to the difference between the actual and desired antenna directions. This error signal is amplified and supplied to the gimbal drive motors to reduce the error to zero. The transducers also send to the cockpit display indicator signals showing the antenna direction so that the display can generate the picture needed.

Parabolic dishes were almost universal until the 1960s. They are still found in simple nose radars for general aviation, and are the most common type for surveillance and anti-ship radars for maritime aircraft and helicopters. The latter radars use a reflector of wide but shallow elliptical or rectangular shape to give a flat beam swept along the horizon. Since the late 1950s a family of slightly more complicated parabolic antennas has become popular for fighter and attack aircraft, especially in Europe. These are the inverse (or inverted) Cassegrains.

The two common forms of inverse-Cassegrain antenna: left, hyperboloid sub-dish, convex as seen by the waves; right, paraboloid sub-dish, concave as seen by the waves. The paraboloid type is used by the radars of the fighter Viggen and Tornado.

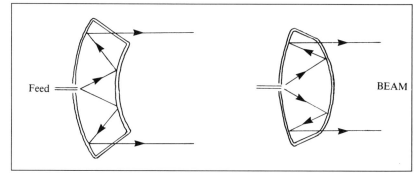

Cassegrain originally used the arrangement for the optics of astronomical telescopes, hence the adjective 'inverse' needed for a radiating antenna. The waveguide feeds straight ahead from the centre of the main parabolic reflector so that the waves are directed on to a sub-reflector in front. This sub-reflector is either parabolic, convex seen from the front, or hyperbolic and concave as seen from the front. The sub-reflector reflects the radiation back to cover the main reflector, with no waveguide getting in the way. Of course, the incoming echoes are received at the main dish first and are then focused via the sub-reflector on to the open end of the waveguide.

The alert reader will ask how it is that the sub-dish reflects the radiation back on to the main dish and then lets it through to form the beam ahead of the aircraft. The answer is that the transmitted radiation is polarized (Chapter 1). If it is vertically polarized, the sub-dish is not a metal sheet but composed of hundreds of fine wires evenly spaced parallel to the plane of polarization (vertical). This acts as an essentially perfect reflector. The main dish consists of identically spaced wires but turned through 45°, backed by a solid reflecting surface. The diagonal wires alone would lose energy (loss is proportional to the cosine of the angular difference between the waves and the wires), but the combination loses very little. Its big effect is to rotate the plane of polarization of the radiation through 90°. Thus, when the now horizontally-polarized waves again strike the front sub-reflector they pass straight through, because Cos 90° is zero and so an antenna at 90° to the plane of polarization cannot extract any energy from the incident radiation. In other words, when the waves meet the sub-reflector the second time it is transparent to them.

In the USA, and now increasingly worldwide, a totally different kind of antenna has become popular. This is the planar-array, sometimes called the slotted-waveguide antenna, which describes how it is made. Instead of having a single feed and a reflector, the planar array sends out the radiation from a large number of slot apertures cut in the face of a flat array. The flat plate has a size and shape which are likely to be broadly similar to those of a parabolic or inverse-Cassegrain reflector. It can be made in two principal ways. In one method the plate is assembled from up to 30 identical linear waveguides each running right across the aperture and tightly packed one above the other or side by side. Radiation is emitted from precisely cut slots in the forward-facing waveguide walls, each slot usually running transversely right across the waveguide, the assembly forming a carefully arranged slot pattern fed from a common 'corporate feed' in the edge. The same assembly operates in reverse in the echo receiving mode, taking in the weak signals through all the slots and feeding them out through a different single waveguide. The other method of construction is to divide up the antenna plate into perhaps thirty rectilinear portions called slot array modules. Of course around the periphery the modules have to be cut off by the curved boundary. Each module may have (say) a dozen slots cut in its face. On the back of the antenna the microwave power is fed in via a multiple branching network of waveguides (power dividers) each termination feeding one module.

An obvious drawback of the planar-array antenna is its greater cost. Another is that it is rather more difficult to send out waves that are circularly or elliptically polarized. Such antennas also have a relatively narrow bandwidth, and in some applications (certainly in multimode radars) this is a disadvantage. The advantages are in general much greater. Aperture efficiency is significantly higher, which means greater gain than any simple dish of

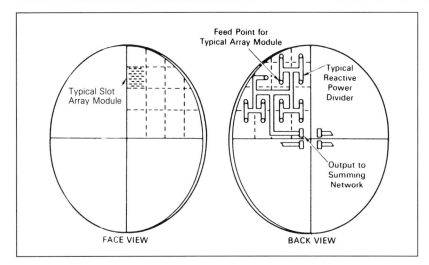

FACE VIEW   BACK VIEW

Modern radars usually use a planar-array antenna. Instead of being a dish, this is flat, and radiation of equal phase is emitted from accurately positioned slots in its face. (Hughes)

similar size. Back radiation, also called spillover, is reduced to insignificant levels. Perhaps most important of all, by controlling the excitation of the slots to increase it across the central region and reduce it at the edges, by fitting non-dissipating attenuators on the back of the antenna, the radiation pattern can be controlled to put almost all the energy into the main beam, with very small sidelobes. This tapering technique was referred to earlier, and it is essential in some MTI (moving-target indication) modes, as described later.

Today there is an even more advanced kind of antenna: the phased-array or electronically scanned antenna. It will be appreciated that the planar array antenna has to be so designed — for example, in the matter of precise lengths of waveguide feeder to each slot — that the radiation from all slots is in equal phase. The whole antenna is then rotated

bodily to aim the beam. But it is possible to hold the antenna still and aim the beam by differentially shifting the phases of the radiation sent out from each slot. This is called electronic scanning. Put another way, the normal operating mode of the planar-array antenna, in which all the 200 or more miniature beams are in phase, resulting in the mainlobe being on the antenna boresight line, is a special case taken from an infinite number of possibilities. It is not difficult to add a phase-shifter to each radiating element so that the phase emitted from each can be varied in any desired way. To steer an electronically scanned beam it is necessary to control the amount of phase-shift so that it is progressive in a series of exactly equal steps from one radiator, or row of radiators, to the next, from top to bottom to tilt the beam in elevation, or from left to right to sweep it in azimuth, or both.

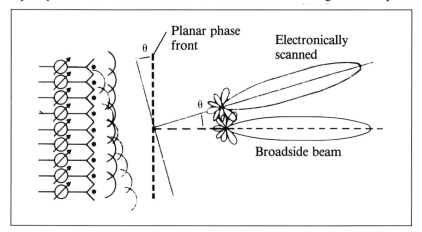

With electronic scanning the antenna does not move, but a phase-shifter (rings with vector arrows) behind each radiating element progressively shifts the phases of the signals from one side of the antenna to the other. The bigger the shift, the greater the steering angle Θ. (Westinghouse)

Electronic scanning does not alter the beam, nor any other aspect of radar performance other than scanning capability. Since the antenna is fixed facing dead ahead, there is no need for gimbals, drive motors and transducers, so weight is unlikely to increase much and can even be saved. The scanning can be flexible and fast in a way utterly unattainable with mechanical scanning. The beam can be given any desired shape, swept about in any desired way, jumped (speed of light) between extreme off-centre positions, and, usually at some penalty in range, split into two or more separate beams each of which can be locked-on to a different target. The main drawbacks of electronic scanning are increased cost and the inevitable degradation in performance at large look angles. This is because the effective antenna aperture decreases as the cosine of the look angle; if you could scan to 90° the apparent width of the antenna would be zero and nothing would be sent out. So this kind of antenna is preferably used where look angles do not extend more than about 30° from the axis. It would seem to make sense to combine an electronically scanned antenna with gimmbals allowing it to look anywhere.

There is another special kind of antenna which does not actually exist but is simulated bit-by-bit by the movement of the aircraft. This is the SAR (synthetic aperture radar) described in Chapter 8.

Before discussing how we measure target range and direction, and how we lock-on and track targets of interest, something should be said about clutter, noise and other interferences. These affect every radar, and can never be eliminated. Clutter is the name given to echoes from objects other than the targets we are interested in. Noise is electrical energy of random wavelength and amplitude which may come from almost anywhere.

We may not be aware of it, but almost everything emits radio waves! For an object not to do so, it has to be a perfect insulator or at absolute zero temperature. Your little finger falls into neither of these categories, though the RF energy it emits would not be a radar problem. This is not the case with many other sources. Noise from the Sun is powerful at many wavelengths, and highly variable, and if the antenna mainlobe happens to point at the Sun at a time of solar activity the noise can swamp the targets we want to see — almost no matter what our operating frequencies. Other sources of noise which can be powerful are the ground and the atmosphere, their output varying with absolute temperature and length of atmosphere through which the radar has to look. Within the aircraft noise is generated, often at the very frequencies we are using, by the radome, the antenna, the feed and waveguides and the receiver itself. The receiver noise is probably the most significant, and that originating in the input stages is of course amplified by the receiver's full gain. Today's radars often minimize receiver noise by adding a low-noise preamplifier between the antenna and the mixer.

Noise gives rise to a continuous random background. If we plot the incoming signal strengths against range, azimuth direction or anything else we inevitably get what looks like the side view of a lawn along the baseline, so for this reason noise is called grass. Unless we are clever weak targets cannot be seen, because they are down in the grass and masked. With a really noisy receiver a hostile aircraft, especially a stealthy one, could be almost upon us before its blip emerged from the noise background. There is no point in increasing the receiver gain; that would amplify the noise and target echo equally. In today's advanced radars we try harder and use doppler filtering and successive integrations, performed by a signal processor.

To begin with, we invariably also insert a matched filter which eliminates all frequencies except those containing most of the energy in real target echoes; such a filter has a bandwidth close to the reciprocal of the pulse width. We then add a large bank of many hundreds of doppler filters, which

Every radar ever built suffers from noise. As range increases, eventually the target disappears into the 'grass' along the baseline. (Hughes)

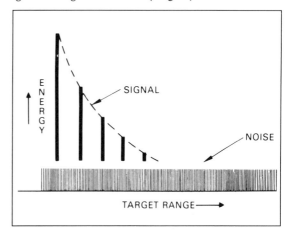

collectively cover the whole anticipated combination of doppler frequencies (generated by the difference in velocity between the radar and the target) but which each lets through only about one-thousandth part of the IF (intermediate frequency) passband. Now we are home and dry. Every second we obtain a few thousand signals, some from noise and some from a real target. Every time the radar beam hits the real target it causes echoes whose waveforms are all approximately in phase. But the noise is a confused jumble of waveforms. The doppler filters therefore repeatedly integrate the incoming signals; this means the signal in each narrow band of frequencies is compared with all its successive values and the differences are added together (for calculus buffs it is summed with respect to time). At the end of, say, a second we have a few thousand noise signals which, being random, all tend to cancel out, and a few thousand real target signals which, all being in phase, add together. The longer we go on, the more the real target stands out from the noise background. Put another way, integrating the returns received each time the beam sweeps across the real target increases signal/noise ratio in direct proportion to the integration time.

The radar designer then has to decide the signal level at which the radar decides it has detected a target. It is a characteristic of noise that it includes frequent bursts of high signal strength, called spikes from their appearance on a display. If we set the detection level only just above the level of the background grass we shall get fed up trying to track false alarms caused by spikes. Too high a level, and

we shall fail to detect real targets. Modern fighter radars have automatic detectors set to a carefully chosen CFAR (constant false-alarm rate) for each operating mode. As this applies mainly to fighter radars this subject is discussed a little further in the next chapter.

The other unwanted interference is clutter. Three types are normally identified: returns from the Earth's surface, from precipitation and other atmospheric reflectors, and from chaff (which is dealt with in Chapter 9). Clutter can be further divided into mainlobe clutter (MLC) and sidelobe clutter (SLC).

As the Earth's surface is by far the biggest reflector around our planet it intrudes into the operation of most radars. Radar altimeters aim straight at it, and doppler navigators aim obliquely at it. Early night fighter radars were almost crippled by the Earth return, except at high altitude. Today sidelobes can be so attenuated that the problem is no longer severe, but it is always present. When we draw sidelobes they look short, but this does not mean the radiation only travels a short distance. The drawings show radiated signal strength, and a short sidelobe means low strength; but the signals go on until they encounter something. Suppose we are flying at 6,000 ft and have a sidelobe with an angular size of 44° with its axis vertically downwards. This will illuminate the ground over a vast ellipse 5,000 ft along the track of the aircraft and extending to the horizon on each side. If we ignore the distant parts and consider only the circular area of 2,500 ft radius centred on the sidelobe axis we have an echoing ground area of 20 million

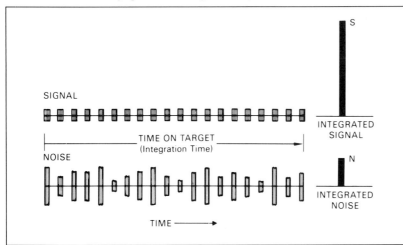

Here we integrate a mere 20 echoes, and 20 associated noise pulses. The latter mainly cancel out in the doppler filter but the true target echoes all add together. In a real radar we may be able to integrate 10,000 pulses in one integration period. (Hughes)

square feet. The nearest point, at the centre, has a range of 6,000 ft. The periphery has a range only 500 ft greater, so we can now see that, even if the sidelobe is very weak, it will generate a massive return from a 20,000,000 sq ft area all at about the same distance.

Thus, we can never forget that sidelobes are always present, there are lots of them, and they extend in all directions from the front round to the sides and rear. Therefore their doppler frequencies cover the whole range from maximum positive, corresponding to a value only just below the radar's groundspeed, to maximum negative. Clearly, maximum positive is dead ahead, while at 90° to the side the doppler frequency (f_d) is zero. In between we can plot lines called isodoppler contours joining all points on the ground having the same doppler frequency. The zero line is straight out to each side. The rest are elliptical curves, getting progressively sharper in curvature and further from the aircraft. Suppose we are chasing a hostile aircraft, and are closing on it. The difference in velocity generates a particular doppler frequency. If the radar differentiates between targets and clutter solely on the basis of doppler frequency, then any target falling amidst the SLC has to compete with the echo from the entire strip of ground between the isodoppler contours bracketing the target's doppler frequency. Not only is this curved strip of ground thousands of times larger than the target but it is also likely to be much nearer. And all these effects are vastly aggravated by flight at very low levels, which is where interceptions in the modern world are likely to take place. So modern fighter radars (we hope) also provide range gating, described later, which eliminates the strip of clutter except for any part passed by the same range gate as the echoes from the true target.

What about mainlobe clutter? MLC is almost inevitable when flying at low level, and it can still be a problem even from high altitude with the mainlobe horizontal. As the mainlobe gain is so high, combined with the vast ground area intercepted, MLC is likely to be far stronger than the return from any aircraft. Of course, some radars point the mainlobe(s) at the ground deliberately, examples being doppler navigators, navigation/bombing radars, SLARs and all kinds of mapping radars. With other types, such as surveillance and interception radars, MLC can be a serious problem. I do not propose to go into great detail in discussing MLC spectral characteristics,

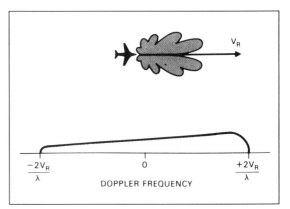

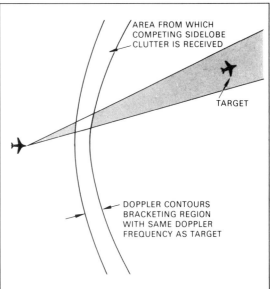

Top *Doppler frequency f_d covered by sidelobe clutter extends over the whole spread of frequencies from that corresponding to the radar's own velocity ($2V_R/\lambda$ dead ahead) to an equal negative frequency astern.* (Hughes)

Above *If a radar differentiates between target echoes and ground clutter solely on the basis of doppler frequency, sidelobe clutter presents a serious problem. Moreover, the ground is much bigger than the target, and in low-level combat is likely to be closer.* (Hughes)

but they are quite complex. For one thing, a lookdown mainlobe illuminates a roughly elliptical area of ground whose size is always thousands of times larger than aerial targets. Imagine this area subdivided into numerous small patches. The look angle is slightly different for every patch, so the MLC covers a band of frequencies. Moreover, as

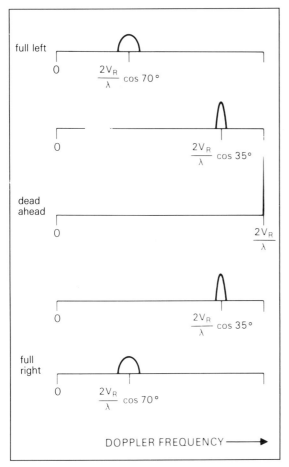

full left

$$0 \qquad \frac{2V_R}{\lambda} \cos 70°$$

$$0 \qquad \frac{2V_R}{\lambda} \cos 35°$$

dead ahead

$$0 \qquad \frac{2V_R}{\lambda}$$

$$0 \qquad \frac{2V_R}{\lambda} \cos 35°$$

full right

$$0 \qquad \frac{2V_R}{\lambda} \cos 70°$$

DOPPLER FREQUENCY ⟶

As the mainlobe sweeps across its full scan, so does its clutter spectrum rise to its peak frequency dead ahead, at the same time being squeezed into a narrow line; then its f_d falls again and spreads at the extreme look angle, in this case 70°. (Hughes)

the beam scans (say, from extreme left to extreme right across one bar of the frame) the MLC spectrum starts as a shallow hump covering a wide spread of f_d (doppler frequencies), steepens and grows in both amplitude and average f_d until, when dead ahead, it is a huge spike with peak amplitude and a single (peak) f_d; then it falls away in both average f_d and amplitude so that the right half is a mirror image of the left. We can imagine it in our mind's eye. This all provides a grounding of basic principles for the next chapter.

There is another important characteristic of some airborne radars which, though hinted at in this and previous chapters (for example in sifting targets

from noise), has not been spelt out in simple words. This is the idea of coherence. A non-coherent pulsed radar merely uses the synchronizer to switch the RF power on and then off again so that the modulator and transmitter send out a succession of pulses. We make the synchronizer as accurate as we can, so that we get pulses of the correct PRF and pulse width. But each pulse is an independent entity. The phases of each pulse are unrelated to those that precede or follow it, or to any other pulses. With a coherent radar we use a stable oscillator to generate a highly stable CW (continuous wave) output which runs all the time the radar is switched on. This low-power train of waves is fed to a power amplifier which is then keyed on/off to send out the high-power pulses. Instead of being independent, each pulse is, as it were, a portion cut from a non-stop CW wave train. Thus, all the phases are in step; the pulses are coherent. The distance from any one wavefront in any pulse is an exact whole number of wavelengths from any wavefront of the same phase in any other pulse. If the radar's wavelength is 3 cm then the gap between the last wavefront of one pulse and the first wavefront of the next might be 3,000,000 cm, or 3,000,003 or 3,000,006, but not 3,000,001 or 3,000,000.25, which could well be the case with a non-coherent radar.

Small diagrams show the spectra of different types of radar. For a CW radar the spectrum is a single line. For a single pulse, or a train (series) of noncoherent pulses the spectrum is a shape, very familiar to radar designers, with a sine-wave form having a tall mainlobe at the centre and symmetric sidelobes half the width of the mainlobe and dying away on each side. The spectrum for a coherent train of infinite length (impossible in practical radars) is a symmetric series of single frequencies separated by the reciprocal of the PRF, and fitting inside the same envelope shape as before. For a practical coherent radar the spectrum is one in which the narrow one-frequency lines are replaced by sine-wave lines whose maximum width is 2/NT Hz where NT is the total length of the pulse train in seconds (or fractions of a second).

How do radars measure the range and direction of a target, and lock-on to track it? Earlier I commented that to obtain target range you merely multiply half the round-trip time of any one pulse by the speed of light. Thus, if the total (not half) round-trip time is 6.67 μs, the target range is 1 km; if the total time is 10.7 μs the range is a mile, and if the

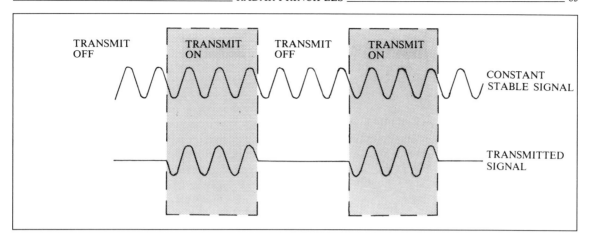

Above *In a coherent radar the waves transmitted in any pulse may be ten miles away when the next pulse is transmitted, yet the waves remain precisely in step. We can add echoes from different pulses without loss, and we can precisely compare echo frequencies with those transmitted.* (Ferranti)

Right *Spectra of different kinds of pulsed signal. CW is naturally a single line at the operating frequency. A single pulse or train of non-coherent pulse gives the familiar shape seen previously (τ is pulse width). An infinite train of coherent pulses would give single frequencies fitting within this outline. A practical short train of coherent pulses gives sine-wave lines as shown.* (Hughes)

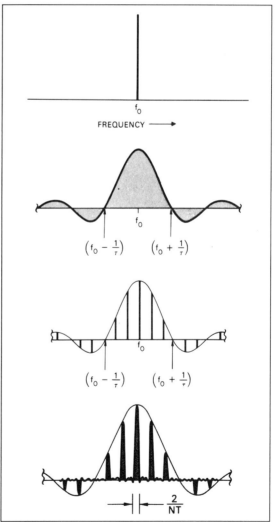

time is 12.4 μs the range is 1 nautical mile. In modern radars the output from the receiver is passed to a large bank of fast electronic switches called range gates. These open (ie, the switch closes to let a signal pass) in rapid succession. When any one gate is open, all the others are shut. The signal processor notes which gate(s) pass the echoes of targets. This can be done in various ways, as explained in the next chapter. For the moment we may just note that this so-called pulse-delay method of ranging is fine so long as targets are near and the round-trip time is less than the interpulse period. But if any target's transit time exceeds the interpulse period its echo will be received after the next pulse has been transmitted. The pulse-delay range gates will think the echo came from the next pulse, and we shall get a false short range output. These range ambiguities are one of the major problems of fighter radars (Chapter 5).

Another subject dealt with in more detail in the next chapter is tracking, which means noting the directions of each target and if necessary locking the antenna on to it. Modern fighter radars have a mode called TWS (track while scan). The antenna keeps scanning the beam all over the frame in its ceaseless search for targets, and every time the beam sweeps across a target the signal processor memory makes a note of the azimuth, elevation and range, or in some other way records the target's position. Older radars could not do this, and in any case we may wish to ignore the possibility of other targets and devote our attention to the first (probably the nearest). To do this we lock the antenna on to it, and this requires measurement of angular errors, and then driving the antenna so that these errors are reduced to zero.

There are several ways of doing this. It can be done with a simple beam, provided it has adequate angular resolution to discriminate between the target we want and any others very close to it. The receiver output from a single target, plotted against antenna angle, is the familiar hump shape. As one target begins to separate into two, the plot grows a notch or saddle in the middle, and, as the two target angles move further apart, the notch grows until we have two separate returns. To lock on to a target the most common technique is lobing, and this can be done in several ways. The earliest way was to aim the beam just to one side of the target, and then aim it just to the other side (or aim just above and then just below). The two mainlobes (rather, the same one but at different times) are arranged to intersect at their half-power points. If the target is centred between them, the left/right and up/down pairs of signals will be equal. If the target is offset from the boresight line the signals will not be equal, and

because of the steep slope of the radiation pattern the difference in signal strength will be large even for a small pointing error. It is simple to arrange for the antenna gimbal drives to aim the antenna so that the signal difference is reduced to zero. We are then very accurately tracking the target.

We noted earlier that targets scintillate, and ECM (Chapter 9) can also cause sudden large variations in apparent target RCS. It is therefore better if, instead of aiming the lobes sequentially, we can aim all four lobes simultaneously. As all the angular tracking information can then be obtained from the returns from a single pulse this simultaneous lobing is called monopulse operation. It is discussed in the next chapter.

One extremely important function of almost all military airborne radars, and also common in simple civil weather radars to avoid ground return, is MTI (moving-target indication). Before radar designers learned to exploit the doppler effect, radars would have been useless in the low-level missions flown by essentially all today's combat aircraft. The massive ground return would have swamped all the real targets, and the concept of a look-down fighter radar would have been impossible. We have already seen how measuring doppler frequencies enables clutter to be greatly reduced if not eliminated. In exactly the same way, since the range rates (rate of change of range) of most aerial targets are greater than those of the ground, rain, ground vehicles and other echoing sources, aerial targets can easily be filtered out. MTI is another subject discussed in the next chapter.

On the other hand another technique, pulse com-

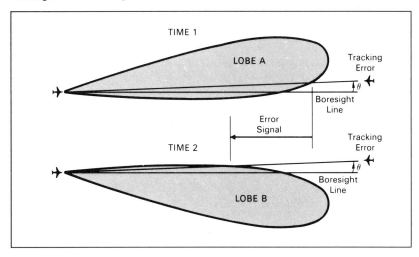

To track a target we compare the return signals from lobe A with those from lobe B. The difference is an error signal, giving a tracking error. It is simple to use this signal to drive the antenna until the error signal is zero. (Hughes)

With chirp, each received echo increases in frequency from front to rear. Since the rear parts pass through the filter quicker, the result is a bunching-up, giving a pulse of greater amplitude and decreased width. (Hughes)

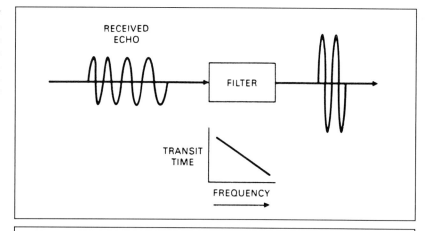

A linear FM pulse can be thought of as made up of segments of progressively higher frequency. Going through the filter, segment 2 catches up with 1, 3 catches 2, and they all end up emerging simultaneously. (Hughes)

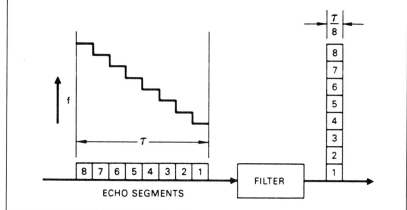

pression (PC), is applicable to many kinds of radar and can be covered here. This again can be done in several ways. PC seeks to overcome the fact that, to increase range, you want to increase peak power, and there are limits to what is practical; and to improve range resolution (accuracy of measuring range) you want to use extremely narrow pulses, whereas, to obtain good detection ranges at PRFs low enough for normal pulse-delay ranging to be used, we have to use quite wide pulses.

The first and commonest form of pulse compression is called chirp, a word sometimes used to denote all PC methods. The name came from the similarity of the frequency spectrum to that of a bird's chirping. A more sedate term is linear frequency modulation. Like all other PC schemes it involves coding the transmitted pulses and then decoding the received echoes. With chirp, each pulse sent out is passed through a filter which increases the frequency at a constant rate throughout the length of the pulse, each fresh pulse of course starting again at the original modulator frequency. Thus, all the received echoes repeat the same waveform. After being received at the antenna they pass through a filter which does the exact opposite: it introduces a time lag which decreases linearly with frequency. Thus the front of each echo is held up and the rate at which the echo passes through gets faster and faster, so that the pulse that emerges is bunched up, with greater amplitude and much less width. Some linear-FM techniques split the received pulses into increments of successively higher frequency. In one method the delay is made to equal the width of each pulse-segment, so that all (in the diagram, eight) segments emerge from the filter at the same instant. Thus the receiver output from each pulse has a fraction of the width but many times the power.

Chirp is simple, and can provide large compression ratios. One of its advantages is that it greatly

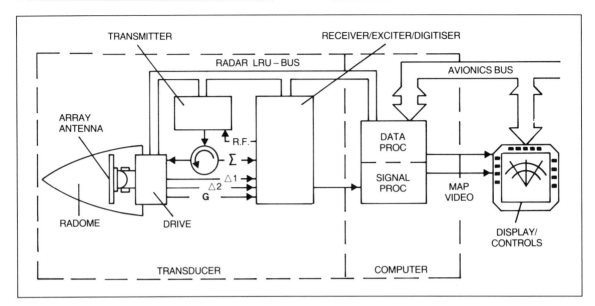

reduces range sidelobes. These are not the same as antenna sidelobes, but result from the fact that each wave in the received echo is not totally at one exact frequency but is spread over a significant band extending equally above and below the nominal frequency. By suitably designing the compressing filter we can do a tapering function, as is done with antenna sidelobes. Tapering the amplitude at the leading and trailing edges widens the compressed pulse slightly but greatly reduces the sidelobes. A more important advantage is much better range resolution. Consider echoes from two very close targets, whose spacing is small compared with our pulse length. The received echoes are thus merged and seemingly indistinguishable, but the coding means that the string of segments of each echo are assembled in the filter in slightly different places. Thus, what emerge, as if by magic, are two clear and unambiguous echoes separated by their small range difference.

I do not propose to go into detail on other PC techniques, which most notably are binary phase modulation, where you reverse the phase of certain echo segments, and polyphase coding in which successive phases may be rotated through, say, 90° or 120°.

To round off this general overview I will touch on various paths along which radar designers are beating out new territory. Some of the more easily understandable developments concern hardware, such as antennas, but (if my postbag is any guide)

Architecture of a modern multimode military radar. Instructions arrive via the avionics bus. The data processor selects the mode, waveform, antenna position and channels, and configures the signal processor to handle these. The exciter generates the waveform, the transmitter amplifies it, the sum channel Σ, two difference channels Δ1 and Δ2 and guard channel G are amplified and digitized in the receiver, the signal processor extracts target data and the data processor compiles tracks for the avionics bus or builds up a map image for display. (Ferranti)

the fastest-growing topic in the whole of aviation is software. Though designers will never cease finding ways of improving the hardware, the crucial differences between modern nose radars for combat aircraft and those in, say, the Mirage III or F-4, are that today's sets are called multimode, or multimission, because they are programmable. Early radars did have signal processors, but they were 'hardwired'. Today's PSPs (programmable signal processors) are not only less costly but enable the radar to be instantly reprogrammed for different functions, missions, processes, algorithms (computational rules) and processing coefficients. One of the major lines of advance is in making processors that work much faster yet use less power. One key to this is VLSI, and this is covered in the final chapter.

Radars designed to work in hostile or disputed environments naturally have to face enemy threats such as jamming and other ECM, and missiles designed to home on our radar, or home on our aircraft which was detected because of its telltale radar emissions. There are various things we can do about this. One method of countering jamming so that we always have a usable signal/noise ratio is to use an adaptive array antenna. These are arrays, arranged in various geometrical ways, of many antenna elements. They can take different forms, such as fully controllable, or phase-control only, or coherent sidelobe cancelling. Much work is still needed to perfect radars that can inspect and filter returns in which are embedded high-power broadband mainlobe jamming power. But with the fantastic advances into the world of VLSI it is possible not just to filter out huge chunks of received frequency containing clutter or jamming but also continuously to examine the outputs of each of perhaps 1,600 receiver filters and to reject only those that actually contain interference. This adaptive cancellation will enable far more targets to be detected, and usable results to be obtained in the face of many types of jamming.

Another new technique for front-line missions is what is called bistatic radar. In such a system the transmitter is in one place (eg, one aircraft) and the receiver in another, perhaps miles away. Thus, in an attack on a surface target the enemy should, we hope, remain ignorant of the silent approach of the attacking aircraft, heading towards the received echoes from the target illuminated by the friendly bistatic partner, who stands off, we hope, out of SAM range. All the thoughtless enemy's ECM are directed towards the transmitting partner. Another advantage is that in creating SAR imagery (Chapter

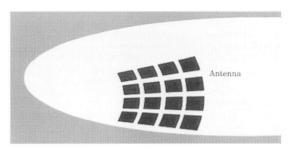

Conformal radar antennas could be built into an aircraft nose, leading edge or any other part facing a direction of interest. The Northrop B-2 probably has some. (Westinghouse)

8) the transmitter must have an angular rate about the target being mapped, but a bistatic partner can fly directly towards it. Yet another possibility is for an illuminating aircraft to co-operate with a bistatic partner whose radar uses a fan of receiving channels to detect targets spread along a large area of illuminated sky. For all bistatic schemes to work accurately there must be absolutely precise keying of relative position information and timing between the two aircraft.

To conclude on the subject of antennas, the future looks bright. For almost twenty years the conformal radar has been a major objective of many design teams, and a few have actually been made. In such a radar the antenna comprises one or several regions of aircraft skin — metal skin, we think — formed into radiating slot patterns. Provided the slots and the patterns are carefully design-

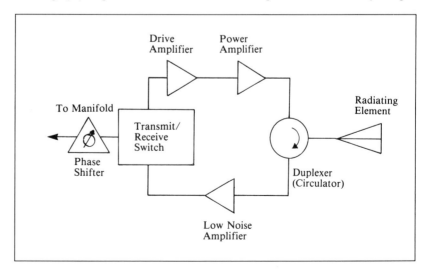

Typical elements found in a T/R (transmit/receive) module in an 'active aperture' electronically steered radar. Each module is about the size and shape of a large torch. The B-1B antenna contains 1,526. (Westinghouse).

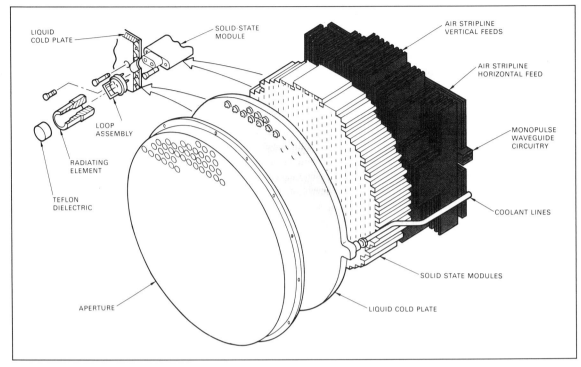

Above *A simplified active-array radar, showing one of the array modules removed and 'exploded' into its main parts.* (Hughes)

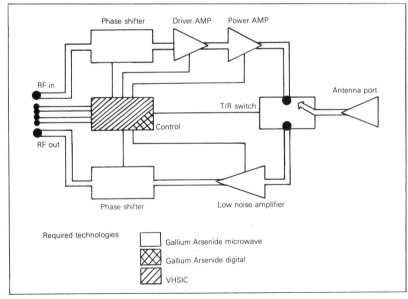

Left *Schematic of a solid-state receiver for a 'year 2000' active radar of EW arrays based entirely on MMIC (monolithic microwave integrated circuit) technology.* (Westinghouse)

ed, the radiating region can exactly correspond with the ideal shape of the aircraft. Such antennas can be formed in the skin of the nose, leading edges of wings, tail surfaces or rotor blades, or portions of fuselage. There are many problems, and it is probable that fully conformal arrays will need to use an active transmit/receive module behind each of the radiating slots.

Active arrays of this type are already flying (though very few are conformal). Their advantages extend into every aspect of radar performance, and at some increase in cost they offer truly remarkable improvements. The active array could be described as many hundreds of radars in one, because behind every radiating/receiving element is a complete solid-state module of a novel kind. In the radar of the B-1B bomber 1,526 modules form a tight pattern across the elliptical fixed aperture. The modulator sends a low-power RF signal to all modules. Each module amplifies this signal in a power amplifier and radiates it through its radiating element. The entire aperture thus radiates a perfect high-power signal with no high-power microwave tube, no dissipative losses from the transmitter, power management and feed circuitry, better transmission efficiency and simpler cooling from a flat liquid plate. The beam is steered electronically by phase-shifters upstream of the final power amplifiers (page 120).

Received echoes are amplified right at the face of the aperture by an array of low-noise amplifiers, almost eliminating transmission-line losses and greatly reducing noise. The phase-shifters are then encountered downstream, with little effect on receiver noise. Target detection and virtually every other task is enhanced by the immediate access to each channel, and, by grouping the modules into different RF feed manifolds, the one radar can perform with different independent or overlapping sub-apertures, whose processed outputs can then provide elegant answers to such problems as finding targets in heavy ECM. Reliability should be outstanding, because failure of one module, or even several, has little effect on performance.

We are likely to see millions of these active array modules, each about as big as a bottle of Liebfraumilch. They can be packaged into a compact block to fit a fighter nose, but with VHSIC processing they could be distributed throughout an aircraft, emitting in various directions. Anyone who wants to design radars will find plenty of work.

5
RADAR FOR FIGHTERS

Having in the previous chapter tried to make a few comments on how radars work, this chapter should be easier for the non-specialist. It outlines some of the history of airborne radars used to intercept hostile aircraft, and concentrates more on the hardware than on theory. It does, however, inevitably include a pretty solid section on PD and medium-PRF radar, because this cannot be avoided.

Radar was pioneered chiefly in Great Britain, from February 1935. As a cover it was called RDF, which the bad guys were expected to translate as radio direction finding. The original gigantic installations were of course on the ground, working at wavelengths of 10 to 13.5 m (22–30 MHz). By April 1936 the team of workers under Watson Watt had studied the problems of what was called RDF. 2: airborne fighter radar. At first this seemed impossible, on such grounds as antenna size and electric power requirement. By March 1937 a Heyford bomber was flying with a big dipole antenna fixed between the spatted wheels, to receive echoes from targets illuminated by the BBC transmitters, feeding a CRT oscilloscope. On 16 August 1937 a complete RDF. 2 set made its first flight in Anson *K6260*. I described the subsequent history in some detail in *Night Fighters*, also published by PSL. Via a set called AI (airborne interception) Mk I, which was the world's first stab at a production aircraft radar, the AI Mk II was available by early 1939. This properly engineered set was made by commercial industry, the transmitter coming from Metrovick, the receiver being based on a Pye TV chassis and A.C. Cossor being a major subcontractor. At a total cost of £4,650 the first 21 production sets were installed in Blenheim IF fighters in summer 1939. Operating at 1.5 m (200 MHz), AI Mk II used horizontal pairs of transmitter dipoles on the nose, and upper and lower pairs of horizontal receiver dipoles near one wingtip. To be of any use the pilot

had to be vectored by ground control so that the target was within a 20° cone ahead at a range between 5,500 ft and 1,200 ft. At heights below about 8,000 ft the ground return blanketed any target echo. AI II also suffered from basic ambiguity problems; for example the observer concentrating on the CRT display could not tell if a target was at upper left or lower right, because the indications were the same.

It is difficult for us to appreciate that in the 1930s the word electronics was virtually unknown, and for practical purposes none of today's avionics concepts had been thought of. In an interview on RAF radio for a BBC TV series Sir Robert Cockburn recalled that, at that time, 'The standard airborne set consisted of a box which had a 120-volt battery and two bright emitter valves. I remember the way you tested these parts was to take the two valves out and drop them on the table and bounce them — Boing! — and catch them. If they did not break you put them back and the sets would pass as serviceable. It was almost unbelievable how naïve and elementary the equipment was.'

Starting from such a primitive baseline it is small wonder that AI Mks I, II, III and IV each made giant strides, yet in timing were separated by weeks rather than (as would be the case today) many years. AI.IV was the first really important airborne radar, and the only interception radar in large-scale service anywhere in the world prior to 1943. Still a 1.5 m set, it incorporated a modulator conceived by A.D. Blumlein of EMI which at one stroke, by slashing the time duration of each pulse, overcame the problem of the transmitted pulses being fed direct to the receiver. GEC created the Micropup thermionic valve which could put out 10 kW. The pairs of dipole antennas could be switched to give four mainlobes, so that by comparing the four received signal amplitudes the target direction could be determined without ambiguity anywhere within a 40° cone ahead of the fighter. The observer could then give the pilot azimuth/elevation directions to try to equalize the heights of the four blips on the CRT display, viewed in succession. Practical range limits above the minimum useful altitude of 10,000 ft were about three miles down to 800/1,000 ft, and this rather long minimum range often proved too great for visual contact at night. The final closure to firing range had to be done blind, not knowing where the target was and in fear of colliding with it from astern. Nevertheless AI.IV was the first radar to make a real difference to a nation's ability to intercept at night or in bad weather. But it was obvious to the tiny British research teams that AI radars ought to operate at much shorter wavelengths.

Need for centimetric radar for night fighters had been obvious since AI was thought of in 1936. Such radar could be miniaturized, and could send out a beam like a searchlight that could be directed by a reflector. It would overcome the problems of minimum range, ground reflection and many other difficulties, besides giving a sharper blip and, in theory, even being able to picture the target's shape. It would also be more difficult to jam. But in 1939 it was simply incapable of being built. One who knew this was a nuclear physicist, P.I. Dee, who eventually headed the relevant team. Percival Rowe knew how vital a breakthrough in this field would be, but wisely played it down in talking to visiting VIPs; nobody knew if it could ever be made to work. And for a time all results were negative.

As explained in Chapter 1 it was the invention of a good magnetron, by Randall and Boot of Prof Mark Oliphant's team at the University of Birmingham, that provided the breakthrough. The Telecommunications Research Establishment (TRE), then located at Worth Matravers in Dorset, received the first supposed centimetric AI hardware on 8 June 1940. Supplied by a klystron, it merely confirmed everyone's belief that it couldn't be done, and it even had to have its own vacuum pumping plant. But the following month the establishment set up the first radar fed by one of Birmingham's new magnetrons. This was wholly practical, the magnetron was evacuated and sealed and thus needed no pumping, and from the start of operation — the target was a boy on a bicycle — it was clear that centimetric AI was 'on' at last.

By May 1941 TRE, GEC and the Clarendon Lab had virtually finished the engineering of the receiver, and in particular had devised a high frequency switch which enabled a single small antenna to serve alternately as transmitter and receiver. Thus with centimetric radar there did not have to be any remote antennas near the tips of the wings. To focus the pulses of 10 cm waves into a pencil beam a paraboloidal metal dish was placed behind the waveguide feeder. Then the combined unit, called a scanner, was mounted on pivots so that it could point anywhere in a large cone ahead of the fighter carrying it. The complete unit comprising pivoted scanner, a mechanical drive system and associated circuitry at the rear, was then mounted in the fighter's nose. The main boxes containing the transmitter, receiver, power supplies and other parts might be anywhere, while the control and display units naturally were in the cockpit. To smooth off the nose contours the scanner was then enclosed by a 'radome' of thin non-conductive (dielectric) plastics. All this was breaking completely new ground, and one of the most difficult mechanical engineering tasks was achieving sufficient precision, speed and angular movement to point the beam everywhere it had to go.

The first airborne centimetric installation was made in a TRE Blenheim at Christchurch in March 1941. The scanner was driven in spiral fashion, starting at the centre dead ahead of the aircraft and rapidly spinning round an ever-increasing cone to a maximum of 45°, then it would spirally scan inwards until, for a brief moment at the centre, it would again be motionless. Other scanners follow-

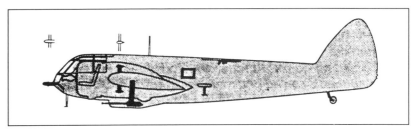

The world's first radar-equipped fighters were Bristol Blenheim IFs of RAF No 600 Sqn in 1939. The 200 MHz AI Mk II used horizontal dipole antennas.

ed different patterns, one obvious one being a sequence of horizontal (or slightly sloping) left/right right/left sweeps working their way up and down between wide angular limits. These pioneer scanning antennas were made by Nash & Thompson, famed for their bomber gun turrets. Rowe commented that when RAF personnel first saw them 'doubts were cast on the sanity of the scientists. Before the system reached a speed of rotation greater than the eye could follow, it could be watched rotating in a curiously irregular fashion, with the one apparent desire of escaping from the aircraft altogether'.

GEC rushed through 150 centimetric AI.VII radars by the end of 1941. The first flight was in Beaufighter IF *X7579* in November 1941. This was the first aircraft to fly with what soon became familiar as a radome, though at the time it was called a thimble nose. The urgency resulted in a compromised design. For example, to sidestep the problem of feeding to a moving scanner the waveguide terminated in a fixed aft-facing horn at the focus of the parabolic scanner which was driven round behind it in increasing and decreasing spirals. This greatly increased beamwidth as look angle increased, so that while targets dead ahead might be seen at six miles they could remain invisible only two miles away at a look angle of 30°. Another snag was that it was difficult to interpret the display to measure angle-off, though as the idea was to reduce this to zero this was not serious. Beaufighters with AI.VII were on operations before the end of 1941, just a year after one of Britain's most eminent scientists had proclaimed 'Centimetric radar is for the *next* war'.

Of course the giant advantages of using a much shorter wavelength, apart from the ability to package the radar and antenna into the nose, were that the equipment could be used at low altitudes and that the minimum range was reduced to something like 300 ft, a distance at which any ordinary target should have been acquired visually. AI.VII was quickly followed by AI.VIII, a refined and productionized set ordered to the tune of 1,500 from Ekco and 1,000 from GEC, and with over 1,000 of the magnetrons supplied from a production line in a lab at the University of Birmingham!

AI.VIIIA made provision for IFF and Racon (radar beacon) interrogation, and VIIIB added the Lucero facility for position fixing from compatible ground beacons transmitting on 1.5 m. Fitted in various Mosquitoes and the Beaufighter VIF and some Xs, these were the standard British AI radars for the rest of the war. Many were used by US forces, but the United States had been given the magnetron valve, along with the Whittle turbojet and many other secret new developments, on 28 September 1940. The official history of the US Office of Scientific Research and Development described the magnetron as 'the most valuable cargo ever brought to our shores'. On 10 November 1940 Dr Lee DuBridge, from the University of Rochester, was appointed Director of the Radiation Laboratory set up at MIT, with Ted Bowen, a pioneer of British AI, assigned to tell the new lab what to do and how to do it. To say the Americans moved fast is an understatement. Starting from nothing, with no research team, the Radiation Laboratory had a prototype radar working on 4 January 1941! On 7 February a fully engineered set was tracking aircraft, on 10 March another was flying in a B-18A, and a little later pre-production sets called AI.10 or SCR-520 were flying in A-20s and in an RCAF Boeing 247 which flew to England for demonstrations and tests.

As it used the standard British magnetron this pioneer US radar worked on 10 cm, but peak power was uprated to 100 kW and PRF was increased. The antenna boldly fed the microwave power to a waveguide feeder which moved with the scanner. The 30 in parabolic reflector nodded up and down, typically between $+50°/-20°$, on a rectangular frame. This frame was mounted on upper and lower gimbals through which passed the transmit/receive waveguides. It was carefully balanced so that, instead of sweeping through a limited arc, it spun continuously at 350 rpm. The feed horn was fixed to curve back at the focus of the dish reflector, and the beam was transmitted through a wide arc head, such as 75° left to 75° right. After delivering 108 SCR-520A radars production switched in early November 1942 to the SCR-720. Fitted to Douglas P-70Bs and almost all Northrop P-61s, this was the most advanced airborne radar of the war. It was basically a marriage of the 520A and the British AI.VIII, but with important new additions including the first ECCM (electronic counter-countermeasures) in the form of anti-jam circuits, two display modes, and the ability to close down the field of view once a target had been acquired.

In Britain brilliant work was done by Dr (and Wing Commander) Derek Jackson on developing

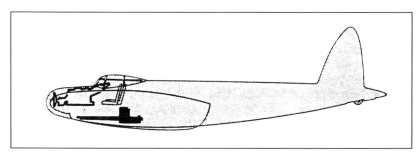

De Havilland Mosquito XIX with universal nose (AI. VIIIA shown installed) and four 20mm Hispano.

AI.VIII into AI.IX able to discriminate individual targets even in the presence of the newly invented Window (chaff). On 23 December 1942 Jackson was engaged in Window trials from a Beaufighter, trying to confuse another Beau fitted with the prototype AI.IX; in a not uncommon example of misidentification they were attacked by a Spitfire, Jackson's aircraft limping home a wreck and the vital Mk IX aircraft being shot into the sea. In a happier test programme starting on 1 April 1943 Mosquito II *DZ659* was fitted with SCR-720 and evaluated against *DD715* with AI.VIII. The US radar had been exhaustively tested in at least one white Wellington and, following the evaluation in Mosquitoes, it was adopted by the RAF as AI.10, made in the USA by Western Electric who had spare capacity. AI.10 was still the RAF night fighter radar in the days of the Meteor NF.11 and Venom NF.2 in the 1950s!

In Germany virtually all radar effort was applied to large sets for ground and ship applications until, in December 1940, Major-General Kammhuber asked Telefunken to begin work on a radar that could be carried in a fighter. The company chose as a starting point the Lichtenstein B coarse high-altitude radio altimeter, developed in 1939. Flight trials began in August 1941 and series production was started in summer 1942. Following operational trials in Bf 110E-1/U1s at Venlo the production set, called FuG 202 Lichtenstein BC, was first fitted as standard to the Bf 110F-4a from September 1942. From October 1942 it equipped the Ju 88C-6b.

German research into centimetric microwaves in the 1930s had yielded such discouraging results that it had been abandoned, but for this new application Telefunken brought down the wavelength to 62 cm, equivalent to 490 MHz. Transmitter power was 1.5 kW, and excluding antennas the weight was 53 lb. Output was fed to an array of antennas on the nose of the aircraft — the Luftwaffe called this a *Matratze* (mattress) — arranged in four groups each

consisting of four vertical dipoles backed by four identical dipole reflectors. A high-speed rotary commutating switch fed the power to each antenna group in turn, upper left, lower left, lower right, upper right, so that the echoes could give range on one display, azimuth on another and elevation on a third. In the first installations the receiver antennas were on the outer wings. Search azimuth was 70° and practical range limits about 11,500–650 ft. Basically an excellent set for its day, FuG 202 was marred by unreliability and many other shortcomings which caused it to be widely scorned until a few *experte* pilots began to make good use of it in 1943.

In January 1943 Telefunken began deliveries of FuG 212 Lichtenstein C-1, a refined version of 202 that was easier to produce and had only two CRT displays, one for range and the other combining Az/El. As described in Chapter 9 the RAF at last used Window on 24 July 1943, and a month later Telefunken began producing C-1 sets whose receivers could be tuned anywhere within the range 420–480 MHz. And from September 1943 the company began delivering a new radar altogether: FuG 220 Lichtenstein SN-2.

Anybody might have expected this to use a shorter wavelength and a small scanning dish antenna. Its design was started in November 1942, long before it was known that the RAF had stocks of Window, yet the decisions taken were quite the opposite. SN-2 used a longer wavelength, greater than 3 m. At first it operated at 73/82/91 MHz, widened by 1944 into the so-called 'dispersal waveband' from 37.5–118 MHz. This meant that it needed an antenna 'mattress' even more cumbersome than before, and the Luftwaffe's name for the huge array of four dipoles, with reflector rods behind them, was *Hirschgeweih* (stag's antlers). At first the dipoles were invariably vertical, and the four struts were heavily braced to reduce their resonant vibration and sway. Power was 2.5 kW, weight of the

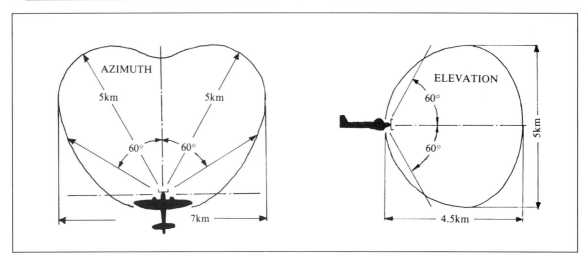

internal boxes about 154 lb, and the effect on performance and handling, especially of the Bf 110G-4 series, quite considerable. Angular coverage was good, but a major drawback was that minimum range was about 1,000 ft, and most crews naturally found this too far for visual acquisition. Accordingly many night fighters were fitted with SN-2b, which was FuG 220 plus a second set, Lichtenstein C-1 *Weitwinkel* (wide angle). The latter added a single-pole quad antenna in the centre of the nose and was switched on as the range was closed. It could look over a 120° sector down to a minimum range from 1.25 miles down to about 500 ft.

The combined SN-2b was widely used at the end of the war, but from May 1944 Telefunken produced SN-2d, with the main dipoles set at 45°, matching the changed polarity of the waves. By reducing the beamwidth this improved performance in conditions of Window jamming. At about the same time drag was reduced by redesigning the strut mountings. By this time the effort on German night-fighter avionics was considerable, Telefunken's research staff numbering over 3,000 and being joined by Siemens, FFO, GEMA, Lorenz and others. Small numbers of FuG 228 Lichtenstein SN-3 high-power (20 kW) sets were built, some having *Morgenstern* (morning star) rod antennas, together with a range of tail-warning radars using rod antennas on the wings or tail. By 1945 Telefunken had copied the magnetron and produced prototypes of the FuG 240 Berlin operating on 9 or 9.3 cm, 3.25/3.33 GHz. There were seven versions under development when the war ended, all hefty sets weighing about 400 lb exclusive of anten-

nas. It is reported that ten examples of Berlin N-1a were delivered and two or three were flown in Ju 88G-6s including one of Stab/NJG 4. (The often reported Ju 88G-7 remained long-span prototypes which never got near any Luftwaffe unit.)

It is remarkable that Britain never fitted radar to any single-seat fighters in World War 2, except for a single Typhoon with AI.VI. Indeed, with the sole exception of the short-range Lightning, Air Staff policy insisted on a crew of two until almost the present day. In the USA, however, the picture was totally different. In January 1941 the US Navy issued a far-seeing and detailed requirement for a radar operating on the record short wavelength of 3 cm, capable of being used by the pilot in air interception and even surface attack missions. The first result was AI-3 (SCR-537), the main contractor being Sperry. First flown in the nose of a Beech JRB in April 1942, this set was mounted behind the fighter's cockpit, feeding via a long waveguide to a spirally driven scanner near the right wingtip. By late 1942, as the AIA, later redesignated APS-4, this set was in production for F6F Hellcats and, as AI.XIVA (ASH) for British Fireflies and Sea Mosquitoes. It was followed in 1943 by the Westinghouse APS-6, first flown in October 1943 in a Beech SNB. The wing pod was pressurized and housed the whole RF system, eliminating the long waveguide. Stromberg made the modulator and Dalmo Victor the scanner, which rotated at no less than 1,200 rpm in covering a cone of up to 60°. Fighters suffered no trouble with vibration or reduced rate of roll, though the installation weighed 242 lb. APS-6 and -6A (with Philco APS-4 type

Left *Angular coverage of the FuG 220 Lichtenstein SN–2. The chief disadvantage of this radar was that it had a rather long minimum range.*

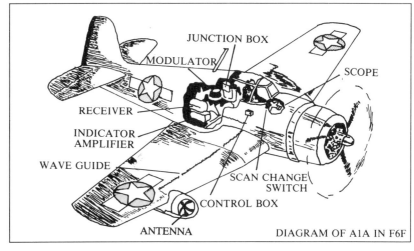

JUNCTION BOX
MODULATOR
SCOPE
RECEIVER
INDICATOR AMPLIFIER
WAVE GUIDE
SCAN CHANGE SWITCH
CONTROL BOX
ANTENNA
DIAGRAM OF A1A IN F6F

Right *Contemporary (1942) sketch showing installation of the AIA, the pioneer 3 cm radar, in a Grumman F6F-3N.*

receiver) worked well at up to 30,000 ft, range limits being 5 miles (40 against coastlines) down to a mere 360 ft. No fewer than 5,260 were delivered, including 2,161 by 1 August 1945, mainly for F4Us and F6Fs.

Thus, by the end of World War 2 Westinghouse had become a major radar company, its AI sets being backed up by deliveries of over 13,000 ASB attack radars, mainly for SBDs and TBFs. In the post-war era the Baltimore-based giant continued to develop improved radars of basically conventional form. The US Army/Navy designation scheme for avionics, published in 1942, allocated APQ to versatile fighter radars, A signifying piloted-aircraft application, P radar, and Q a combination of purposes. Likewise, in APG the G meant fire control, in APS the S meant detection or range/bearing search, and in AWG the W meant armament. Westinghouse continued to have a near-monopoly of Navy radars, with APQ-35 and 43 for such aircraft as the Skyknight and (with UK designation AI.21) Meteor NF.14 and Sea Venom FAW.21, APQ-41 and 65 for the Banshee and Aquilon, and closely related AI.22 for the Javelin. In Britain GEC developed such sets as AI.18 for the Sea Vixen, while similar traditional radars were developed in the Soviet Union for many prototypes and for the production Yak-25.

In 1948 the recently created US Air Force asked industry for a completely new radar fire-control system for all weather interceptors. It was to incorporate a computer and had to meet a very demanding specification. To the amazement of other bidders the winner was Hughes Aircraft. Under

General Harold L. George the aviation empire of Howard Hughes was being steered in the direction of the world's most challenging electronics, and a team of great talent was quickly created. Hughes had been the only bidder to agree to have the radar flying in one year. Five months later the Soviet Union tried to seal off Berlin. On the following day the USAF asked Hughes if it could fly the radar in four months and be in production six months later. This 'impossible' schedule was agreed to, and Hughes met it. A little later a Lockheed F-94A out of Eglin AFB intercepted and destroyed a target drone without either of the crew seeing it.

This original Hughes radar, the E-1, was the ancestor of the biggest range of fighter radars in the Western world. With the E-10 the California upstart replaced Westinghouse on the final model of the Navy's Banshee. With the E-4, fitted to the single-seat F-86D Sabre, Hughes tied the radar to a pioneer computer to give the pilot such accurate steering information that the fighter could perform a collision-course, making the interception from abeam where the target RCS was much greater than that from astern. The system was not accurate enough for guns, but worked adequately with a salvo of 2.75-inch Mighty Mouse rockets. Many related fire-control systems were fitted to such aircraft as the F-89D, F-94C and CF-100. With the E-9 of 1955, for the F-89H, transmitter power was increased to match the range of the Hughes Falcon guided missile. With the MG-10, in production in 1956, Hughes created a fire control capable of controlling the supersonic F-102 Delta Dagger in any weather, converting digital guidance from the ground SAGE network into analog form for display to the pilot and subsequent independent guidance of the interception. Once locked on, the MG-10 automatically guided the F-102, opened the weapon-bay doors and fired the Falcons or Mighty Mouse rockets.

An almost exactly similar system was MG-13 for the F-101B, with the differences that this aircraft had a full-time backseat operator and could fire Genie nuclear rockets which needed a long stand-off distance. These and other contemporary fire-control installations were necessarily bulky, occupying about 25 cubic feet and weighing some 1,425 lb. The next generation, however, was even bigger.

Interceptor radars reached a peak of weight and bulk with the mighty MA-1, around which the Convair F-106 was designed.

The F-106 Delta Dart, originally called the F-102B, was required to have an electronic navigation and fire-control system giving virtually total automation of each intercept mission, the pilot having a supervisory role. Starting by translating SAGE target vectoring information, the MA-1 system thereafter guided the aircraft before and after radar lock-on, managed the attack and then recovered the aircraft back to base, navigating by Tacan and homing on preselected beacons and then linking the ILS and flight controls. Apart from the A3J (A-5) Vigilante, the F-106 was the first aircraft in service with a digital computer. But this was in the era of thermionic valves, so MA-1 comprised 200 LRUs occupying 45 cubic feet and weighing 2,520 lb! Yet its computational speed was a mere 9,600 arithmetical calculations per second or 6,250 decisions in one minute, and the self-test program took five minutes. (At the time this was no mean achievement.)

The MA-1 had a good innings, the last Darts having just left the ANG squadrons as this chapter was written, after some 28 years. Another good innings was enjoyed by the Lightning, the only single-seat radar-equipped fighter the RAF has ever had. The original F.1 had a rather simple radar mounted in the inlet centrebody feeding echoes to a PAS (pilot attack sight) resembling a gyro gunsight combined with a HUD. This AI.23 radar put out 175 kW via a quad feeder to give four overlapping beams for monopulse lock-on. Like other radars of the 1950s it had a single low PRF and pulse width. In the 1960s the F.3 and F.6 were fitted with the AI.23B, which had an HDD (head-down display) instead of the PAS. Both installations weighed about 287 lb. In many respects they were similar to the radars fitted to such aircraft as the Mirage III, MiG-21MF and Su-11. Skilled pilots could use them to get within missile- or even gun-firing parameters, but today they seem prehistoric. Not only was the work of interpretation considerable, but they were useless against aircraft flying at very low level, and from 1960 onwards that is where the targets were going to be.

The answer was PD (pulse doppler) radar. Today this is virtually universal in combat aircraft, and it is necessary to explain how it works in more detail than in the previous chapter.

Let us imagine the mainlobe of a fighter at low level. When pointing ahead the radial velocities (relative speeds of radar and ground targets) are very close to our own groundspeed, and there is

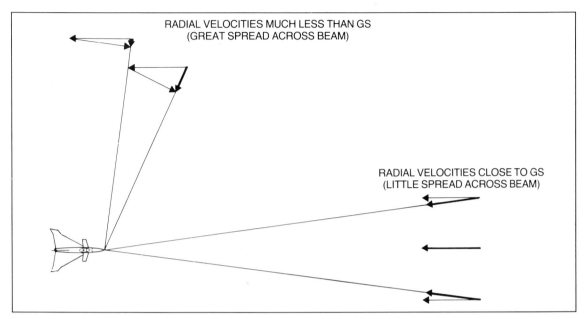

RADIAL VELOCITIES MUCH LESS THAN GS
(GREAT SPREAD ACROSS BEAM)

RADIAL VELOCITIES CLOSE TO GS
(LITTLE SPREAD ACROSS BEAM)

When a fighter radar is pointing ahead the radial velocity vectors of the clutter are only slightly less than the groundspeed, and hardly vary across the beam. When the beam is pointing to one side, the opposite is true. Thus (see next diagram) the clutter moves down from the velocity scale and becomes wider. (Ferranti)

little spread across the beam. We can plot this in a standard form, called an environmental diagram, in which the X-axis is range and the Y-axis is radial (doppler) velocity. Thus, closing targets come in the top half of the diagram and separating targets in the lower half. Clearly MLC, also called MBC (main beam clutter), with the beam pointing ahead, appears on such a diagram as a horizontal line along the top. Its velocity is just below our GS, because the beam is not horizontal but angled slightly downwards, and it starts at the range at which the beam first touches the ground (which in a modern

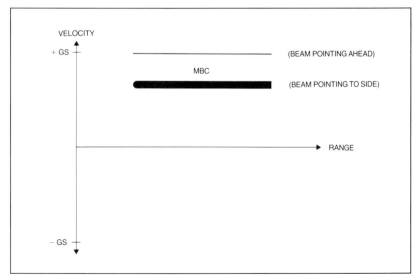

VELOCITY

+ GS — _____ (BEAM POINTING AHEAD)

MBC

(BEAM POINTING TO SIDE)

RANGE

− GS —

This is an R/V diagram, or delay/doppler space or environmental diagram. Closing targets have a positive velocity and appear in the top half (they can be far above the groundspeed line); separating targets have negative velocity and appear in the lower half. All are relative radial velocities, taking into account movement of both radar and target. Here we have merely plotted the MBC (main-beam clutter). (Ferranti)

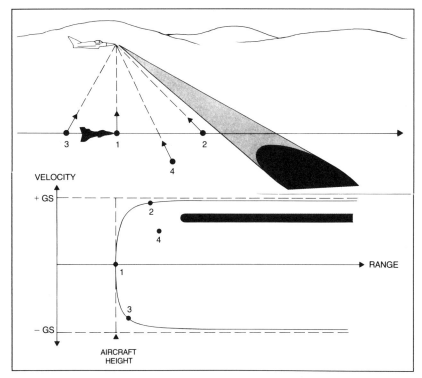

Here we have added the curved boundary within which clutter must lie. It cannot be quite equal to plus or minus the aircraft groundspeed, and cannot be at a range less than the aircraft's height. Ground points 1, 2 and 3 are on the aircraft's ground track and thus fall on the clutter boundary. Point 4, off-track, falls inside the boundary. (Ferranti)

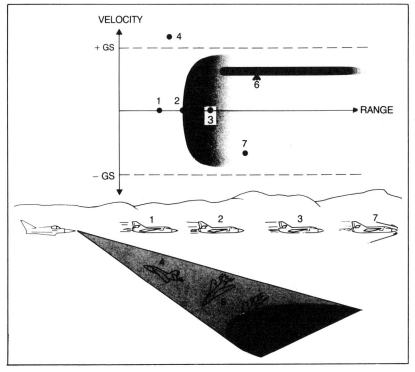

Now it gets more complicated. Targets 1, 2 and 3 are formating with us, so they come on the zero-velocity line, but 2 may be lost in the boundary clutter as it happens to be at the same range as the altitude line. Any approaching target (4) will usually have V greater than the GS and so should be above any clutter. Beam-on targets have radial velocity similar to the MBC and so may be lost in clutter (6) unless they are very close (5). Targets flying away (7) need to be moving at twice our own GS before they emerge clear of clutter. (Ferranti)

scenario at about 200 ft altitude might be half a mile or less). If the beam is pointed out to one side the velocity falls progressively (it would reach zero at 90°, if our radar could achieve such a look angle) but the spread across the beam increases. Thus, plotted on the environmental diagram the MBC for the beam at one side moves down the velocity scale and changes from a line to a broad band.

When we add SLC (sidelobe clutter) we get a lot more returns that fill in the bottom half of the environmental diagram. Obviously SLC cannot be returned from a range less than our altitude, and must have a velocity inside the limits of ± GS. We therefore get a characteristic picture, symmetrical about zero relative velocity, which we can shade to indicate clutter intensity. On this we can then plot real targets. Targets 1/2/3 are in formation line ahead and thus on the zero-V line; 2 is at the same range as the altitude line (where the main beam intersects the ground) and so may be lost in dense clutter. Target 4 has a very high relative speed, taking it far above clutter. Beam-on targets 5/6 have a heading which gives them the same V as the MBC and so cannot be seen. Target 7, dead ahead in afterburner, has a receding V putting it well in the lower half of the diagram, but until its GS is double

our own it will not move out of clutter. So things are much more complicated than we thought!

We should also briefly look at two 'domains', which have off-putting names but which are really simple in conception. The waveform from a radar can be expressed in these two domains. The time domain is a plot of amplitude against time. Typically it looks like a straight line of zero amplitude interrupted by the pulses of sine-wave power. The frequency domain is a plot of amplitude against frequency. Any repetitive waveform — no matter how complicated — can be broken down into the sum of one, two or more regular CW signals. For example we can generate one particular pulsed signal by adding CW above and below a chosen fundamental. The frequency domain of that particular signal is thus three spectral lines fitting within the profile of the wave. Many radar waveforms are much more

We portray a pulse train as electrical signal strength plotted against time; this is the time domain. We can also portray the waveform as amplitude plotted against frequency; for example, our waveform may be made up of three discrete frequencies, each appearing as one spectral line. This is the frequency domain. Time-domain measures are ranges; frequency-domain measures are velocities. (Ferranti)

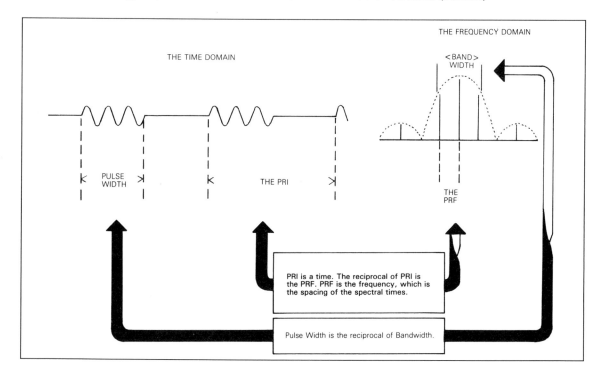

complex, but by what are called FFTs (fast Fourier transforms) the signal processors of modern radars can, in about a thousandth of a second, convert any radar echo signal into both its time domain and its frequency domain. This is important, because in a modern fighter radar both domains play a central role. Target range is measured in the time domain; accurate ranging demands a narrow pulse width, in other words a broad band of frequencies. Target relative (doppler) velocity is measured in the frequency domain; accurate V_d or f_d (doppler frequency) measurement demands a broad span of time.

MTI, moving target identification, is important to almost every user of airborne radar. As explained in the next chapter, airborne radars differentiate between slow ground targets and fast aerial targets by switching the PRF. Trucks and other slow targets give an f_d that is the true value, so when PRF is switched these targets remain in the same doppler filter. The fighter pilot therefore eliminates these; or, rather, the fighter radar has its circuits so designed that such targets do not appear. This leaves just the targets which move so fast that their f_d is their true frequency minus some multiple of the PRF. Thus, on switching PRFs, they jump to a different doppler filter. We design our radar so that such targets will be aircraft, but setting the dividing line can be hard. We want to eliminate BMWs on the Autobahn and high-speed trains, yet catch tactical helicopters lurking in wait for our own armour. And we will certainly fail to see the MiG-29 cunningly hovering at zero airspeed; at Farnborough in 1988 Mikoyan test pilot Anatoly Kvotchur pointed out that vanishing off the screens of hostile fighters can be a tactical advantage. Designers of fighter radars are scratching their heads, except in the Soviet Union where all modern fighters also have IR search/track sensors which are not bothered by such tricks!

Early radars used magnetrons to send out powerful short pulses at low PRF. This usually had the advantage of giving unambiguous range, because all the echoes from each pulse were received before the next was transmitted. On the other hand magnetrons do not maintain coherence from pulse to pulse, so velocity data could not be extracted. This is fine when looking up at a high target, and the need for hardly any signal processing results in little signal loss and good detection performance. But by 1960 fighter radars were having to look down, and traditional radars could not detect targets within the background of completely overwhelming clutter.

A search for a solution began in 1949, when Boeing and the University of Michigan started the IM-99 Bomarc programme for the USAF. This large ramjet cruise missile was to intercept enemy aircraft far beyond the horizon or any effective ground control. Thus the missile needed its own active seeker, and to intercept targets at all altitudes the answer appeared to be a radar that could extract target echoes from ground clutter. Boeing hired R.A. Glaser from the Radiation Lab. He had already done pulse-doppler research, but the USAF hoped the simpler CW doppler system could work and placed a research contract with Ryan, who were pioneers of CW altimeters. Glaser believed transmitter spillover noise would prevent a CW radar from achieving the required 20-mile detection range against a 100 sq ft target. Accordingly his team went to work on the first PD radar.

It was not until late summer 1951 that Glaser and Leroy C. Perkins, in a night-long session at the blackboard, hit on a major breakthrough. First they drew the spectrum of a CW doppler seeker closing in level flight on a target. The sidelobe clutter forms a hump on either side of carrier frequency F_c, and the clutter from the depressed main beam a sharp peak at a frequency (velocity) between F_c and the target. Then they drew a PD spectrum, with essentially the same echo spectrum repeated at intervals of F_r, the PRF. It was obvious that, if the PRF was too low, the target at one line would be overlapped by the SLC from the next higher line. Assuming the X-band F_c of 10 GHz and a Bomarc speed of 2,600 ft/s the SLC could be calculated to spread 50 kHz above F_c and 50 kHz below. Assuming a target head-on speed of 1,000 ft/s its echo would add a further f_d of about 70 kHz. Therefore, to create the necessary clutter-free space for the target, the PRF had to be $50 + 70 = 120$ kHz. At this time fighter radars had PRFs of one or two kHz!

Such a very high PRF would immediately make range determination next to impossible, because ambiguities would rear their head at about 0.8 mile. For Bomarc this was no problem; the missile did not need to know range, only sightline rate, in order to steer a collision course. Another problem was that of 'eclipsing' echoes by the rapid outgoing pulses, but this was partly solvable by increasing PRF gradually from 125 to 250 kHz and then starting afresh at 125. A major difficulty was that no source of high-power coherent CW, from which pulses

Right *The spectrum of a CW doppler radar compared with that of a PD radar. The latter was first drawn with chalk on a blackboard in 1951. Note: a = amplitude, f = frequency.* (Westinghouse)

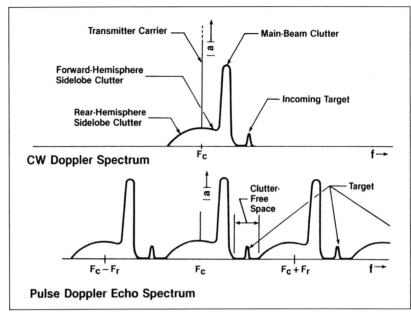

Below *Despite many problems, the radar flown in a DC-3 in 1956 was a major advance, with a 100 W klystron and a duplexer permitting a single search/track antenna.* (Westinghouse)

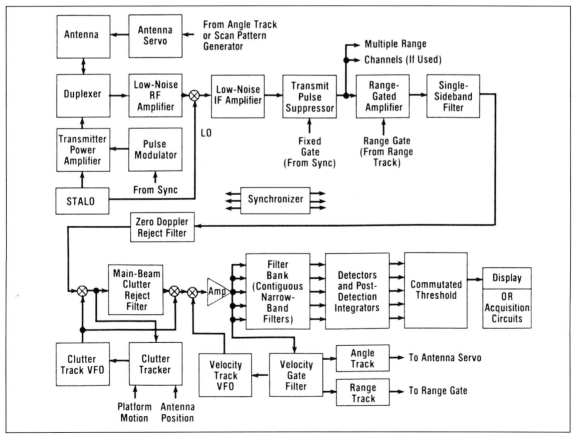

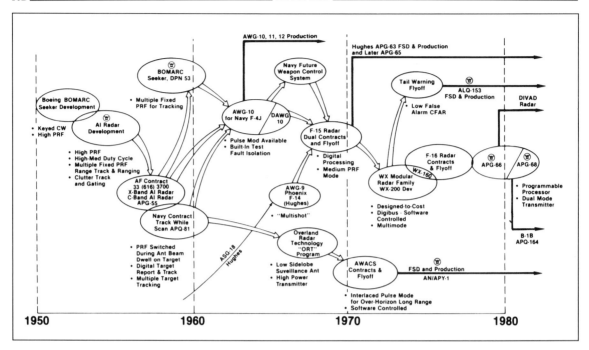

PD radar was pioneered in the United States (see text). Note the profusion of small Westinghouse symbols. (Westinghouse)

could be chopped, was known. The answer was for Varian Associates to add a control grid to one of their high-power klystrons and injection-lock the phase of each successive RF pulse to the Stalo (stable local oscillator). With such rapid pulses TR tube recovery time was too short for the receiver to recover sensitivity, but the time was shortened by pulsing the TR keep-alive electrode. By autumn 1952 a breadboard PD radar was tracking a C-47 from take-off to six miles out, and this was followed by air tests in a C-46 and ground tests against chaff and jamming from an EB-29. In summer 1953 Ryan's CW backup was terminated and, following a competition, Boeing awarded development of the Bomarc IM-99B seeker to RCA. But in the meantime Westinghouse had not been idle.

Westinghouse was not only a staple producer of traditional Navy aircraft and ship radars but it also had major research programmes on the totally new doppler radars. In April 1953, Harry Smith got a large in-house programme going on PD radars, which only eight weeks later bore fruit in an Army contract to study PD for the active seeker of the Hawk missile, which even today is still the chief SAM throughout NATO. The world's first PD fighter radar, in a bulky breadboard state, flew in a DC-3 in 1956, suffering from severe problems. Klystrons had to be cathode-gated with a pulse of

around 20 kV at 1 ampere and PRF exceeding 100 kHz, jitter requirement was a few nanoseconds, birdies (spurious signals) were extremely hard to eliminate, and the duplexer which protected the receiver had to be fully recovered in $1\mu s$, a demand eventually solved by gas-tube switches developed in-house. In 1957 a breadboard X-band PD radar was flown, followed in 1959 by the productionized APG-55, flown in a B-66.

Meanwhile, in 1956 Westinghouse spun off a smaller, simplified version of the fighter radar to compete for the production buy for IM-99B Bomarc. The result was DPN-53, an extremely neat PD radar with a coherent gridded klystron, multiple fixed PRFs to distribute eclipsing in the search mode, PRF switching to eliminate eclipsing in the tracking mode, and a Stalo that could stand up to the severe missile vibration. The rest is history. Westinghouse delivered 301 examples of this radar — the first production PD radar — and Bomarcs successfully intercepted targets at all altitudes.

In 1957 Westinghouse began work on APQ-81 for the Navy XF6D-1 Missileer. This was the pioneer TWS (track while scan) PD radar, and it used many new techniques such as multiple range-gated channels to increase information rate and provide time gating for additional clutter rejection. This aircraft and its giant Eagle AAM were cancelled, but the radar work went on. By 1959 DPN-53 and APQ-81 had made possible the AWG-10 fire control for the F-4B, using the APG-59 PD radar. This was one of the first solid-state designs, with built-in test and fault isolation. Ferranti sent engineers to Westinghouse and collaborated in the AWG-11 and -12 for British Phantoms. Like AWG-10, these could switch from PD to pulse operation, the latter using Chirp. After 1960 the TWS and missile multishot features of APQ-81 were incorporated in the very powerful AWG-9 fire control, matched with the Phoenix missile, for the F-111B. After this aircraft was cancelled, the same fire control was produced by Hughes for the F-14A.

Hughes had competed with Westinghouse every inch of the way, and in 1956-59 had developed the ASG-18 PD radar for the F-108 Rapier. When this was cancelled the ASG-18 was put into the YF-12A 'Blackbird', and in that aircraft it was the first fully developed PD radar to fly in a combat aircraft. In 1957, in breadboard form, it was probably the first airborne radar to have a slotted-waveguide planar antenna. The ASG-18 not only provided the

knowledge for the AWG-9 but also the starting point for the APG-63 for the F-15A and (with a programmable processor and other updates) F-15C, the APG-65 for the F/A-18, the APG-70 for the F-15E (described later) and APG-71 for the F-14D. Though they are totally digital, have vastly greater computing power (thanks to VLSI and VHSIC as explained in the final chapter) and many other improvements, all these radars work in basically the same way as the pioneer PD sets of the late 1950s. Westinghouse meanwhile beat Hughes in the competition for AWACS (Chapter 8) and the F-16, the latter with the APG-66 derived from the 1972 'design to cost' WX radars, described later. Westinghouse also supplied the tail-warning radar for the B-52 and the ALQ-161 forward-looking radar for the B-1B, described in the next chapter.

Though they are PD sets, today's fighter radars differ from the previous generation in one significant way. Their duty cycle (proportion of the time

Though nothing in it was completely new, the APG-63 for the original F-15A of 1972 was a landmark in fighter radars. The transmitter contained a solenoid-focused gridded TWT as well as a 500 W magnetron for beacon operation. The signal processor was hardwired; in today's F-15s it is programmable.

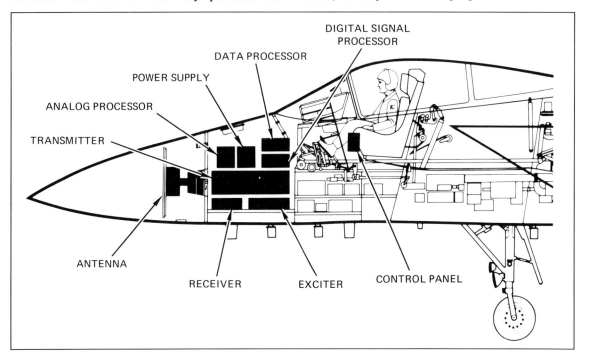

they are transmitting), and thus their PRF, are both lower than before. The high-PRF sets typically had a duty ratio of 0.5, which meant that for half the time no information could be received. In practice, when overlap of transmitting and receiving periods is taken into account, eclipsing was nearly 70 per cent; in other words the radar could make use of only one-third of the echoes arriving back at it. Moreover, we have seen that any target that turns away will be brought down into clutter by the reduction in radial velocity, and any target at a range just beyond the altitude line will move into the densest clutter of all, unless it is coming towards us. The only way to extract range information is then to use FM techniques, or simultaneous transmission on two frequencies close together. These methods, called FMICW (frequency modulated interrupted CW), are inherently inaccurate, and with multiple targets often fail completely at 0.5 duty ratio. It took real brain power to find the answer, which is medium PRF.

Today's medium-PRF (or low duty cycle) fighter radars send out short high-power coherent pulses separated by relatively very long listening periods. In these periods we receive target echoes, but have no way of knowing which pulses caused them. In the same way, in the frequency domain we can no longer link together particular received spectral lines with those transmitted. It sounds disastrous, but there's a method in our madness.

During each brief transmission the received data are digitized and stored, and then converted by multiple FFTs to give a velocity output for each target. A typical PRF is 15 kHz and pulse width about 1μs. With this PRF we can unambiguously measure ranges up to 6 miles (10 km) between pulses and up to 450 kt between spectral lines. So we draw these limits on our environmental diagram. It forms a small rectangle. Now the big bit of lateral thinking is that, whenever we get a target, we 'fold it over' so that it occupies the same relative position in our small rectangle and also in all the other equal-size rectangles throughout the whole range/velocity space. Thus, each target could be at any of perhaps half a dozen ranges and half a dozen radial velocities. How do we remove these appalling ambiguities?

What is the highest relative V we are likely to encounter? If it is 4,500 kt, we could measure this unambiguously with a PRF of 150 kHz, but this would reduce our unambiguous range measurement to only 1 km. What is the greatest range we might wish to measure? If it is 150 km we need a PRI long enough for us to receive echoes from that distance between pulse transmissions, and this works out to a PRF of about 1 kHz, which reduces our unam-

With a PRF of 15 kHz we can unambiguously measure ranges up to 10 km and speeds up to 450 kt, so our folded-over plot (if we could see it, which we can't because it's all inside the signal processor) would look like this. (Ferranti)

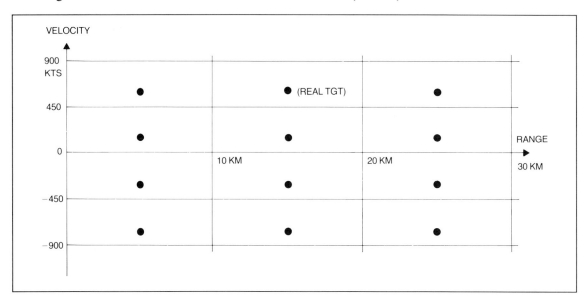

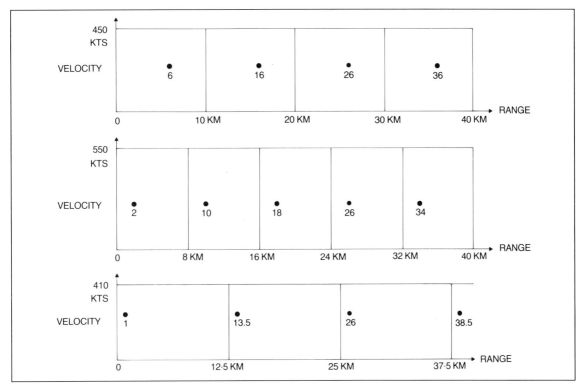

The removal of ambiguities shown as a graphical plot. The target need only appear on two pulse bursts with suitably different PRFs. (Ferranti)

biguous V measurement to only 30 kt. So we begin to see that we need to vary PRF. But we do not need to go to extremes; suppose we transmit in groups of pulse bursts and vary the PRF within each group from 15 to 18.7 and then 12 kHz? At 15 kHz the PRI is 67 μs, so the unambiguous range limit is 10 km. Our radar processor outputs targets at 6/16/26/36...km. Switching to 18.7 kHz (PRI 54 μs) we instantly shift the ranges to 2/10/18/26/34...km, while the third switch, to 12 kHz (83μs) gives targets at 1/13.5/26/38.5...km. The processor ignores all ranges except the obvious real one, common to all PRFs (26 km). The answer comes in a split second.

There is one other point to note. The 'folding' process converts the previous limited patches of MBC and altitude-line clutter into a rather formidable-looking grid of horizontal (MBC) and vertical (altitude line) bands. These bands are quite real blind zones, but by careful choice of the PRFs within each burst group (called a schedule) we can invariably eliminate all blindness problems except those due to the original fundamental MBC velocity and altitude-line range. Other points to note are that, because of the complexity of the processing,

we lose signal strength and thus, for given detection range, we need more transmitter power in a medium-PRF radar, and that we need detection on several bursts in succession for targets to be confirmed as valid.

Thus, if we are not interested in low-flying targets we are better off with low PRF, and can use a non-coherent waveform, because this can be a cheap radar with simple processing and thus have the longest detection range. Against low targets we can get results from a simple high-PRF PD radar giving us velocity information but nothing accurate on range. If we can afford it we should use a radar which switches between, say, three medium PRFs. This has excellent detection, range and velocity performance, even in look-down operation, but suffers greater processing losses, which reduce initial detection performance.

In the past the operator had to decide when a target was detected, and in single-seat fighters this workload was compounded by the long frame time

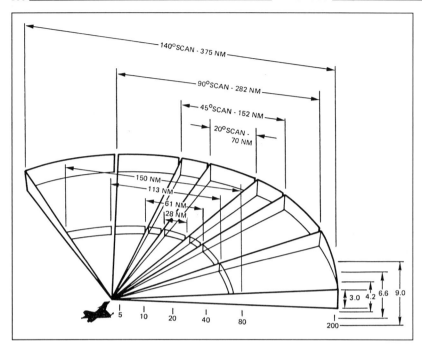

with laborious multi-bar scanning. Today the pilot flies the fighter and leaves the radar to decide how it scans. As soon as the processor has detected a target it puts a clear bright symbol on the display. In the search mode the processor may choose to use medium PRF looking down, a high or medium PRF on the level, and low PRF looking up. Once a target is detected, the processor may switch fulltime to high-medium or high PRF for maximum rate of data extraction. Modern radars can also operate in different modes, which may be automatic or punched in by the operator:

Multi-target discrimination is a high-resolution mode which can identify a target as actually consisting of two or more aircraft. Discrimination may be on a basis of range or velocity.

Target recognition is an even higher-resolution mode which, usually by measuring jet-engine modulation or propeller/rotor echoes, obtains a target signature which can be matched with a particular aircraft type in a library of known hostile signatures.

Air combat acquisition is a mode confined to close (visual) combat; the operator selects a particular box of sky (a particular az/el shape in a particular direction), presses the accept button, and the radar locks on the first target to appear within range inside the angular box limits.

STT, single target track, is one of the two auto tracking modes, and the traditional form in which the antenna locks-on and follows that target within its limits of az/el. The usual method is phase-comparison monopulse, the antenna being bore-sighted to the target by three closed control loops, one for range, one for angle, and the third for doppler velocity. In each loop the sequence is: discriminant formation (estimating the error between the true value and the radar's best knowledge of it), filtering, gate command (following refinement of estimate) and gate repositioning, the result being fed back to the input. STT is essential for guiding semi-active radar AAMs, and can also be used in gun aiming.

TWS, track while scan, is a data-processing function normally performed with two independent loops, one combining angles (az/el) and the other range and range rate (doppler V). Each loop is different from the three used in STT: measurement formation (data preprocessing), correlation, track initiation/deletion, filtering (prediction/update) and, via gate formation, back to correlation. Correlation and gating are two steps in the difficult process, performed by a complex computer algorithm, of deciding whether each target detected on particular scan bars is a new target or one detected on a previous scan. The computer keeps a record of all non-degraded tracks (tracks which keep appearing) and displays them, but the scan process is never interrupted by any attempt at tracking, and no targets are ever alerted as being subjected to special interest. The Hughes AWG-9 (F-111B/F-14A) was the first TWS radar, able to carry on searching whilst simultaneously keeping tabs on 24 individual targets.

Track prioritization is commonly based on TTG (time to go, target range divided by closing speed). Invariably, the target with the shortest TTG represents the greatest threat. For this target the frame time may be longer than the desired TWS update rate, and the computer can modify the scan pattern so that the mainlobe flashes across one or two high-threat targets much more frequently.

Almost all these functions were provided in the Westinghouse/Hughes flyoff for the FX in 1970, which led to the Hughes APG-63 fitted in the F-15A. A further provision introduced at this time was a guard channel, a broadbeam receiving channel with gain a little greater all round than the sidelobes. A response in the 'sum' channel of the signal processor must come from the sidelobes if it is less than the equivalent response in the guard channel. This assists in suppressing SLC and in recognition of sidelobe jamming. Westinghouse used a single signal/guard channel arrangement in its WX family of low-cost radars of 1972. Being entirely an in-house development, WX made many

advances. They were totally modular, and ranged from a baseline WX-200 (i.e., estimate $200,000) to a WX-60 at one extreme and a WX-400 at the other. The number of parts of all versions was about one-sixth as many as in 'comparable radars in the field' and an important advance — long before MIL-1553B became the NATO standard — was that all the modular LRUs were linked to a digital 'mux bus' (multiplex bus), which Westinghouse called a Digibus. Together with a wholesale transfer of functions from hardware to software, this revolutionized flexibility, reliability and cost, and for the first time made it possible to swap LRUs on and off the bus without any need for adjustment. A radar engineer as recently as 1965 would have thought this amazing. To prove they could produce more than brochures it was the mid-range radar that formed the basis for the APG-66 for the F-16, and in 1974 dollars this was produced not at a cost of 200,000 but only 174,000.

One detail I have overlooked is that powerful radars need a lot of cooling. One reason for the APG-66's low cost is that it is air-cooled, a rare thing among modern fighter radars which usually use Freon refrigerant, Glycol or some other liquid coolant. Air cooling is continued in today's APG-68, but when this fighter radar was used as the basis for the B-1B bomber radar liquid cooling was found desirable (next chapter).

At this point it is helpful to outline the develop-

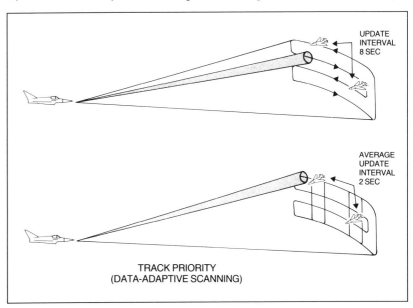

When a target becomes a serious threat a radar with data-adaptive scanning can automatically switch from search priority (upper drawing) to track priority (lower). (Ferranti)

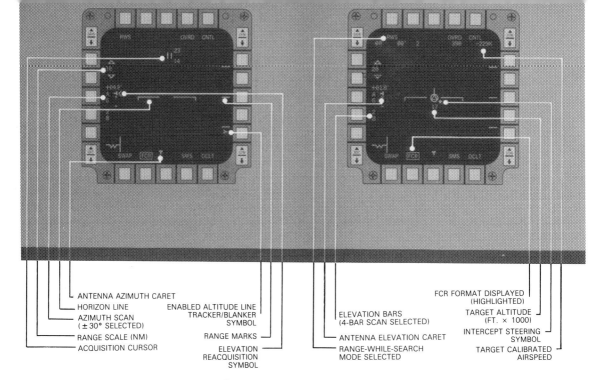

ANTENNA AZIMUTH CARET
HORIZON LINE
AZIMUTH SCAN
(± 30° SELECTED)
RANGE SCALE (NM)
ACQUISITION CURSOR

ENABLED ALTITUDE LINE
TRACKER/BLANKER
SYMBOL

RANGE MARKS

ELEVATION
REACQUISITION
SYMBOL

ELEVATION BARS
(4-BAR SCAN SELECTED)
ANTENNA ELEVATION CARET
RANGE-WHILE-SEARCH
MODE SELECTED

FCR FORMAT DISPLAYED
(HIGHLIGHTED)
TARGET ALTITUDE
(FT. × 1000)
INTERCEPT STEERING
SYMBOL
TARGET CALIBRATED
AIRSPEED

Examples of modern fighter radar displays (APG-68 used in the F-16C). These are called RWS (range while search) modes, that on the left being search priority and that on the right being track priority. (Westinghouse)

ment of one contemporary fighter radar, the APG-70. As already noted, this Hughes product began with the ASG-18 and led to the APG-63 fitted to the F-15A from 1973. This was very capable by the standards of the day, but it had a hard-wired signal processor and 16 K memory. By October 1979 the memory was upgraded to 24 K and a PSP (programmable signal processor) was provided, making a big difference to the F-15C. The main new capability was a raid-assessment mode in which tightly clustered targets can be identified individually. Subsequent software changes have added TWS (track while scan) and partial capability to fire AMRAAM missiles.

From 1980 further software, and minor hardware, changes have led to today's APG-70, fitted to the F-15E which entered service in December 1988. The first software tape was released with the first production APG-70 in May 1987. The vital second tape, written like the first in Jovial, further upgrades air/air and provides totally new air/ground modes (the latter are standard in the F-15E but are not provided in F-15C fighters fitted with the APG-70). There are also four new LRUs: a higher-power liquid-cooled transmitter with a gridded TWT for rapid PRF switching; two new A/D signal converters, one for air/air with 100 ft resolution and high clutter rejection and the other for air/ground with remarkable 8.5 ft resolution; and a new receiver/exciter with 32 coherent RF channels, frequency agility and 75 per cent increase in bandwidth to provide the 8.5 ft ground map resolution.

We have already seen how modern fighter radars interleave medium and high PRF, and need many doppler filters to exclude ground clutter. The APG-70 will be the first fighter radar known to have range-gated high-PRF, giving good detection against nose-on or tail-on targets without interleaving. It has forty gates, each with 500 doppler filters, or 20,000 in all. This bold step is right at the edge of the technology, but seems to work as planned. Hughes breathe a huge sigh of relief, and now have a radar which allows the pilot to detect targets at long range, sort them extremely quickly, switch to TWS and concentrate on the closest or highest-threat targets. The key is computer power. The FFTs necessary to 'build' 20,000 filters in 5 milliseconds requires 33 MCOPS (million complex operations per second). This would need 200,000 Apple IIE personal computers, yet the APG-70 computer is a 1 cu ft box weighing 60 lb (27 kg). The second computer, the radar data processor, has been upgraded to 1,024 K, 64 times that of the first APG-63, and is about five times faster. Use of Jovial eliminates a vast amount of software rewriting and validation testing.

The 8.5 ft ground-map resolution is achieved by adding hardware and software for an SAR

(Chapter 8) mode, a rare capability for an aircraft that, even in the F-15E, is basically a fighter. SAR capability adds only 2.5 lb to the weight, and nothing to reliability problems. The APG-70 has unprecedented BIT (built-in test) provisions, and mean time between removal of a faulty LRU is expected to begin at 25 h. This compares with 16 h for the APG-63, which includes removals of serviceable LRUs, something the APG-70 is hoped to eliminate.

To conclude this chapter I should add comments on the use of avionics to guide fighter weapons. Where guns are concerned the implicit short range has normally meant that aircraft are violently manoeuvring in close combat, using the HUD to provide an aiming 'pipper' which the pilot attempts to place on the target by flying manually. If radar is used, its function is usually only the provision of target range. In the MiG-29 and Su-27 a laser is used for this purpose, and many years of experience have confirmed that the multi-sensor fire-control systems of these aircraft result in (among other things) first-round gun accuracy of a wholly new order.

At the same time, suitable radars can serve as an all-weather aid to accurate gunfire under combinations of range and fighter/target manoeuvre that today are 'impossible' by the fighters our pilots actually fly. The only known Western system is an extension of the USAF-funded IFFC/Firefly III called the Maneuvering Attack System. Since 1982 tests with this fitted to F-15s have repeatedly confirmed the ability to destroy violently manoeuvring jet targets at ranges of up to two miles, even crossing from frontal positions. Of course, to achieve such accuracy the fighter's flight-control system has to be commanded entirely by the fire-control computer, not by the pilot. The author has long since ceased to be surprised at the decisions of air staffs, but it seems strange that supposedly thoughtful air forces should put guns in their fighters and then leave the pilot to aim them in the traditional way, when they could score a first-round strike on a target a mile away crossing at 90°.

AAMs can be guided by various forms of passive (eg IR) homing, and in the past there have been several AAMs which used different kinds of radio command or beam-rider guidance. Today, however, the preferred methods for all-weather guidance at BVR (beyond visual range) involve use of the fighter's own radar. The common methods are SARH (semi-active radar homing) and a mid-course phase followed by active terminal homing.

In SARH the target is illuminated by the fighter's own radar, and a crippling disadvantage of this method is obviously that, with the conventional fighter radar mounted in the nose, this means that the fighter has to keep flying towards its enemy until the missile hits (or misses). The whole objective of medium-range SARH missiles is to engage beyond the range of IR-homing dogfight missiles, yet the method of guidance throws all this advantage away and puts the big, capable fighter in deadly peril! Be that as it may, the way we do it is for our radar to hold single-target track throughout the flight of the missile. Some missiles, such as Sparrow variants, need CW echoes from a transmission sent out by the main antenna interleaved with the main radar pulses but on a different frequency. Others, such as Phoenix, can home on intermittent echoes, which explains how the F-14 can illuminate targets whilst still searching for others, or ripple away up to six Phoenix in rapid succession and guide all of them to different targets with interleaved target echoes. Phoenix also adds active terminal homing.

The author fought an ineffectual campaign against SARH in the 1950s, but today at last we are moving into the era of 'launch and leave' AAMs, of which by far the most important in the West is AMRAAM AIM-120A. Like its Soviet counterparts this is fired in the general direction of its target, which has previously been detected and its range/V measured by our radar, at far beyond visual range. For most of the way the missile flies on a simple strapdown INS, which keeps it flying in the right direction — towards a predicted future target position — and right way up. In some attack modes, especially if we think the target is alerted to our presence, we occasionally 'paint it' with single brief sweeps of our radar, the processor then having the job of checking that the echo does indeed belong to the same target. After each paint we can transmit a quick (hopefully secure) coded digital update of target future position, each of which results in a small alteration of missile trajectory. When it is within range, the missile switches on its own active seeker radar. Of course, the need for periodic mid-course updating of target position throws away some of the chief advantages of having an active missile. In the author's view the true launch-and-leave AAM must eventually become standard, unless there are good reasons for continued reliance on the fighter's own radar.

6
RADAR FOR ATTACK

In World War 1 many attack missions, often called trench strafing, were flown by fighters. From the 1920s the US Navy equipped its fighters to carry bombs, and in World War 2 more attacks on surface targets were flown by fighters than by bombers. In the 1950s the fighter species tended to diverge into expensive radar-equipped missile-armed all-weather interceptors and simple single-seat 'day fighters' which attacked surface targets with bombs and rockets. But it was repeatedly shown that attack aircraft need just as comprehensive a suite of avionics as do air-combat fighters. They need the equipment partly to find and hit their targets at night or in bad weather, and partly in order to penetrate hostile airspace and survive.

Accordingly, today we have attack missions of several distinct types. We have large traditional bombers able to search for and hit moving targets (fixed targets, such as airfields and cities, are obviously ideal for strategic missiles). A second category are dedicated anti-ship aircraft armed with sea-skimming missiles useless for any other purpose; this category includes major helicopters and fixed-wing aircraft ranging from the Hawk and Sea Harrier to the B-52G. A third category is the dedicated all-weather attack aircraft, which may carry self-defence close-range AAMs but has no pretensions at air-combat capability; examples are Tornado IDS, Su-24, A-6E and F-111. A fourth group are the fighters so well equipped with avionics/displays/weapons that they can fly fighter and attack missions at night or in any weather; examples are the F-15E, F/A-18C/D, Su-27, Sea Harrier FRS.2 and Harrier GR.7. A fifth category is filled by a motley collection of jet, turboprop and even piston-engined trainers and various helicopters, but these impinge on this chapter only peripherally.

At least we can see that, though in the two preceding chapters we have already investigated in some detail how modern airborne radars work, there is still quite a lot more ground to cover. And from the start of consideration of the attack mission we can see that, in this chapter, the ground is no longer regarded as the most serious kind of clutter but becomes the target. Some radars, especially in traditional bombers, are used primarily to picture the ground in a way that assists navigation and the aiming of free-fall bombs, especially through cloud cover. Leaving aside for the moment the possibilities of low-observable 'stealth' bombers, this form of attack is today impossible over territory protected by a modern defence system, but, even in a small 'penetrator' flying at very low level, radar can still be used in a ground mapping mode. On the other hand, to be stealthy we do not want to broadcast detectable signals, but we do not yet appear to be clever enough to fly at high speed only just above the ground without using at least one kind of emitter to warn us of obstructions ahead, and to steer the aircraft automatically around or over them.

Mainly in order to divide the book into chapters of manageable length, I have discussed many other avionics systems that may penetrate hostile airspace in the next three chapters. Tactical devices includes the non-radar systems needed by such diverse aircraft as fighters, ASW patrol aircraft and anti-tank helicopters. Reconnaissance systems is self-explanatory. Electronic warfare deals with detecting and identifying hostile threats, finding out details of hostile emitters (also covered in Chapter 8), interfering with the enemy's EM defence systems (over the whole band of wavelengths from light to VLF) and trying to prevent the enemy doing the same to us (which includes ECCM/IRCCM and stealth technology).

Historically, the first avionics for bombers were radios. There is no objection to a bomber receiving radio transmissions over enemy territory, and with modern communications this can be done at any distance and right down to ground level. The next types were navaids, such as Knickebein and Gee and their successors. Next came the pioneer ground mapping radar, H_2S. Like many new developments this had proponents and opponents, was driven through in the face of severe difficulties, and finally made a notable contribution to RAF Bomber Command's night campaign against Germany. Yet, with the benefit of hindsight (in the author's opinion at least), we can see that it ought to have been restricted to a mere handful of aircraft, not thousands.

During the early experiments in March 1937 with a Heyford bomber equipped with a primitive radio-wave receiver and CRT display (using a powerful ground transmitting station) it was discovered that identifiable echoes were being received from a ship and from the harbour and railway station at Harwich. There is no record of anything being done at that time, but when a few weeks later TRE physicist P.I. Dee noticed recognizable ground returns, work was quickly put in hand on air/ground radar. This was initially thought of as being useful in attacks on ships. Sir Philip Joubert, AOC Coastal Command, was quick off the mark in seeing what could be done. Anson *K6260*, mentioned in the preceding chapter, was sent off on 3 September 1937 with its radar modified to look mainly downwards. The battleship *Rodney* and carrier *Courageous* were positively identified, and distinguished from their destroyer escorts. A few weeks later work began on ASV (air to surface vessel) Mk I radar, and this made good progress, soon joined by ASV.II which had some capability against what by 1938 was recognized as at least as serious a threat as the Luftwaffe: the U-boat. ASV.I was first demonstrated in September 1938, long before any AI set was ready, and before the outbreak of war ASV.II was virtually ready for production. This 1.5-m set was amazingly troublefree, and several thousand examples were installed in such aircraft as the Hudson, Whitley, Wellington, Beaufort, Warwick (ASR.IA), Liberator I, and Sunderland. The author well recalls the thrill he and his thirteen-year-old friends experienced whenever, from 1940, we saw aircraft festooned with arrays of what we called 'washing lines'. We even knew what it was!

This was the first time in history that aircraft had been significantly changed in appearance by their avionics. The smaller twin-engined aircraft had just a forward transmitting antenna of horizontal Yagi type with a central feeder, the receiver antennas being angled slightly outwards under the outer wings. In all technical essentials this installation was a close relative of 1.5 m AI, such as Mk IV, with the same problems of glass valves and a pestilential carbon-pile voltage regulator, yet reliability was better in the ASV sets, and the positive attitude of the aircrews could hardly have been more different. I am grateful to Richard Walker who wrote me the following in a private letter:

'My first job at St Athan in January 1940 was to

The modest Yagi transmitter antenna of ASV.II under the nose of a Beaufort II.

develop a homing beacon for Mk II ASV-equipped aircraft, and this was done very quickly. It took the form of a simple inexpensive super-regenerative receiver attached to a pair of horizontal dipole aerials connected by a coaxial feeder so as to put them a half-wave out of phase, giving a lovely circular polar diagram. The receiver was switched by a motor-driven cam, and by choosing different cams the thing could be coded. In those days, any device that could get a lost aircraft safely home was greatly appreciated by aircrews. Those of Coastal Command may not have had much more confidence in ASV than Fighter Command had in AI, as a device for finding a target, but they soon found that the ASV homing beacon worked beautifully. That endeared the ASV to them right from the start of 1940, and this may have had a very important bearing on its later successes. If we had had a similar beacon that Fighter Command aircraft fitted with AI could have used, with an optional extended timebase on the azimuth tube, at the same time, I think it would have made a great difference to the AI situation, especially through the autumn and winter of 1940/41.

'I think that the methods of selecting aircrews for the three RAF Commands also had a bearing on the whole business. Fighter Command pilots were selected for qualities appropriate to daytime dog-fighting, and in 1940 — at least it seemed to me — they were death-or-glory boys expecting to win a VC and bar within a few weeks. They were not of the temperament that is desirable for handling complex scientific apparatus, nor were they in any way sympathetic to those who could handle it. There were exceptions, but not many. Coastal Command chose aircrews for different qualities, which happened to be much more suitable for handling radar; and in any case the ASV was simpler, being concerned only with azimuth and range, and consequently having but one CRT.'

The Sunderland and other large aircraft backed up ASV.II with the first surface surveillance radar. It was this that excited me, and other young spotters of the period. Lateral beams were broadcast by eight simultaneously pulsed horizontal dipoles on each side, the received signals being picked up by the 'washing line' row of four dorsal masts each carrying two pairs of horizontal dipoles. By 1941 the whole installation was fully operational. It made surprisingly little difference to the flight performance of Coastal Command aircraft, which seldom

exceeded 150 kt anyway, and despite its long wavelength (though called 1.5 m it actually operated at 1.7 m, 176 MHz) it proved highly effective not only against surface ships but also against such small targets as U-boat periscopes, except in really severe sea states. The operator could select two range scales, 0–9 or 0–36 miles, and had no target elevation problem as in AI radar. As the target came down the range scale it gradually became more submerged in the sea clutter until, in the case of a periscope, it was lost at about a mile. At night this was a problem, solved — after a big hiccup injected by Helmore's Turbinlite — by the 22-million candlepower Leigh light. But by mid-1942 U-boats had the FuMB.1 Metox passive receiver which could detect 1.7 m radar. The obvious answer was to use the newly invented magnetron to emit microwaves at about 10 cm: and such radar already existed.

In the previous chapter we saw the difference the magnetron made to AI sets, and in November 1941 a Blenheim took off from Christchurch fitted with a night-fighter AI Mk VII with the scanner modified to point a very narrow fan beam obliquely down so that, with the scanner rotated about a vertical axis at 30 rpm (one revolution in 2 s) a picture was painted of the surface ahead of and below the aircraft. It was found to give a clear indication of coasts, rivers and lakes, towns and even (from below 5,000 ft) individual large buildings such as hangars. A BN (blind navigation) group was set up at AMRE at Worth Matravers (soon to become TRE, later moved to Malvern) under Prof P.I. Dee. Group leader was A.C.B. Lovell (later Sir Bernard, pioneer of radio astronomy). He recalled that Lord Cherwell said the idea was 'stinking because it ought to have been done years before', leading to the code name H_2S (hydrogen sulphide, which stinks), but the designation actually came from the fact that aircrew were briefed on a fictitious homing device, to be popularly called Home, Sweet Home, to explain away new installations and wiring in shot-down aircraft still lacking the new radar. In fact H_2S first flew in Halifax *V9977* on 16 April 1942 (this aircraft soon crashed, killing most of the research team including EMI's brilliant Blumlein), and was first used to mark Hamburg on 30 January 1943.

Fitting H_2S disrupted bomber production, cost a great deal of money, cut severely into bomb load, increased drag, made it impossible to fit a ventral gun turret (it was not then realized that that was the only turret that was needed), and provided a marvellous broadcasting beacon on which Luftwaffe night fighters could home from over eighty miles away. Initially H_2S was fitted only to Pathfinders and not to aircraft carrying out diversionary attacks, so it told the Luftwaffe which was the target for the main force. It also gave away (near Rotterdam on 2 February 1943) the secret of the magnetron, which being of solid copper was likely to survive being shot down. To cap it all, H_2S was no precision aid, as was Oboe; moreover, many times it was misled by spoof ground features, with the result that (for example) on 3 March 1943 a major attack missed Hamburg by 17 miles. The only advantage of H_2S was that, being fitted to the aircraft, it could go wherever the aircraft went. It was because of this pioneer mapping or PPI (plan-position indicator) radar that the 10 cm waveband became designated as the S-band. In the USA work on the 3 cm wavelength resulted not only in radar for small fighters but also in a better BTO (bombing through overcast) set called H_2X, this waveband therefore being given the letter X. The RAF called it H_2S Mk III, and in 1944 began using H_2S Mk VI operating in the previously 'impossible' 1.5 cm K-band. Such a short wavelength gave pictures of improved clarity and definition, but suffered more from cloud and rain.

These H_2S sets pioneered air/ground radars used for navigation and, as their definition improved, for blind bombing. Similar sets were developed in the Soviet Union, France and Sweden, and for the next decade British and US nav/bombing radars followed along similar lines, getting progressively better in performance. Even the Vulcan's H_2S Mk 9A would have been immediately comprehensible to a wartime Lanc navigator. So too would the later ASV radars operating on centimetric wavelengths, such as Mk VIC (9 cm) whose twin transmit/receive scanners were in flush (today we would say 'scabbed on') radomes under the outer wings of the Sunderland GR.V. Corresponding German sets, notably FuG 200 Hohentwiel, were similar in principle; Hohentwiel had much in common with Lichtenstein AI sets, and was used mainly against ships. Even today many aircraft, such as the B-52G/H, with ASQ-38(V), Mirage IVP, with Arcana, and certain variants of Tu-16 and Tu-20/142, all have main nav/bombing radars which can be traced back 45 years to H_2S. On the other hand they are installed as part of a com-

The elliptical scanner can dimly be seen through the translucent radome of the H_2S Mk VI fitted to Avro Lincoln RE364 Aries II. *Taken by the author when it visited his Harvard training station in S. Rhodesia in 1947.*

prehensive system which is linked by a (usually digital) bus to one or more computers in a system which can control the trajectory of the aircraft horizontally and vertically, both for navigation and the accurate delivery of free-fall bombs. Moreover, today almost all missions against surface targets are flown by fighter-like 'attack' aircraft flying at the lowest safe level, and this has resulted in several new requirements, of which perhaps the most obvious is that on-board sensors no longer look down but straight ahead. Before discussing the modern scene, however, we should learn how air/ground radars work.

Once we regard the Earth's surface not as clutter but as the target, we become interested in its texture. When a radar beam strikes smooth water most of the energy is reflected; little is scattered back to the radar, so this bit of the picture (in conventional formats) looks black. Rough terrain, stormy seas and most other surfaces give rise to various intermediate tones; we often call them grey, though they are usually bluish-green, depending on the phosphor used in the display. Built-up areas reflect strongly, and so stand out brightly. We must remember that the tonal values of any given scene may be totally different for a radar, for our eyes, for TV, for IR, and for different kinds of photographic film. For example a 'camouflaged' building may give a brighter radar or IR image than one painted brilliant Day-Glo orange!

In traditional 'hi' bombing missions shadowing was minimal but foreshortening severe, whereas in

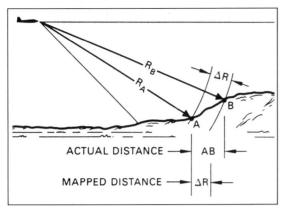

Foreshortening of mapped distances at steep lookdown angles can usually be automatically corrected, but not when it is due to sloping terrain. (Hughes)

today's 'lo' attack profiles there is little foreshortening but severe shadowing. This is easy to understand. Foreshortening is caused by the fact that a radar does not measure distances horizontally along the Earth, as in a map, but slant ranges. But the normal display format of a mapping (or nav/bombing) radar makes no allowance for this. Its picture is constructed from the azimuth (direction) of the beam and from the slant range at each azimuth. The greater the lookdown angle, the greater the foreshortening of the mapped distances. In the extreme case consider a radar looking down at a mountain whose profile is a semicircle centred on the radar: at each azimuth direction the entire mountain would be mapped as a single point, because all the distances would be the same. Advanced mapping radars correct foreshortening, but only on the basis of the varying lookdown angle and assuming terrain all at one local level as in a huge lake. The presence of our mountain could thus be detected because of the spread of lookdown angles all giving the same slant range.

Shadowing can immediately be understood if we reduce the radar wavelength until it is that of visible light. The powerful beam coming down from a source at high altitude, with an incident angle close to 90°, would illuminate the whole of the local Earth's surface. Now let us dive to make a lo attack. As the incident angle decreases, so do the shadows appear. First they will be significant behind tall buildings, then steep mountains until, as we get closer to the ground, trees, shallow hills and even vehicles will all cast shadows. Our display becomes,

in effect, full of holes where we can see nothing. We cannot do much about this until we can invent EM radiation that goes round sharp corners.

From the dawn of mapping radars half a century ago engineers have striven to make the picture better. Obviously, the definition depends on the size of the resolution cell, just as the picture quality in half-tone printing (until recently common in newspapers) depends on the spacing of the dots. The resolution cell is the slightly curved box of space bounded at the edges by the periphery of the beam and in slant range by the pulse width. To make it smaller (a half-tone printer would say 'to use a finer screen') we have to improve the resolution in both range and azimuth. To improve range resolution we either transmit extremely brief pulses or we use pulse compression, as explained in Chapter 4.

To improve azimuth resolution we must be cleverer. The narrower we make the beam, the bigger our antenna aperture has to be, and we do not want (say) a scanner 15 ft across in the nose of a supersonic jet. Yet even a beam as narrow as 3° still has a width of 0.5 mile at 10 miles range. As with pulse compression we can get range resolution down to a few feet, this azimuth resolution sounds very poor indeed. We could try to keep down the antenna size by reducing the wavelength, but we have already seen that down in the millimetric range our radar soon becomes unable to pierce far through rain, dust and fog. The answer, yet again, is to use the differences in radial (doppler) velocity. Except when the beam is looking dead ahead, the different reflecting features inside each resolution cell all have significantly different doppler velocities, falling progressively as we traverse the beam in the direction away from the area ahead of the aircraft. Thus, even though echoes from all these features are received at the same time, we can differentiate between them. In effect we subdivide the resolution cell into numerous small segments whose cross-beam width is limited only by our ability to resolve doppler frequencies.

This makes a tremendous difference, but we can in fact do even better than this, as hinted in the chapter on radar principles. We can integrate successive echoes, from pulses sent out from successive aircraft positions, to create the same picture that would be received if we had used a gigantic antenna covering many hundreds of feet along the track of the aircraft. Such a radar, called an SAR (synthetic-array, or synthetic-aperture, radar), does have

Shadows leave 'holes' in radar maps, and the problem is accentuated in low-level attack. (Hughes)

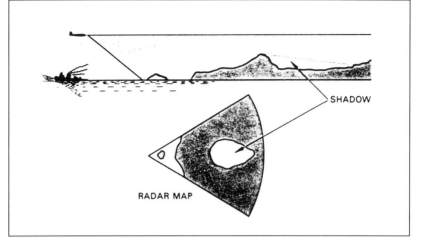

With a conventional mapping radar, the dimensions of the resolution cell are determined by the beamwidth and the pulse width. Generally, a coarse picture results. (Hughes)

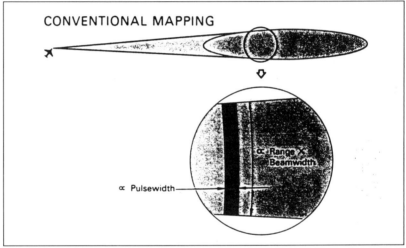

Resolution can be dramatically improved by sensing the different doppler velocities (frequencies) across the width of the beam. (Hughes)

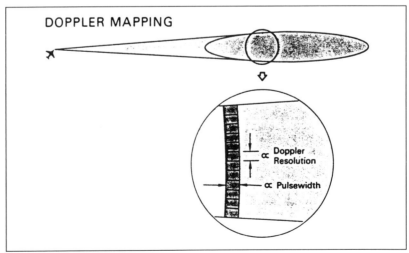

important applications in attack navigation and air/ground weapon delivery, but its primary purpose is in ground mapping for reconnaissance, and so it is discussed in Chapter 8.

Just what lo-observable 'stealth' aircraft can do is arguable, but the author concurs with today's opinion that the only way to have any chance of penetrating defended airspace is at the lowest possible altitude. We could still be seen and shot down by surveillance radars and SAMs on mountains or even on towers, and our maximum speed will be much less than that of defending fighters looking down from thin air at high altitude, but on balance we have rather better chances 'down among the weeds'. But trying to fly manually at full throttle at the proverbial 'nought feet' is extremely dangerous, even over the sea in broad daylight; among mountains, in bad visibility, it would be suicidal. So, unless we delude ourselves that we shall not encounter any defences, our attack aircraft must be equipped with one of three methods of radar navigation enabling us to fly automatically at low level, without needing external visibility.

The simplest of the three is the TFR (terrain-following radar). In principle this appears to be straightforward. The TFR is a high-power radar operating at a short wavelength, usually in the Ku-band. Its small antenna nods up and down in the vertical plane whilst pointing straight ahead. It thus obtains a continuous profile of the terrain ahead. The TFR's own radar data processor, or a computer elsewhere, is programmed to link the outputted terrain profile to the vertical (pitch) axis of the aircraft's flight-control system so that the aircraft is automatically made to follow the contours of the ground at a chosen height above it. It is common to describe a TFR as projecting an invisible 'ski toe locus' ahead of the aircraft. This imagines that the aircraft rides on a huge ski whose front end is always pressed to the ground, but the software for a

practical TFR has to be much more complicated than this. The TFR echoes detect the rise and fall of the ground, and their slope. The software has to know the airspeed, the engine thrust and the aircraft's performance limits. If an F-111 at 200 ft at 500 kt (a typical 'for real' attack situation) came up against the World Trade Center in New York City it would correctly pull up and not hit the building, but if heavily loaded it might stall out and crash in trying to climb the vertical face.

There are many other obvious problems. The most basic one is that the safety of the aircraft depends totally upon the TFR's correct operation. This kind of radar must therefore have the highest standards of integrity, reliability and fail-safe operation. In the Texas Instruments APQ-110 TFR designed for early F-111s almost everything, including the antennas, was duplicated. The contemporary (1960) Ferranti TFR designed for TSR.2 incorporated monitoring and self-checking circuits which, upon there being any output disagreement, automatically warned the pilot and pulled the aircraft up into a climb. In today's TFRs the pilot can select terrain-clearance heights from, say, 1,000 ft/300 m for initial confidence-building training down to 100 ft/30 m for the most heavily defended target areas. It is also simple to add to the software three ride qualities, 'soft' giving gentle undulations, 'medium' getting more severe, and 'hard' where the selected terrain clearance is held rigorously (at 100 ft you cannot have 'soft'). The system also has to decide whether to go over or under power cables and to react correctly to the most difficult small obstructions detected at very close ranges. Just like a car fitted with auto cruise control, sustained steep gradients call for considerable extra power, and

In the TA (terrain avoidance) mode, the radar scans not only vertically but also (usually less often) laterally. This enables the flight-control system to wend the optimum low-level path around obstacles. (Hughes)

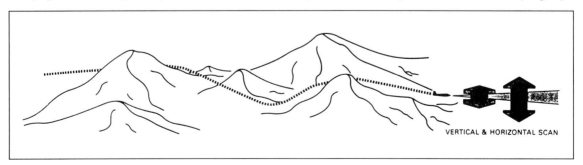

VERTICAL & HORIZONTAL SCAN

While the basic TF or TA radars are used simply to avoid flying into the ground, if we store details of the terrain over which we expect to fly we can use TF as a very accurate navaid. A variation, terrain-referenced nav, is described later.

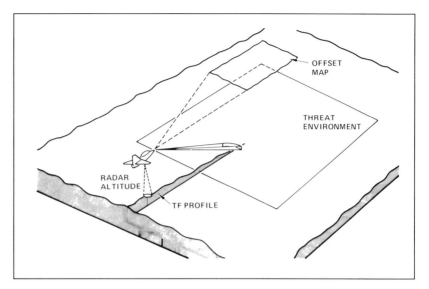

maintaining the desired airspeed is also usually handled by the TFR software.

The system as described so far could lead to silly results. For example we could thunder across flat desert at Mach 1 and climb up and over the top of a 2,000 ft TV mast, with no other obstruction in sight. Worse, we might fail until too late to detect the mast's lateral guy cables. Moreover, even holding a straight course we may not always hold the wings level, and this could make the up/down TFR antenna scan diagonally and not look where we are actually going. In the TA (terrain avoidance) mode the radar interrupts its up/down scanning every 2 s or so to do a quick side/side scan in azimuth. This results in a more efficient flight path, which would for example fly round our solitary TV mast instead of trying to clamber over it, and would thread the most lowly track along mountainous valleys. In practice the software needed to control a TA radar is quite complicated, and a totally debugged program could be sold by a spy for a lot of money.

The third modern method of radar navigation is Tercom (terrain contour matching, or contour mapping). From aircraft overflights or, more probably, satellite navigation measures, we first obtain precise profiles of the ground on particular tracks across enemy territory leading to particular targets. These, assuming a more or less constant attack profile (height above mean sea level), are stored in our attack software in the form of many millions of digital numbers, each representing the vertical (radar altimeter) distance between our aircraft tra-

jectory and local ground level. These attack profiles are unique for each track from the enemy coastline or frontier and the target; the software is carefully programmed to sense the overall picture, and not be misled by any local error or false height caused by local countermeasures. It must be emphasized that the resulting digital sequence covers many tens of thousands of linear metres, and is far beyond the capacity of any enemy to falsify except in very local areas, which do not mislead the software. To fly by Tercom we merely navigate by doppler, inertial and/or GPS Navstar or other means, and continuously compare the radio-altimeter profile with that stored in our nav memory. It is not difficult to program the nav system to reduce the error between each stored and measured height error to zero, which means that the aircraft flies the programmed track within an error of maybe two to three metres. Not only is this method extremely precise but it also almost eliminates detection by the enemy, because a short radio-altimeter wavelength is used (rapidly attenuated except in very dry air) and it looks straight downwards and thus cannot be detected except by receivers directly below the aircraft flight path.

At the conclusion of this chapter I shall look at some contemporary attack radars and navigation systems, including advanced forms of Tercom, but before doing so there are several other radar modes to be mentioned. Use of CW doppler as a full-time dedicated navaid was explained in Chapter 3. It was not then pointed out that an oblique beam can serve

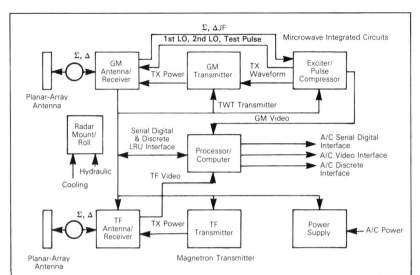

Block diagram of the two interlinked radars fitted to Tornado IDS. They comprise the main GM (ground map) radar and the smaller TF (terrain following) set. Both are extremely versatile Ku-band radars. (Texas Instruments)

as a source of accurate information on altitude relative to the terrain ahead. One could use one beam of a doppler nav radar for this purpose, but it has to point dead ahead, be angled down at an appropriate angle (for low attack profiles the angle has to be shallow, especially if the terrain ahead is rising) and ideally should comprise upper and lower overlapping monopulse lobes. Such a radar then outputs the slant range to the point at which the centre of the beam intercepts the ground, from which the signal processor can derive the required height difference. This is essential for accurate laydown of free-fall bombs over undulating terrain.

An attack radar can also be used periodically to update or refine the readouts of aircraft velocity and position from an INS. Even the most precise INS suffers from random errors which are cumulative, and at suitable intervals (say, every thirty minutes) it may be a good idea to use an on-board radar to start the INS off again with zero error. For example a doppler, or a forward-looking radar of PD type capable of directing three beams symmetrically ahead, can give intermittent measures of velocity which are almost perfectly accurate, and can be used to refine INS velocity. An INS position is almost bound to be less accurate than its velocity output, and in this case any error can be virtually zeroed by using a real-beam or SAR radar (Chapter 8) to display a high-resolution radar map of the terrain ahead or obliquely to one side. By manually driving a box or crosshair cursor over a clearly identified landmark the navigation computer can almost

instantaneously output the aircraft's position at that moment, greatly reducing the error in the INS and improving all subsequent INS position outputs.

Another mode is radar map matching. Luftwaffe F-104Gs pioneered the technique of producing detailed radar maps of an entire region. On a combat mission the required radar maps, or map strip, can be stored in the aircraft's nav computer and displayed as accurately as possible by the INS. The aircraft's own real-beam radar is then used to produce an actual real-time map, which can be compared with the stored one to correct INS errors.

In general, as it is obviously sensible to use precision missiles to destroy fixed targets, attack aircraft will be used only against moving targets such as ships or mobile armies. In both cases, over land or water, GMTI (ground moving target indication) can be used to separate the targets from the surface clutter by sensing the different doppler shifts. For targets dead ahead the velocity required for detection is only a few knots, but, as the beam angle away from the future track increases, so does the spectral width of the clutter. On top of this, problems may be caused by such false moving targets as leaves and crops blowing in the wind, and spume from the crests of waves.

It is rare for an attack aircraft to want to look more than 40 km ahead, so a low PRF of only 2 to 3 kHz can be used without range ambiguity. On the other hand, the use of low PRF can cause problems from severe doppler velocity ambiguities, depending on whether we are a fighter interested only in aerial targets or an attack aircraft interested only in moving ground targets. The usual way of separating GMTs from aerial targets is to switch PRF between values that differ only slightly. As we have seen (Chapter 5) most aerial targets move so fast that their apparent doppler frequency is generally the true frequency minus some multiple of the PRF. Thus, any change in PRF will change the target frequency. GMTs, on the other hand, move so slowly that their observed doppler frequencies are usually true frequencies, and so do not change when the PRF is switched.

This enables us to separate our MTs. In the fighter mode we disregard those threshold crossings which remain in the same doppler filter after PRF switching, thus preventing GMTs from appearing on the display. In the attack mode we discard all those threshold crossings which move to a different doppler filter when PRF is switched, thus preventing airborne targets from appearing. The remaining difficulty is knowing where to set the dividing line. It must have been around 1970 that a fighter pilot in Germany pointed out that 'If the Warsaw Pact armour rolls westwards they'll be preceded by

The traditional way of separating GMTs (ground moving targets) from aerial targets is to change the PRF slightly; the aircraft doppler frequency changes, while that from the truck does not. The huge humps, of course, are mainlobe clutter. (Hughes)

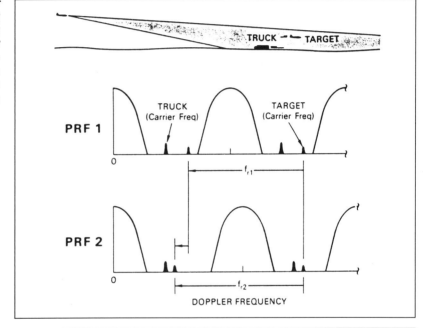

Radar displays without and with an AMTI (airborne moving target indicator) which eliminates ground clutter, but leaves echoes from vehicles or low-flying aircraft in ground clutter. (Norden Systems)

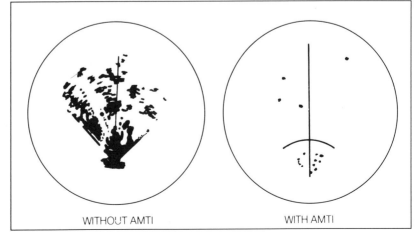

so many Mercs and BMWs going over 200 km/h along the Autobahns that we'll think they're all Hind helicopters'.

Note: mapping, DBS and SAR are all discussed in Chapter 8, though all have applications to attack missions. The remainder of this chapter gives an overview of some modern attack avionics.

The most advanced and instructive attack radar of which details are known is the ORS (offensive radar system) of the B-1B, the Westinghouse APQ-164. Many of its parts rest on technology developed in the USAF/Westinghouse EAR (electronically agile radar) of 1974–79, notably including the phased-array antenna. Remarkably, other parts, including the dual-mode TWT transmitter, modular low-power RF, and '4th-generation' programmable signal processor, are based squarely on a small fighter radar, the APG-68 fitted to the F-16C. Basic data include: weight 1,256 lb; frequency X-band PD; input power 15 kVA; azimuth scan $\pm 10°$, $\pm 30°$, $\pm 60°$; range scales 10, 20, 40, 80 and 160 nm. Moreover, in order to meet the unprecedented reliability requirement of 99% availability throughout a fifteen-hour mission, the APQ-164 is really two radars, one being on standby ready to come on-line, the only unduplicated parts

being the antenna, RVSP and RTI, as described shortly.

Though based on EAR experience, the electronically scanned antenna is a completely new design optimized for the many operating modes needed for a strategic manned bomber. Normally fixed, it is elliptical, 44 in high and 22 in wide, and incorporates 1,526 phase-control modules which, in comparison with those of the EAR, show many dramatic improvements. Westinghouse claim that the antenna combines wide bandwidth, low sidelobes, linear and circular polarization, rapid scanning (beam switching under 200 μs), beam shape variety, and the high pointing accuracy needed for terrain following. A low RCS is maintained both in and out of band whilst the radar is operating. The antenna and its BSC (beam steering controller) are mounted on a roll-detented gimbal using the normal forward-looking position for strategic attack modes. A future growth mode, Conventional Standoff, will use a side-detented

Major features of the Westinghouse APQ-164, the most advanced attack radar in service, fitted to the B-1B. The oval antenna is fixed, the beam being aimed electronically.

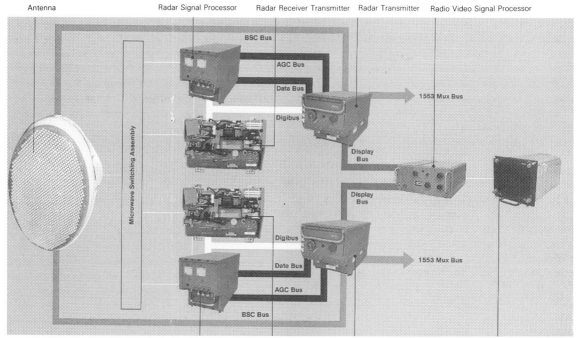

position giving broadside coverage extending behind the B-1B's wing line.

The antenna is connected via the microwave switching assembly to the duplicated parallel chains of LRUs, each comprising an RRT, RSP and RT. Each RRT (radar receiver/transmitter) contains a receiver protector, low-noise FET amplifier, receiver, A/D converter, stable local oscillators, system clock generator, range gate attenuator for the TF mode, and high-resolution circuitry for precision ground mapping. Each RSP (radar signal processor) contains an embedded dual RC (radar computer) to manage the radar via the internal digibus. It uses expanded AP (array processor) architecture, with 384K words of non-volatile nuclear-hardened bulk memory, which accommodates growth requirements for the future conventional standoff mission. Software is written in 1589B HOL (higher-order language). Each RSP contains 32 SRUs (shop-replaceable unitsd) of dual-board pair design, with spare slots for future growth.

The two RTs (radar transmitters) differ from those of the F-16C's APG-68 only in having liquid cooling, the gridded multiple peak-power TWTs being the same. It is optimized to the B-1B's various air/ground modes (doppler INS update, weather detection, GMT indicate/track, beacon and high-altitude precision calibration of the barometric altimeter) and also provides an air search mode out to ranges of about ten miles for tanker rendezvous. The F-16's full air/air modes remain available as future growth capabilities.

The single RVSP (radar video signal processor) accepts and stores processed data from the RSPs via the display bus. Its output feeds the RTI and also refreshes the VSDs (vertical situation displays) and MFDs (multifunction displays) with the radar data selected by the crew. Its interface, processing and storage functions are controlled by a MIL-1750A CPU (central processor unit) identical with that in the RSP's RC, with software which is downloaded from the RSP's bulk memory at turn-on. There are two video channels for complete redundancy.

The RTI (radar target indicator) is a high-resolution, high-contrast display featuring linear detection amplifiers which provide a basic 875-line TV format plus capability of pattern raster and stroke symbology or alphanumerical data. The TV picture can be used for various modes and external data (one imagines, giving real-time pictures of all external hostile emitters and other threats) while the pattern raster provides the highest-quality real-time radar mapping displays for accurate updating of the navigation system.

This describes the APQ-164, but it is worth adding a note on how it works during lo penetration. In TFR it looks ahead along a corridor prescribed by the flight path to a distance of 10 nm (18.53 km). It continuously generates and stores in the RC a range/height profile, which is also sent across the 1553B bus to the TF control unit which generates the climb/dive commands. The RC's azimuth/elevation extent processing algorithms (claimed to be unique) enable the radar to differentiate between terrain, towers/wires, rain/snow and electronic interference. Normally a TF scan takes about 0.8 s, but, whenever groundspeed, altitude and terrain roughness permit, a variable TF update rate can be selected which permits the radar to interleave TF with various other modes. These are sequentially time-shared and seemingly performed simultaneously, permitting the pilot, copilot and OSO (offensive systems operator) all to have quite different displayed modes at the same time. Each display is appropriately motion-compensated, and thus appears to be dedicated. The APQ-164 can also function in the TA (terrain avoidance) mode, with an azimuth scan that identifies objects off the future flight path that are higher or lower than the selected clearance plane. Thus the aircraft can be guided around the terrain rather than over it, maintaining a lower overall altitude. As the aircraft banks into turns, the radar looks round past the instantaneous flight vector into the future flight path.

Of course, at all times the radar serves as a primary navaid, with precision mapping capabilities which update the INS and can be essential for weapon delivery. The basic radar navigation mode is high-resolution mapping, and in this mode the APQ-164 can behave as an SAR (Chapter 8). It takes the coordinates of a suitable clearly identifiable checkpoint from the avionics and scans the antenna beam over the predicted checkpoint. Assuming a reasonably accurate INS input the radar radiates, gathering data for the image over a short period (during which the synthetic-aperture antenna is formed along the flight path) and then turns off or reverts to another mode. The stored image is presented on the display as a precise rectangular ground-coordinate map, frozen so that the operator can study it and make positive identification. When he is satisfied, he moves a range/

azimuth cursor over the checkpoint and designates new position coordinates. These are sent to the avionics, which automatically update present position and destination heading in the INS. Should the B-1B have to make a cold launch (ie, with the INS not aligned) the radar can go into the real-beam mapping mode to permit rapid INS alignment. This mode is a backup navigation method in the event of INS failure.

For small attack aircraft GEC Avionics has produced a compact Integrated Navigation System (which can hardly be abbreviated to INS!), called AD.620K. Apart from a pushbutton CDU (control display unit) which you could slip into your pocket, it consists of a single LRU about the size of a large book, weighing 13 lb (6 kg). The beauty of the 620K is that it can fit any attack aircraft, new or old, and without needing a digital bus can link almost anything to anything in order to present the pilot with the aircraft's position and guidance to any of 1,000 inserted waypoints. The main LRU, called the NCU (nav computer unit) contains five PCBs (printed circuit boards). The first (reading from left to right with the front removed) provides digital interfaces, linking with Tacan/DME, VOR, ILS, doppler, AHRS, INS or Hudwac (head-up display and weapon-aiming computer), and with the CDU and, if needed, a small readout display to go on the HUD. The next board is the processor, carrying out R-Nav calculations, checklist menu data, storing data for all navaids and airfields, managing I/O between boards and also providing a real-time clock. The next board interfaces with video: MFDs, video recorders, missiles and cockpit or gun cameras, and outputting checklists and R-Nav map displays. The fourth board handles analog inputs: compass, vertical gyro, air-data sensor, outside air temperatures and fuel flow (presumably angle of attack could be added). Last comes the analog output board, providing (where necessary) D/A conversion for: HSI, ADI, BDHI, RMI and FDC (flight director computer). This is an ideal totally flexible integrated package for attack aircraft that do not need terrain following and which may be able to use external navaids.

Unfortunately, in a major war an attack mission will have to fly very low, in any weather or at night, with no external navaids and without any high-power emissions. GEC Avionics has addressed this much more severe problem also, and so have British Aerospace and Ferranti. Ferranti's system, called

Penetrate, an exceptionally good acronym from 'Passive Enhanced Navigation with Terrain-Referenced Avionics', is for truly advanced aircraft but is flexible enough for users to pick and choose from a range of LRU modules. The heart of the system is a data store housing a digital 3D model of the terrain to be traversed, including cultural details and tactical intelligence information. From this database the optimum flightpath is calculated and the pilot offered display options and enhancements tailored to external visibility. A typical installation might include a HUD, two HDDs (head-down displays), an INS, barometric and radar altitude, FLIR, terrain-scanning laser, JTIDS, DTM (data-transfer module, hand-held), and a computing suite comprising a mission computer, display processor, bus control, ridge-line generator, perspective displays, threat avoidance displays (data storage, terrain-referenced navigation, intelligent GPWS (ground proximity warning system), digital map and intervisibility shading (see below). Emphatically, there is no TFR — which, say Ferranti, 'shines out like a searchlight from many miles away, can be jammed, or used as a SAM homing beacon'.

Penetrate offers a plan-view digital map display and a forward-looking 'highway in the sky'. The map display can be produced either by digitizing ordinary paper maps or by using an existing database to generate a bright full-colour map stored in 3D form. Nav and intelligence data are inserted via the portable DTM. The map enables the pilot to select the colours he likes, taking account of ambient or cockpit lighting and NVGs, to zoom the display when desirable, and to eliminate (declutter) redundant information. The DTM and JTIDS can then be used to insert threats such as SAM sites and display them as a function of aircraft height. This 'intervisibility shading' highlights vulnerable sections of track to permit optimum terrain masking. Terrain hidden from the aircraft can be shaded to allow covert use of radar or other emitters.

The basic terrain-referenced navigation system, using the terrain model, INS and radar altimeter, has consistently demonstrated accuracy of around 100 ft (30 m) with no external aids or emissions. The required flight trajectory is electronically generated and displayed on the HUD. It is 'simple to follow, and regardless of deviations will always guide the pilot back to his planned route. No interpretation of symbology is required'. Knowledge of present position, in three dimensions, attitude, aircraft perfor-

Typical of the systems proposed for future attack aircraft is Texas Instruments' Covert Attack, or enhanced terrain-masked penetration programme. This is a block diagram of the system as proposed in 1986; work is continuing.

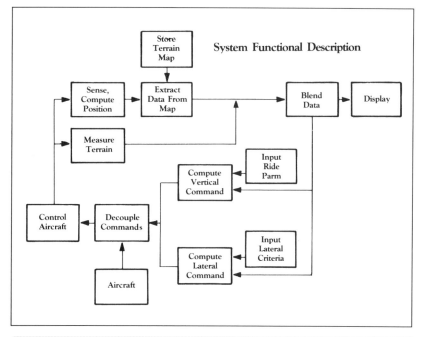

A typical synthetic digitized map displayed by Ferranti's Penetrate system. We are in the small black ring and will automatically follow the black dots. Large rings show effective radius of threats.

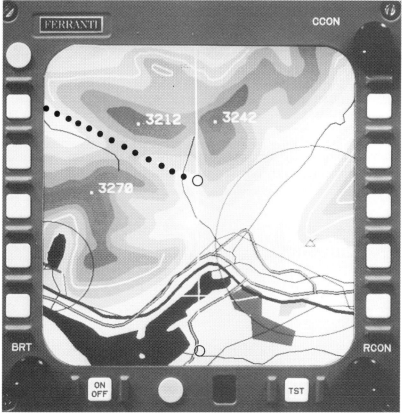

mance and the terrain ahead, enables the system continuously to calculate the vertical acceleration (g) needed to avoid hitting the ground. A special feature of Penetrate is that the pilot can enhance the HUD forward view depending on the weather and the EO sensor performance. In ideal conditions no enhancement may be necessary, but the pilot may switch from 'normal' to 'obstructions', a mode in which, as well as target cueing, obstructions such as masts, pylons and cables are highlighted as bright cursive or raster symbols. In poorer visibility or at night the HUD can be switched to 'ridge lines' which overlays bright lines exactly along all summits, ridges and edges. In the worst conditions the HUD can be switched to 'perspective' in order to display a complete synthetic 3D image. In suitable conditions additional integrity can be obtained by using a laser ranger in a terrain-scanning mode. Similar perspective displays can be displayed on an HDD or MFD for preflight briefing on waypoints, threats, IPs and target acquisition.

BAe's system, Terprom (registered all in capitals), from TERrain PROfile Matching, is similar in concept to Penetrate but relies entirely on the stored 3D digital map. This provides the vital terrain profile along a strip of perhaps 200,000 sq miles to and from the target. The stored profile and the aircraft's nav and air-data systems are used to predict aircraft altitude. This is then continuously compared with radar-altimeter readout to correct the navigation system. The same system can give intelligent GPWS and auto terrain following without using forward-looking radar. Terprom was started well before Penetrate, and has seven years of flight experience in a Jetstream and Tornado in the UK

and F-16 in the USA. Results have been so consistently good that in September 1987 Collins division of Rockwell signed an agreement to market Terprom for military applications in the USA.

The GEC Avionics solution to the problem of a 24-hour stealth nav system is called T²A (pronounced T squared A), from Total Terrain Avionics. It too rests upon the provision of a huge digital database covering all the terrain over which missions might be flown, with especial care taken over the precision of the data over hostile territory. The company were quick off the mark, working with RAE Farnborough since 1977 to create such a database and the necessary avionic hardware. The data comprise a 3D map with cultural and intelligence information continually updated. As in Penetrate T²A uses this to interface with a comprehensive range of sensors, controls and displays.

One of the central LRUs is a digital map display, which can also be retrofitted in aircraft on a stand-alone basis without T²A sensors. At first this display had either to display existing paper maps, or digital data extracted from such maps. Today DLMS (digital land-mass system) data are being extended to cover large areas of interest, presumably by using specially equipped satellites. The only other way of doing it is laboriously to digitize the information from the colour separations (transparent films) used in printing existing maps. GEC Avionics has been doing this for years, but feels it ought to be a centrally funded (eg, NATO) activity. To be of value the terrain data then have to be augmented by adding details of obstructions to low-flying aircraft, friendly urban areas, animal sanctuaries and such things as mink farms (or even the CO's house) and,

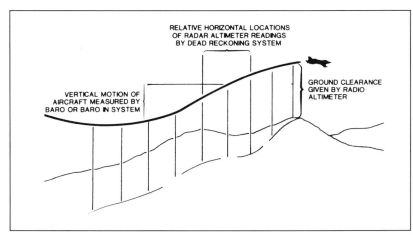

RELATIVE HORIZONTAL LOCATIONS OF RADAR ALTIMETER READINGS BY DEAD RECKONING SYSTEM

VERTICAL MOTION OF AIRCRAFT MEASURED BY BARO OR BARO IN SYSTEM

GROUND CLEARANCE GIVEN BY RADIO ALTIMETER

The principle of terrain-referenced navigation used in Penetrate. There are no detectable emissions.

The T²A database is stored on typical circuit cards. The E-scope is an az/el display for a navigator; SOM is stand-off missile.

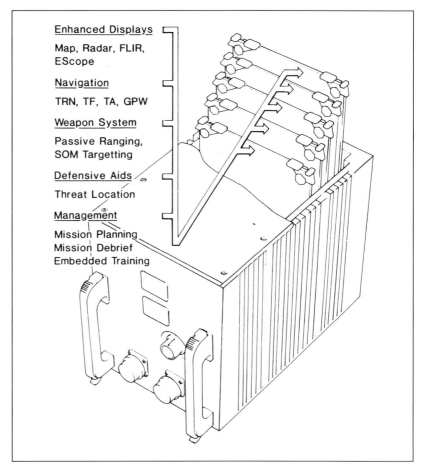

Enhanced Displays
Map, Radar, FLIR, EScope

Navigation
TRN, TF, TA, GPW

Weapon System
Passive Ranging, SOM Targetting

Defensive Aids
Threat Location

Management
Mission Planning
Mission Debrief
Embedded Training

finally, all hostile threats which must be updated at least on a daily basis. T²A is completed by a precise radar altimeter, with near-zero sidelobes that might be detected at a distance, a Lins (laser INS) and a suitable suite of stealth sensors (including a FLIR and Locus (Ch. 10), displays and controls.

Early trials of the basis T²A nav subsystem, called Spartan, are continuing in an RAE Andover. In 1986, in Project Real Night, testing began in a Hunter and a US Naval Air Systems Command A-6E, followed in 1988 by very severe testing in a development Tornado. The world's first pro-

duction contract for a terrain-referenced system followed in April 1989 for the RAF Tornado mid-life update programme. By this time the displays were becoming sophisticated; for example, terrain above the aircraft's clearance height can be coloured red, no matter how the aircraft's actual (eg, local barometric) height may vary, and hostile radar or missile threat zones can expand or shrink as the aircraft selects different heights. Throughout, detectable emissions are virtually zero — but a lot of today's aircraft are easily seen, thunderously noisy, and radiate IR like a lighthouse.

7

TACTICAL DEVICES

This chapter groups numerous devices and sub-systems which need to be discussed in one place, but it also spills over into almost every other chapter in the book. Broadly it deals with nav/attack systems, both new and retrofit; sights and weapon-aiming systems, including data transfer and target handoff; a vast range of IR devices, notably including NVGs (night-vision goggles) and HMDs (helmet-mounted displays), or HMSs (ditto, sights), which impinge upon Chapter 13; almost as wide a range of lasers, TV and other EO (electro-optics) devices; and the whole subject of ASW (anti-submarine warfare). Elint/ESM is covered in Chapters 8 and 9 and ECM entirely in Chapter 9.

Target hand-off systems are really a branch of communications (Chapter 2). They comprise an interlinked computer memory and secure radio link, enabling (for example) a helicopter on leaving the battle area to tell a new arrival the precise position and other details of all worthwhile targets, such as tanks. The link is computer memory to computer memory; nothing is heard by humans, though they are aware of the transfer, which is in cryptographic binary code and takes a split second. The newly arrived helicopter could then start launching missiles without ever needing to look at the battle-field. Other target handoff links are used in ASW, where possibly 500 million or 1 billion bits of data need to be transferred in a second or so from a long-range patrol aircraft nearing 'bingo fuel' to another aircraft coming to relieve it.

In World War 2 the only nav/attack system one could be sure of finding on a combat aircraft was a sight, either for guns or for bombs. A modern N/A system may contain 20 LRUs, but nothing called a sight! Today the function of gunsight is performed by the PDU/HUD, and that of a bombsight by putting a marker over the target as seen on an MFD, or by various other methods. A diagram of a fairly simple N/A system, linked by two parallel 1553B buses, appears on page 244.

Typical of first-generation integrated systems is the very simple Ferranti INAS (inertial nav/attack system), which is still important as the basis of retrofit installations. It needs no digital buses, and comprises one large box and one small one. The big box is the INU (inertial nav unit) which comprises an inertial platform and digital computer, the latter able to handle not only navigation but also air data, weapon aiming and release computations. The small box is the CDU (control/display unit); it comprises the INU controls, a fibre-optic alphanumeric display and the display control keyboard, and in cramped cockpits these portions can all be mounted separately. The system stores ten waypoints or destinations, and the display can show: hdg/drift, wind/v, tk/GS, present posn, cmd tk/GC distance to waypoint, time to go, Xtk (cross-track) dist/tk angle error, and waypoint co-ords. Outputs can be fed to a gyro sight or HUD, and for greater capability this basic package should be linked with a radar or laser, projected map or Comed (combined map and electronic display) and other sensors.

In theory it is possible to fly a useful, if primitive, training mission using a system of this type and merely tapping in a few waypoints on the keyboard. In a more sophisticated environment the number of items of information to be inserted can run into thousands, and so mission planning has itself become largely automatic, with some form of DTS (data transfer system) or DTM (ditto, module). The task is quite complex. The information includes hundreds if not thousands of bits of data which do not vary with time; it also includes perhaps a similar quantity of data which varies very much with time, and which is often applicable to one mission only. The time-invariant data include geographical coordinates of waypoints, terrain profiles, sensor discrete points, sensor operating data, aircraft performance for all weapon configurations, weapon performance and ballistics, and details of the on-board EW/ECM suite. Much of the data describing enemy threats may be time-invariant, while some may only have been discovered while the mission was being planned. Obviously the details of the actual mission, and the expected location of a moving target, cannot be known in advance.

Some of the earliest forms of DTS were called a CPGS (cassette preparation ground station), where map coordinates and similar data could be digitized and recorded on a cassette of film. This in turn could be taken on board the aircraft and used to drive a projected map display or other navaid. Today the number of bits is hundreds of times greater, and new avionics are needed to gather it on the ground and download it on to the aircraft 1553 bus. Ferranti followed the CPGS with Tacplan 2100, the ground units of which store over 250K on each of a number of floppy discs. Coordinates read off a 50K map are accurate within about 65 ft (20 m), and reliable within 1 bit in 10^7 because of the sophisticated verification procedure, yet a mission with 20 turning points can be programmed in 5 min. The pilot can if he wishes take much longer, repeatedly running through the mission on a VDU, editing and refining it until he is satisfied. It is then loaded into a Pods (portable data store), somewhere between a pack of cards and a fat paperback in size, housing an 8-bit Eeprom (electronically erasable read-only memory) of up to 128K capacity. The specification requires ten years retention and an access time of 250 ns (one-quarter of a millionth of a second). The Pods flies the mission, receiving inflight data from the aircraft, and is subsequently played back for analysis. Future DTS may use bubble memories in order to download up to 1 Mbit or more, and at all times it is necessary to maintain not only data integrity but also security of secret information.

Once downloaded into the aircraft the mission data are linked via the 1553 buses to the on-board sensors, flight controls, EW and weapon aiming. This last requirement has suffered a progressive diminution in its relative importance. Half a century ago a bomber might have a complex (purely mechanical) bombsight and up to five optical sights for turret guns. Today's attack aircraft has a device called a HUD (head-up display) which includes the aiming of weapons as just one of numerous func-

tions. The HUD is used to aim every type of weapon, in air/air or air/ground modes, with the exception of self-guided, cruise and anti-ship missiles, and such specialized devices as anti-armour bomblets fired by a downward-looking tank sensor (a modern version of various downward- and upward-firing weapons tested in Germany in World War 2).

In traditional air combat using fixed guns the target obviously will travel some distance forward between the time the attacker on his tail fires his guns and the time the bullets reach the target. If the attacker is dead astern there is no problem, but in manoeuvring combat this simple state of affairs is uncommon. Accordingly the attacking pilot had to estimate aim-off, or lead angle: the angle between the actual sightline to the target at the moment of firing and the gunline (aiming direction) for the bullets and target to arrive at the same place and time. Even using tracer ammunition this has always

A traditional DTS (data transfer system) is the program loading unit seen here being inserted into the cockpit control box for the Ferranti FIN1064 INS which has been retrofitted to RAF Jaguars. It stores all mission data on PCBs (printed-circuit boards).

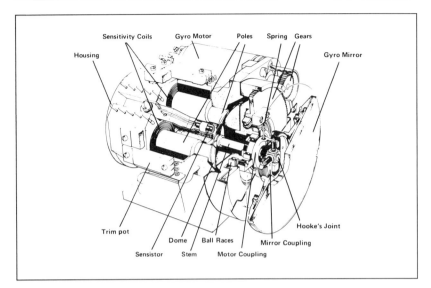

Sensitivity Coils Gyro Motor Poles Spring Gears
Housing
Gyro Mirror
Hooke's Joint
Trim pot
Mirror Coupling
Dome Ball Races
Sensistor Stem Motor Coupling

Today's Isis is identical in concept to the pioneer Ferranti GGS of 50 years ago.

been difficult to do, and even though lead angle almost never exceeds 11° it has to be calculated with precision for the target to be destroyed at modern gun-firing ranges, which are almost always 1,000 ft or more.

The first successful attempt to provide a lead-computing gunsight was the British GGS (gyro gunsight), devised at Farnborough from 1937 and licensed to Ferranti in 1942. The key element was a spinning mirror mounted on a Hooke's joint, allowing it to pivot relative to the drive shaft. At the other end of the shaft was a conductive but non-magnetic copper dome with a part-spherical surface. This dome spun whilst almost touching four poles of powerful electromagnets which, by causing eddy currents within the dome, could control the spin axis of the mirror. In straight and level flight the axis is aligned with that of the housing, and the four poles are disposed symmetrically around the dome. Suppose the aircraft turns, in following a target. Initially, thanks to the Hooke's joint, the gyro rotor does not turn with the aircraft. The spin axis remains unchanged in spatial coordinates, so the four poles are displaced around the dome. The resultant of the four drag forces they impart to the dome will act in one direction, causing a precession of the dome centre (on the spin axis) at 90° to the applied force. The rate of precession depends on the strength of the magnetic field, which is proportional to the range to the target, and to the rate of turn of the aircraft. The result is that, when installed in the optical path of the sight, the illuminated reticle on

the combining glass is displaced to give the required lead angle. A further refinement is that, by applying a proportional current to the upper and lower magnetic coils, the magnetic field may be biased in the vertical plane to take account of the gravity drop of the projectiles.

In the 1960s Ferranti developed the GGS into a range of more advanced sights called Isis (integrated strike and interception system), fitted to RAF Hawk T.1s and to various F-5s, A-4s and, recently, S.211s. These sights incorporate provisions for surface attack. They can also use range information from a laser, and display pointing information from a laser seeker. The main advantage of this type of sight is low cost.

As it projects the aiming reticle on a sloping combiner glass such a sight looks like a HUD, but the latter is more versatile. The key factor is that a HUD presents not only weapon-aiming information but also all essential information needed for navigation and aircraft trajectory control. The need for such a device was obvious even during World War 2, when pilots engaged in air combat and surface attack at low level survived mainly through sheer experience. Doing the same things at jet speeds in Korea accentuated the problem, and in 1955 the US Navy played with the first HUD in which basic flight, nav and sighting data were displayed on a large CRT and reflector glass in front of the pilot. Remarkably, US industry was slow to study the problems, and until after 1960 the only sight systems were electro-mechanical, such as Isis and the French CSF products. Then in 1962 a tiny British firm, Specto, produced the first properly engineered HUD, with a small computer to process incoming information and generate symbols and waveforms for presentation on a CRT. A collimating and combining lens system then projected the display on to a combiner glass in the pilot's forward sightline, focussed at infinity so that he could look at the terrain ahead and at the HUD display simultaneously. Following successful trials, the HUD was selected for the RAF Harrier and Jaguar (French Jaguars staying with the traditional type of sight), and Specto became part of Smiths Industries. Another British firm, Elliott Flight Automation, won the contract for a HUD for the US Navy's A-7, and this at last spurred US companies to get into the HUD market. However, British firms SI and GEC Avionics (which took over Elliott) still remain world leaders.

The pioneer Harrier HUD received nav and weapon-aiming information from a separate hybrid electromechanical computer, with time-multiplexed analog switches to control processing and symbol generation. By 1968 semiconductor technology had reached the point where the Smiths HUD could go digital. A rather simple (and, being serial, slow) central processor was added, plus a separate symbol generator giving precise, bright, repeatable symbols. The symbol memory was 500 words, and the main memory 1K; both used the first LSI ROMs (read-only memories) in a British airborne system. This Hudwac (HUD weapon-aiming computer) was fitted to Jaguars, AV-8As and retrofitted on Harriers, all of which could provide analog inputs only.

By 1971 digital processors of a given size had multiplied in speed and memory, aircraft were becoming digital rather than analog, and the result

Simplified optics for a traditional HUD of the refractive type, showing how the exit optic 'porthole' size determines the IFOV and total FOV.

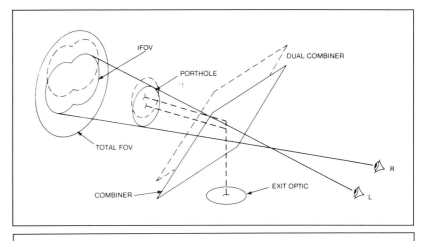

Over 600 different HUD formats have been studied, and some dozens are in service. A typical HUD can switch to at least three — usually Nav, Attack and Air Combat — and each of these may have subdivisions. This is an air-combat mode ('missile'). (GEC Avionics)

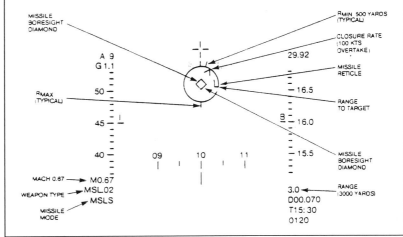

was a vast expansion in capability with far greater reliability and total flexibility, with any desired change effected merely by rewriting software. Thus, in the early 1970s HUD processors quite suddenly became faster (about 400,000 operations per second) and able to handle any operational mode or weapon system. Smiths Industries used a central processor with a main memory, a buffer store and a separate symbol generator. At that time most of the main memory of 10K–20K was usually ROM, with programmable PROM or RAM for the buffer (about 1K) and symbols (up to 2K). One of the first applications of this new style of HUD was the original Sea Harrier, which had a main core store of 16K, mixed ROM/PROM symbol memory and 1K of RAM scratch-pad memory which could be altered within minutes. It introduced a further improved raster symbol generator to provide overlays for the head-down radar display, but the main change was that the HUD became the central package in the navigation and weapon-aiming system. Memories and software are covered in Chapter 15 and displays in Chapter 13.

Gradually, introduction of 1553 bus technology brought realization that there does not have to be a central focus. Every avionic item in the aircraft has its place, and the processors are no longer dedicated to the HUD only. Meanwhile, rather different HUDs were being developed for transport aircraft, and an almost completely different species of weapon-aiming sight was developed for helicopters, as described later in this chapter.

Following their breakthrough into the US market with the A-7 HUD, GEC Avionics (formerly Elliott) won the contract for the HUD for the F-16. This aircraft set a wholly new standard in many things, not least in almost total absence of obstructions to the pilot's all-round view. The winning 'Hudsight' operates in three modes: air combat, ground attack and cruise flight management. It has a 16K Eprom memory, communicates via 1553 bus with the radar, fire-control computer, air-data computer and INS, and has quick BIT (built-in test) to isolate faults to a particular LRU, giving MTBF which began at 500 h and is now close to 1,000. FOV is about 13.5° laterally and 9° vertically.

This served as a spur to further developments, one radically new and the other conventional. The conventional work led to the HUD now in production for the F-16C/D. This obviously has a new control panel, but the most striking change is its

increase in size. The combiner glass has a total FOV of 25°, and an instantaneous FOV (ie, without moving the head) of 21° azimuth and 15° vertical. GEC Avionics believe this is the limit attainable with conventional refractive optics. The processor is that developed for the Lantirn (described later in this chapter), with 64K (48K Eprom, 16K RAM) giving outstanding TV-like pictures for guidance at night or in bad weather. This was the first HUD to combine 1553B links, 1750A processor architecture and Jovial 73 HOL (higher-order language). MTBF in service began at over 1,000 h for the electronics unit and double this for the PDU. Software and optical features automatically correct for distortions of the F-16 canopy.

Despite this, the USAF set its sights even higher. Part of the F-16 MSIP (multinational staged improvement program) was the introduction of the Lantirn sensor pod, and it was evident that this new capability for night and bad-weather missions would need an FOV even greater than that of the new F-16C HUD. The only answer appeared to be to use holographic techniques, with diffractive optics. By this time HUDs had become displays rather than mere sights, and from this point on they are featured in Chapter 13.

Today sights, as distinct from displays, are found almost exclusively on helicopters. The earliest of these was the APX-Bézu series made in France to aid the operator trying to guide the tricky SS.10 and SS.11 missiles fired from Alouettes. Like almost all such sights prior to 1970 this family were simple optical devices of the monocular (ie, like half a pair of binoculars) periscopic type, mounted on the cockpit roof above the operator. They were manually steered in azimuth and pitch, and it was soon realized that it was desirable for the sight to be gyrostabilized, so that it could be kept on target. It was also found that there should be two magnifications. For search and target acquisition a wide FOV is needed, the magnification being a modest ×2.5 to ×3.5. Once a target is acquired, the operator switches to the higher magnification of ×10 to ×16, with a much narrower FOV.

Purely optical devices are not thought of as being avionic in nature, despite the fact that light is EM radiation, but today battlefield helicopters have sights which interface with many other sensors, data links and displays. As an example we can use the Swedish Saab Helios (for scout/rescue) and Helitow (for TOW firing). Both use Pilkington

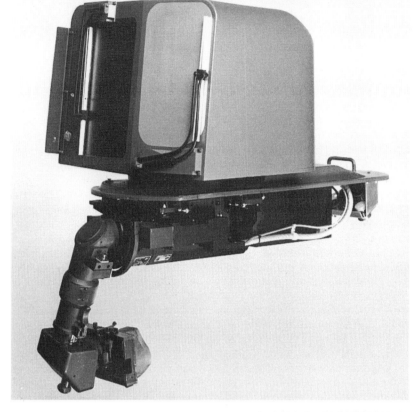

The Swedish Saab Helios (helicopter observation system) is more complex than it looks. The optical path contains no fewer than 36 lenses, mirrors and prisms. It can slew in azimuth and has 50 mm (about 2 in) eyepiece vertical adjustment. It incorporates a laser for precision ranging, but also protects the user against hostile lasers. FOV is 20° at ×3 and 5° at ×12.

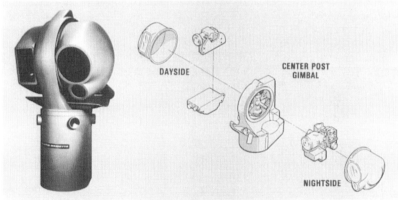

DAYSIDE CENTER POST GIMBAL NIGHTSIDE

Fitted to the A129 helicopter, the Martin Marietta modular MMS has a dayside with magnifying optics and TV and a nightside with a FLIR and laser. The centre post gimbal provides superior stabilization even in the helicopter's vibrating environment. Today's sights face only forward, but future air-combat helicopters will have to have sights telling the pilot if there is an enemy on his tail (even at lower level). In the author's view, this means a second sight head in the extreme tail.

high-resolution optics, with precise stabilization accuracy, with ×3 or ×12 magnification. The sightline can be slewed 120° to left or right at 50°/s and to 25° above or below the horizontal. The optics can accept commands from the manual operator, a radar warning receiver, a laser-warning receiver, a hostile-fire indicator, a helmet sight or an on-board avionics system. It generates outputs for weapon aiming and can be coupled with a laser ranger, laser ranger/designator or FLIR thermal imaging system. The Helitow can be used with a TOW missile simulation system for training, and both systems provide a port for a film or CCD (charge-coupled device) recording camera.

For obvious reasons of helicopter self-preservation the latest sight systems are of the MMS (mast-mounted sight) type, which can be used whilst keeping all the rest of the helicopter concealed. An MMS has to be mounted on a vertical tube which, though light in weight, can pass all the required control and sensor signals and yet remain rigid enough for the perceived images to be sharp. One of the newest sight systems is being developed by SFIM and SAGEM of France for the Eurocopter HAC and PAH-2 versions, derived partly from today's Viviane sight. The chief weapon of these helicopters will be the Trigat-LR, a 'fire and forget' missile with a passive IIR (imaging infra-red) sensor in the nose.

Once the round is fired the helicopter can attend to a different target, but before launch the missile has to be definitely locked-on to the correct target. The helicopter's 1553B bus therefore must correlate the sight's own IIR target image with that seen by the seeker in the missile, to make certain the missile knows where it is going. On the other hand, the sight system does not need to output the target's precise bearing and distance, as does that of the Eurocopter HAP version. This version will be armed with a new 30 mm gun (GIAT 30/781) and Mistral or Stinger AAMs. The MEP (mission equipment package) includes an optical channel, TV, FLIR, laser ranger, HUD, NVGs and HMSs. The latter (helmet-mounted sights), worn by pilot or gunner, can command the helicopter sight to the target sightline by pressing a button. Corresponding symbology immediately appears on the HUD.

Curiously, the only sights used by the US Army for anti-armour helicopters are all in the nose of the helicopter. Unless in receipt of target-handoff data, this forces exposure of the whole machine whenever the enemy is engaged. The AH-1S uses either LAAT (laser-augmented airborne TOW) or Facts (FLIR-augmented Cobra TOW sight), while the AH-64A

has the large Tads (target acquisition designation sight) with direct-view optics, laser spot tracker, TV and FLIR, and the PNVS (pilot night-vision sensor) which is an independent FLIR. Targets can be tracked manually or automatically. The laser, essential for illuminating targets for the Hellfire homing missiles, can also designate targets for attack by other friendly forces.

Obviously, from now on, every combat aeroplane or helicopter is going to have to be able to 'see' at several EM wavelengths, and these will almost always include IR and laser (light or near-light) wavelengths. Fundamental principles were outlined in Chapter 1, but it is now necessary to go into more detail on how these wavelengths are used in tactical devices.

To be of value, an IR sensor must meet certain standards of spatial resolution and thermal sensitivity. If the first parameter is inadequate the picture will be blurred and fuzzy like an out-of-focus photograph. If the second is inadequate the whole scene may appear the same shade of off-white or grey. So far as the author knows, every thermal imager used in avionics is of the opto-mechanically scanned type in which 100 or more sensitive detec-

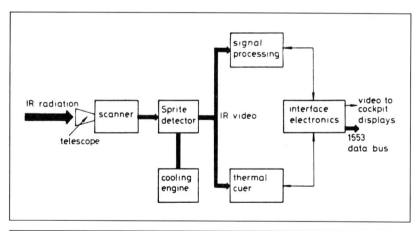

A simple block diagram for an airborne FLIR. Scanning geometrics were illustrated in Chapter 1.

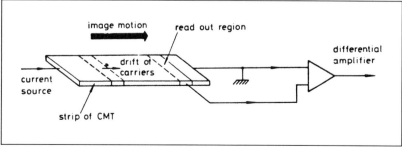

Schematic sketch of a Sprite (signal processing in the element) detector.

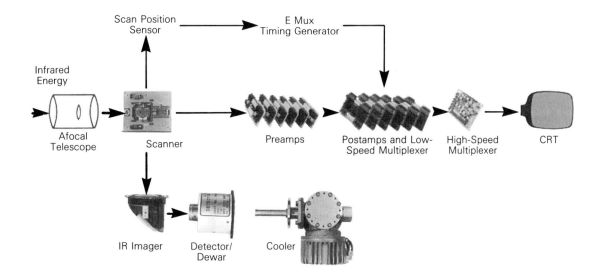

E Mux
Timing Generator

Infrared
Energy

Afocal
Telescope   Scanner   Preamps   Postamps and Low-   High-Speed   CRT
                                                     Speed Multiplexer   Multiplexer

IR Imager   Detector/   Cooler
                    Dewar

tors are mounted in the focal plane of an optical system which collects the received IR, focusses it and scans it in a prescribed pattern over the detectors. The result is an output current which, after processing, is used to construct a raster-type TV picture. The scanning system often involves an IR mirror spinning about a vertical axis and another spinning about a horizontal axis, plus collimating and focussing optics. The mirrors may be internal or external polygons, and may spin at speeds as high as 160,000 rpm.

As illustrated in Chapter 1, in early imagers the whole field was scanned across one detector, but soon as many as 400 elements were being arranged so that each detector scanned one row or column. After arguments over the relative merits of parallel or serial scanning many imagers now use S/P (serial/parallel) scanning in which there may be 6 serial elements arranged in 8 rows which scan across to build the picture in a series of adjacent swathes. But in 1981 Dr Tom Elliott at RSRE Malvern announced the Sprite (signal processing in the element), today the key factor in the outstanding British TICM II (thermal imaging common module 2nd generation). The IR is focussed on a detector in the form of a strip of CMT (cadmium mercury telluride). This strip is voltage-biased so that the released charge carriers are swept along its length at exactly the same linear speed as the scanning speed. Thus the charge is delayed and integrated to yield the same output current as a long array of discrete

Elements of a typical TICM system, in this case with low- and high-frequency multiplexers used to provide a CRT picture. (Hughes)

elements. Various functions are eliminated, and eight Sprites give an imaging performance that would otherwise need 50 to 100 detectors. This has had a dramatic effect on the performance and cost of the TICM II module, which is the basis of most of the latest FLIRs for British and US combat aircraft.

It was sensible for nations, and if possible friendly international groups, to adopt common thermal imaging modules, but this objective has little chance in the face of chauvinistic nationalism. Several countries have naturally copied the USA, whose common modules use parallel scanning, which demands 60 to 180 detectors and a full-frame storage scan converter. The British TICM II is a generation newer, and after development by the MoD, GEC Avionics and Rank Taylor Hobson is standard on Harrier IIs, including at least ninety AV-8Bs of the US Marines, and has performed so brilliantly in an F-16 and a TA-7C that it could soon become a US standard.

TICM II imagers can be internal or podded, and controls and displays can be integral with either the imager or the host vehicle. The telescope uses germanium lenses and has magnification matched to the required FOV (thus, 20° FOV = ×3). Some imagers have a choice of two magnifications or even

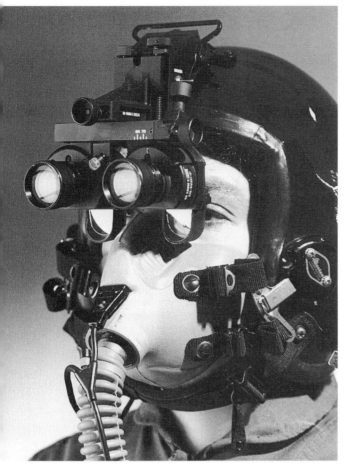

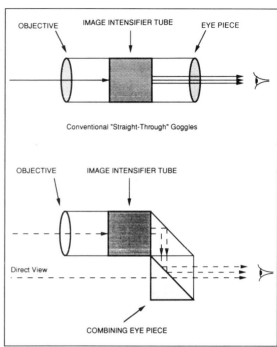

Above *Schematic outline of Cat's Eyes NVGs compared with the traditional type. Makers of the traditional type are fighting back, and claim that Cat's Eyes can cause distortions.*

Left *The revolutionary Cat's Eyes NVGs, already selected as standard for all USN/USMC fixed-wing night attack pilots.*

of zoom optics. The scanner has a high-speed rotating polygon and oscillating mirror. The drive mechanisms are independent, both to facilitate future enhancement and to allow for different scan arrangements (eg, the UK uses 625-line 50-Hz and the USA uses 525-line 60-Hz). The scanner head contains the detector and 8 parallel head-amplifier channels. Detector cooling to 77°K is provided by repeated expansion of gas either from a bottle or a small compressor, the latter probably being the preferred solution in the longer term. The eight channels are carefully matched and then converted to serial form. The TV signal processor performs the usual sync mixing and blanking insertion, provides for the overlay of symbology and alphanumeric data and, most importantly, provides for manual or auto selection of the thermal window (gain, the part of the scene to be displayed) and absolute level (offset). For modern air warfare

automatic control by clever software is crucial; no pilot could keep switching to get a good picture throughout the rapidly changing scene of cold sky, variably warm terrain and hot targets. The picture may be presented on an HDD, but in a fast jet would always be matched to the FOV of the HUD, where the picture would be exactly superimposed over the real view ahead.

Thermal imagers of this type give a picture with thermal sensitivity and resolution almost as good as daytime viewing, and alone are enough for a pilot to fly with confidence at jet speeds at low level on the darkest night. Various people have toyed with LLTV (low-light TV) for this role, but such aids become useless once ambient light has fallen to about the 'quarter-moonlight' level, whereas thermal imagers need no light whatsoever. The only drawback is that the FLIR and HUD FOV is limited to a forward-looking cone of about 15°–25° total angle, and in low-level manoeuvres, especially in rugged terrain, the pilot has to have vision at least throughout the forward hemisphere, ie, including to each side. The only way this can be provided is to use what were originally called PNGs (passive night goggles) and now are known as NVGs (night-vision goggles).

Early NVGs were often monocular, but today the binocular type is almost universal. They are made by many companies, and usually give a ×1 (natural size) view of the world at night, with the light output multiplied millions of times by an optical-wavelength image intensifier of the kind described in Chapter 1. With Gen 3 tubes NVGs give adequate vision with background illumination of only 0.5 mlx (millilux), which most people would say was pitch black. But there are problems. One is that a pilot looking through NVGs cannot normally look at instruments and other things in the cockpit without the use of specially compatible cockpit illumination (very undesirable in hostile airspace) and filters. Viewing the HUD through NVGs can seriously degrade its resolution and dynamic range. It is normally impossible to combine NVGs with other sensor imagery or HMDs (helmet-mounted displays), and one of the most serious shortcomings is that NVGs usually eliminate peripheral vision, giving the pilot a blinkered view of the outside world.

Again, it is British work that has shown the way to go. In 1978 the Royal Aerospace Establishment (as it now is) began a wide-ranging research programme called Nightbird, seeking answers to the central problem of flying low attack missions at night with passive sensors only. After discovering the limitations of LLTV, a FLIR was mounted in the RAE two-seat Hunter Mk 12, feeding two HUDs and an HDD, and with the pilot wearing NVGs. Compatible lighting was soon found in a soft blue-green for instruments and an orange-red for warnings, but an important advance was the development of NVGs resembling miniature inverted HUDs, in which the wearer looks directly at the outside world through two combiner glasses on which are also projected the images seen through the intensifiers, which are above the direct sight-lines. These NVGs, marketed by GEC Avionics as Cat's Eyes, are a true breakthrough. As the direct and intensified images are exactly superimposed the pilot retains a perfect view of the HUD or HDD and, perhaps even more important, can look either direct or out sideways at the outside world. The

shorter length of the intensifiers reduces problems should the wearer have to eject and confers better head mobility than other NVGs, and it is simplicity itself to feed in images from other sensors, each having its own plastics slide or lamination in the combiners. Cat's Eyes could be worn by day; as dusk falls all that happens is that the intensified images gradually become predominant. After establishing that the correct choice for air warfare at night is a FLIR and NVGs, the Nightbird programme has gone on to investigate automatic marking (with small chevrons) of possible targets, zooming between wide-angle search and high-magnification tracking, weapon aiming and laser ranging.

While the TICM II and Cat's Eyes combination probably represents the best mix available at the end of the 1980s, more than twenty companies are actively working on airborne thermal imagers, often in conjunction with a laser or other sensor. One of the most important is the Martin Marietta Lantirn (low-altitude navigation and targeting infra-red for night), packaged into two pods. The AAQ-13 navigation pod has the drawback of including a TFR, whose forward emissions can be detected at great distances; it also incorporates a navigation FLIR. The partner targeting pod, AAQ-14, combines a stabilization system, wide and narrow-field FLIR, laser designator/ranger, automatic multimode tracker, auto IR Maverick missile handoff system, and provision for a future automatic target recognizer. Another production system is the Ford Aerospace AVQ-26 Pave Tack, carried by some F-4s and F-111s, which is a large pod containing a stabilized and common-boresighted Texas Instruments AAQ-9 FLIR and Laser Systems laser designator/ranger. The French Thomson-CSF Atlis pod has the unusual combination of a laser designator/ranger and a TV giving a ×20 picture of the target scene. This is fine for use with laser-homing 'Smart' weapons, but does nothing to help find elusive targets and is of little use except in clear daylight.

In 1988 Thomson-CSF revealed a much newer pod with a 'convertible' front end. The middle is the usual electronics unit and the tail the usual ECS (environmental control system). The hot exhaust at the back discharges overboard surplus heat from the pod and, as in other pods, could form a lock-on source for IR-homing missiles. At the front the operator can attach either a 'day' head, with a TV

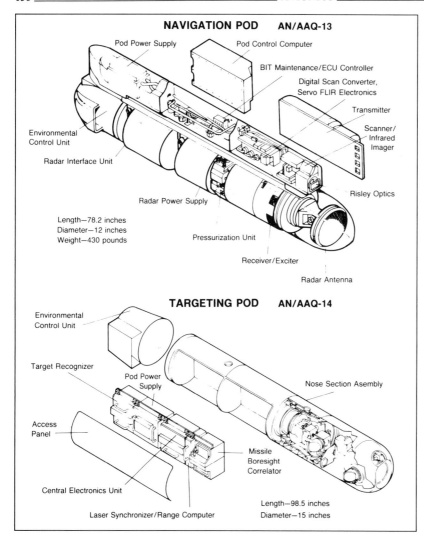

NAVIGATION POD   AN/AAQ-13

Pod Power Supply

Pod Control Computer

BIT Maintenance/ECU Controller

Digital Scan Converter,
Servo FLIR Electronics

Transmitter

Scanner/
Infrared
Imager

Environmental
Control Unit

Radar Interface Unit

Risley Optics

Radar Power Supply

Length—78.2 inches
Diameter—12 inches
Weight—430 pounds

Pressurization Unit

Receiver/Exciter

Radar Antenna

TARGETING POD   AN/AAQ-14

Environmental
Control Unit

Target Recognizer

Pod Power
Supply

Nose Section Asembly

Access
Panel

Missile
Boresight
Correlator

Central Electronics Unit

Laser Synchronizer/Range Computer

Length—98.5 inches
Diameter—15 inches

Left *The Lantirn system is packaged into two pods. Annotation of the targeting pod omits the rotating (roll-stabilized) forward section containing a FLIR and a laser.* (Martin Marietta)

Right *Block diagram of the AAS-38 FLIR pod carried by the F/A-18 Hornet. WRA (weapon replaceable assembly) is the same as LRU: such a package can be replaced as a single unit on the flightline.* (Texas Instruments)

or EO (electro-optical) sensor, or a 'night' head, with a FLIR. This pod was one of no fewer than 26 displayed at the 1988 Farnborough airshow. Probably the front runner is Tiald (thermal imaging airborne laser designator), originally developed by Ferranti (laser), GEC Avionics (thermal imager) and British Aerospace (video auto tracker), and now part of a growing team which includes Aeritalia and may soon be joined by others. Weighing 330 lb, this pod can be used for passive air/air detection and target recognition, and for any kind of ground attack, in any weather, by day or night. FOV can be switched to 12° for search or 3° for tracking, and, once acquired, a target can be tracked automatically. Tiald can be cued to a target

by the crew or by other sensors, and conversely it can itself feed target data to the aircraft's weapon-aiming system or designate targets for smart weapons fired from any friendly platform.

On the other hand, US companies such as Texas Instruments and Hughes are certainly going to hold on to their leading overall EO sensor position. They have developed second-generation focal-plane arrays containing literally thousands of detectors 'on an area the size of a thumbtack' (say Hughes), giving resolution rivalling that of the best still photography. Despite the difficulty of achieving resolution good enough to identify an aircraft as an aircraft (Chapter 8) Hughes has for many years worked on devices able to identify aircraft according to type at BVR (beyond visual range). The latest Imprint automatic identification system actually uses a TV camera sensor, flown in an F-14, but FLIRs are now also giving impressive results.

Hughes is one of the few companies to be promoting Lidar (light, ie laser, radar). There is no problem in forming raster (TV type) images from a laser, but so far not many customers have agreed that 'Hughes laser radar devices are ideal for terrain-following aircraft and missile targeting because they sense the shape of the world ahead in three dimensions'. Many Hughes laser radars are of CO_2 type, while others are solid-state and use a patented 'phase conjugation' process, a passive beam correction technique. In the author's view laser radars are of value at present chiefly for detection of turbulence, particulate matter (including war chemicals), perhaps combined with optical communications, and also possibly for avoiding wirestrikes (Chapter 10).

In a two-seat aircraft there should be no problem in managing all the sensor inputs, aircraft instrument displays and other information sources, but in a single-seater the problem is severe. It is beyond question that penetrating hostile territory at jet speed at 'treetop height' demands that the pilot's attention be focussed 100 per cent outside the cockpit. One answer is to present all information on the HUD, but a severe limitation is imposed by the HUD FOV, which even in the latest and biggest types only just touches 30° laterally and is often half as much. For twenty years workers have tried to solve the problem with displays actually mounted on the helmet, called variously HMDs (helmet-mounted displays), HMSs (sights) or, in the case of the MCAIR/Kaiser Agile Eye, an HMDS (system). Quite apart from such work, there is an unrelated effort which attempts to link the movements of the helmet with a gun turret, missile seeker or some other device, so that the hardware could be aimed merely by looking at the target. Today these disparate efforts are becoming merged in the concept of an ideal integrated helmet.

We have already seen how vital NVGs are for modern air warfare. Even if they permit straight-through direct viewing (Cat's Eyes) NVGs are

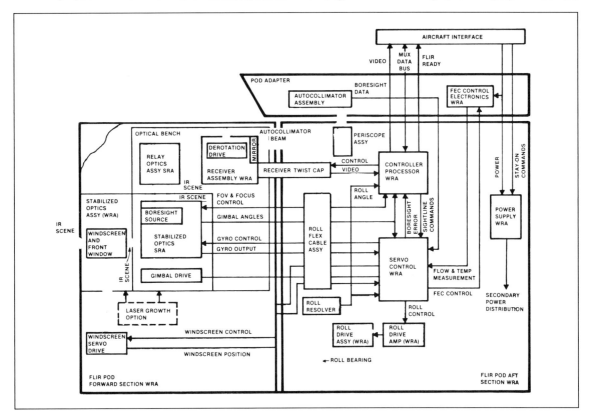

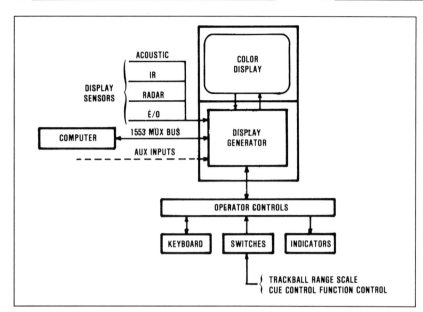

Left *Simplified integrated tactical display for a multi-seat aircraft, generating TV raster and random write alphanumeric, graphic and video displays.* (Loral)

Far right *The pioneer helmet incorporating an optical (miniature CRT) display and sight system is Falcon Eye, seen here in the initial (F–16 trials) form.* (GEC Avionics)

somewhat clumsy, add about 2 lb on the front of the helmet, upsetting the balance seriously when pulling 9 g, and pose a hazard when ejecting. The obvious next stage is to incorporate the image intensifiers into the helmet body, if possible whilst preserving balance, displaying the enhanced scene on two miniature HUDs, one in front of each eye.

The next step is to combine such a helmet with the

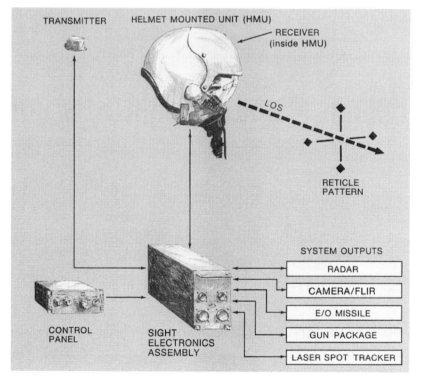

Left *Most helmet pointing systems use a magnetic field to sense helmet position. In the Advanced Helmet Mounted Sight a small transmitter creates a magnetic field which induces signal voltages in a receiver mounted in the helmet. These are processed in the SEA to output pilot's LOS (line of sight) angles and also cue sensors.* (Honeywell)

Right *Block diagram of a proposed Super Cockpit of the future in which all inputs to the pilot are synthetic, including those from a Visual World Generator. In the author's view such cockpits are bound to come in the near future.* (Médécine Aéronautique et Spatiale XXX-VIII–110, 1989) use of head/eye pointing as a means of aiming sensors or weapons, whilst preserving Hotas (hands on throttle and stick) philosophy. There is now a wealth of information on many methods of determining head/eye position. One of the most obvious is to fix a simple sight to the front of the helmet which the wearer can align with the target, the steering coordinates then being transmitted to the sensor or weapon. GEC Avionics did extensive trials with an LED array, but eventually managed to use a miniaturized CRT. This resulted in the Falcon Eye trials helmet which has been extensively evaluated in F-16 flying in the USA. Helmet position is sensed by a link between the helmet and cockpit, using a magnetic field or optics (LEDs).

The next stage appears to be quite dramatic. It involves integration of an INVS (integrated night vision system) and inbuilt CRTs and HUDs into one 'helmet system' fitted with a head-positioning link. The basic need is for one or more colour displays on to which can be presented a high-resolution FLIR image of the world ahead, exactly superimposed on the pilot's vision, plus all the usual HUD symbology. The FLIR sensor would be steered by the head. Terrain, obstacles and upcoming threats would all be observed by wide-FOV sensor/ intelligence systems, and cued to the pilot by an AI (artificial intelligence) processor. The same data channel could be linked via databus to all on-board and internal systems, information from these sources being displayed only when necessary (ie,

upon the occurrence of a fault or battle damage).

Thus, the pilot can fly the entire mission with his own multisensor head wrapped up in a helmet giving him an enhanced binocular wide-FOV picture of the outside world wherever he looks, plus all necessary steering and aiming information. The scene is fed by several sensors operating at different wavelengths, and can include intelligent cues telling the pilot where to look next. In 1990 this helmet is wholly achievable, and work is centred on reducing

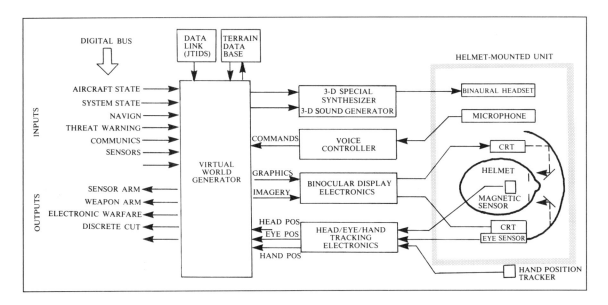

weight and cost. It is also not yet certain whether it is preferable to retain a direct external view or to make the front of the helmet opaque and thus eliminate laser eye threats and dazzle at night. Another possible add-on would be active noise reduction in the headphones, together with artificially generated stereoscopic sound cueing to bring the pilot the recognized and amplified sound of a distant air threat, to cue his head movement towards a threat out of the FOV of forward-looking sensors. Helmets of this type will be essential for all tactical pilots, but the most urgent need is in armed helicopters.

Some tactical devices are intimately linked with particular weapons. For example the MBB VBW (vertical ballistic weapon) fires armour-piercing munitions downwards upon command from its own sensors. These include a sensitive FLIR to detect heat sources, a laser scanner to determine the geometry of targets and a radiometer (instrument for detecting and measuring) operating in the microwave range. These sensors, by Eltro and AEG, have perhaps a second or so to detect, positively identify and locate individual armoured vehicles, whether in the open or under cover. Signals then fire the munitions to hit the tops of each vehicle, without pilot action.

A somewhat similar system is Rapid Fire, developed by Hughes to help pilots select targets for the AGM-65D and G versions of Maverick, with

The actual sensor of an NMR type of MAD. This product is the Crouzet Mk III, fitted in a 'bird' towed by helicopters and feeding an on-board computer and CDU (control/display unit).

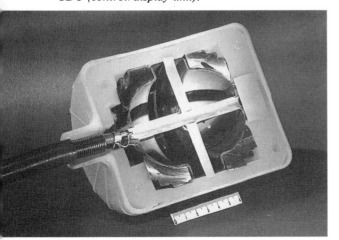

imaging IR guidance. Flying at jet speed at treetop height, a pilot has little chance of even noticing targets before he has gone past them. Rapid Fire searches ahead through the IR seeker of one of the missiles and, by analysing such things as shape and size, picks out likely vehicle targets and aims up to six Mavericks, one at each target. The pilot then has the task of glancing at the display and either firing the missiles, or of altering the firing order or holding his fire. In practice, in real threat areas, one suspects that pilots would be only too glad to let the system get on with it. There is certainly substance in the claim that Rapid Fire allows four missiles to be locked-on and fired in less time than it takes a pilot to fire a single missile manually.

Of course, modern weapon fuzes are avionics items. Even ordinary 'iron bombs' today have the option of airburst at any selected height, burst on impact or at a chosen small distance above the ground, or after any selected post-impact delay. To ensure safety of the low-flying attacker, the bombs can be left safe in flight and armed only after impact.

The last subject covered in this chapter is ASW (anti-submarine warfare). Here the main problem is detection and exact location of what can be a very deep and fast-moving target, surrounded by a medium which is itself noisy and highly variable. Radar is useful only against anything that projects above the surface, and even then the echo can be masked by heavy seas with blown spume. MAD (magnetic anomaly detection) requires a sensor unlike anything else. It detects and measures the extremely small distortions in the Earth's magnetic field caused by the presence of a submerged submarine. Most MADs in the past have used optically pumped He (helium) atoms, but all the newest types use NMR (nuclear magnetic resonance) which measures the absorption of RF energy by certain atomic nuclei which spin in a magnetic field. At particular exact frequencies the nuclei resonate, and, provided the undisturbed terrestrial field has been accurately mapped in advance, the extremely small disturbances caused by submarines can be detected from a sudden change or loss of resonance.

For seventy years the most important methods of detecting submarines have relied on the transmission of sound waves through the ocean depths. The sensors are called sonars if they are big, powerful, permanent, and dipped or dunked on the end of a cable from a helicopter, and sonobuoys if they are relatively small, expendable, and dropped without any physical interconnection. Different sensors are designed to detect either or both the discrete noises of submarines, mostly at low frequencies below 300 Hz where the ocean itself is very noisy, and the broadband noise of the hull's passage through the water. Passive buoys merely listen, while active ones behave like underwater radar and send out high-frequency 'pings' of sound and listen for reflections. Some buoys are omnidirectional, while others are directional and beam-steerable, providing an even closer deep-ocean equivalent of a radar, giving the target's bearing, range and doppler (relative) speed. Command-active buoys remain dormant until, at the last moment during the attack, when the submarine's position is already fairly well established, they are switched on by the attacking aircraft to give an exact position.

All sonics systems need an on-board acoustic processor. The most important of those in NATO is the GEC Avionics 900 series (900, 901, 902 and 903 so far), which can variously be packaged to fit fixed-wing or helicopter platforms and receive data from all types of sonobuoy, dipping sonar or a MAD. The latest systems use extensive digital software architecture and high-capacity 'pipelines' for data. The system has to receive on any of NATO's 99 assigned sonobuoy frequencies. The command system can control pulse length, type and PRF of active buoys, and can translate the signals from any type of buoy into real-time target position. With omnidirectional buoys, fixes and velocities are achieved by hyperbolic and doppler methods, and with sophisticated directional-array active buoys the processor uses frequency-domain and correlation analysis, whilst continually rejecting false targets such as surface vessels, friendly submarines, wrecks and whales. The processor can provide a hard-copy printout, but during the attack the operators will concentrate on one or more CRT displays which may be switched to different formats, such as passive data, active data, sonobuoy tote or a localization plot.

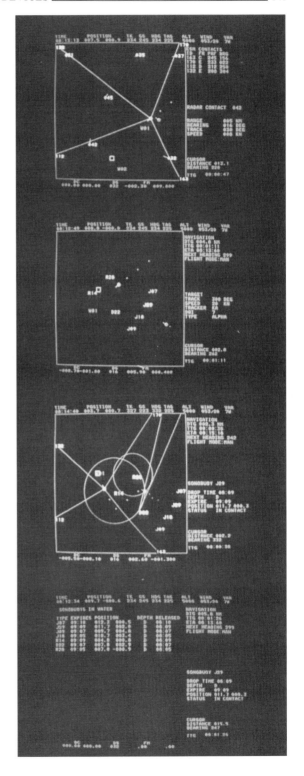

ASN-902 Tattix is an ASW tactical processing system. These four displays are: ESM/radar, showing four radar emitters and five surface contacts (small square = aircraft position); acoustic, showing contact approaching barrier of Lofar buoys; acoustic, contact localized using one passive and two active buoys; and sonobuoy tote, with added nav display. (GEC Avionics)

8
RECONNAISSANCE SYSTEMS

The first military mission ever flown, in 1794, was tasked with reconnaissance. This historic event, at the Battle of Fleurus, involved a balloon. On 22 October 1911 the first reconnaissance mission was flown by an aeroplane, with a note-pad; the same pilot later used a massive plate camera. Subsequently aerial cameras were developed out of all recognition, the ultimate form being the Lorop (long-range optical) series fitted to the SR-71A which have resolution better than 30 in at a range of sixty miles.

At first glance a camera might not be thought of as an avionic item, but modern reconnaissance cameras are complicated enough to need electronic controls. The control can extend to shutter speed (if the camera has that kind of shutter), film speed (very often exactly synchronized automatically with ground speed), cross-track panoramic angular coverage, automatic print of alphanumeric or binary data on each frame (with exact lat/long or other form of location fed by the nav system) and, of course, on/off.

The task of reconnaissance basically means finding out what the enemy is doing. Thus, many of the devices covered in earlier chapters (such as a radar, FLIR or NVGs) could be said to be recon aids. Chronologically, however, the first avionics items to be used in a reconnaissance role were quite simple radio receivers bought on credit from a radio shop in London's Soho district, as noted earlier. After slight modifications they were used to detect, measure and track the Luftwaffe's Knickebein beams in June 1940, in what is today called Elint (electronic intelligence). Later, on the night of 3/4 December 1942, Wellington *DV819* flew a mission which demanded exceptional courage. It deliberately tried to get itself intercepted by a Luftwaffe night fighter, and succeeded. Flying the first Elint mission 'in the face of the enemy', it carried a receiver tuned to the 490 MHz (62 cm) signals that were believed to

come from hostile night fighters. It ditched into the sea a shattered wreck, with nobody on board uninjured, but not before it had confirmed the wavelength of Lichtenstein SN-2.

Today Elint sometimes goes under the name of ESM (electronic support measures, or electronic surveillance measures) or a PDS (passive detection system) or just electronic reconnaissance. It forms an important part of what the Soviet Union calls RES, Russian for radio-electronic combat (next

An example of a relatively small reconnaissance camera is the Type 751 panoramic camera, which sweeps rapidly across track (typically with 60% overlap between sweeps) from a fast jet at 200 ft. Focal length 76 mm, film size 70 mm. The covers have been removed to show the control electronics. (Vinten Military Systems)

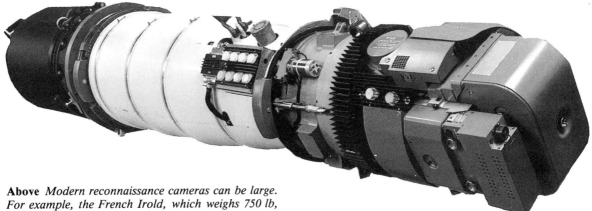

Above *Modern reconnaissance cameras can be large. For example, the French Irold, which weighs 750 lb, contains a video unit which relays its pictures to the pilot's cockpit display, and a symbology generator which superimposes flight data on each picture. It is carried in an external pod, the optics looking out to left or right at 65°–85° to the vertical. Resolution is 3 ft at 62 miles.* (Omera)

Below *Avionics are needed for annotating recon photographs. These are actual examples of data blocks applied in real time by the ASQ-154 DDS (data display set).* (McDonnell Douglas Electronics)

chapter). Indeed, the Elint/ESM concept merges into the RWR (radar warning receiver) and other avionics which are certainly part of a warplane's EW (electronic warfare) suite. This chapter therefore concentrates on 'electronic reconnaissance', as distinct from immediate self-protection.

The early missions by the USAAF and USAF in World War 2 and later were called Ferret opera-

tions. During the so-called Cold War they were perilous, and several aircraft, such as ERB-47s, P4Y-2s and P4M-1Qs, were shot down. Subsequently the chief Elint platforms became various bizarre subtypes of C-135, backed up by variants of U-2 which, via the U-2R, led direct to today's TR-1. Such aircraft continue to fly the various species of Elint mission, which include: Rint, radiation intelligence, technical and intelligence info obtained

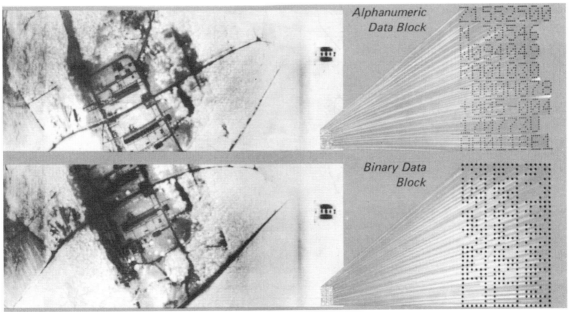

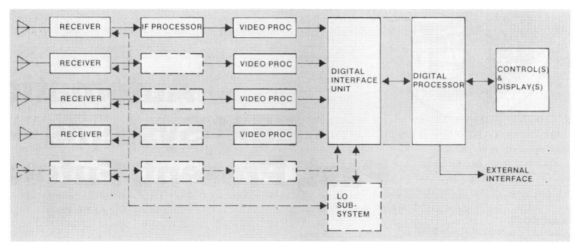

from EM energy unintentionally emitted (for example, by vehicle ignition systems); Comint, communications intelligence, which of course has to be carefully evaluated to screen out deliberate attempts to deceive; and Telint, telemetry intelligence, which can reveal much about hostile missiles and RPVs. Collectively, all these sub-disciplines are known as Sigint, signals intelligence.

The passive receivers used vary considerably. Most are dedicated and specialized equipments matched to a particular type of signal within a narrow waveband, or possibly to only a single frequency. Thus, to cover a wide range of frequencies in the same mission is likely to require the use of perhaps 24 or more different receivers, each served by its own antenna. This explains the profusion of blade antennas seen on the underside of such aircraft as the RC-135V and U-2R, which are popularly called 'antenna farms'. Each channel feeds through an interpretative filter to a recorder, typically with a large reel of Mylar tape. When the whole aircraft is dedicated to an Elint mission, and especially when it

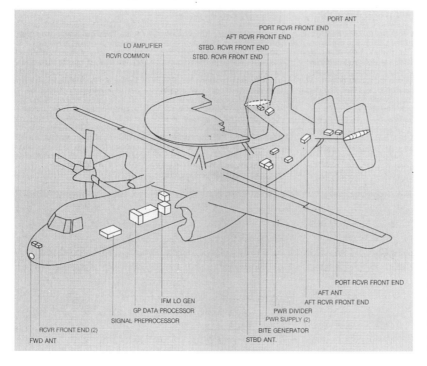

Above *Block diagram of a generalized ESM system. Antennas at extreme left. LO = local oscillator.* (Litton)

Left *Major elements of the ALR-73 PDS fitted to the E-2C Hawkeye. This is a multiband parallel-scan mission-programmable superhet system needing little crew attention.* (Litton)

is looking for specific hostile emissions, then clearly it is possible to use extremely sensitive receivers giving a high-quality full-time output. But in many cases Elint is just one of many tasks. For example, the P-3C Orion has the General Instrument ALR-66(V)3 and is now flight testing the Eaton ALR-77, while the E-2C has the Litton ALR-73. Both aircraft have many other things to do, so the ESM has to occupy only a fraction of the available payload bulk and weight.

Despite this, it can be quite capable. The ESM/Elint/PDS installation should ideally detect surface and airborne emitters, measure range and azimuth direction, and identify each source. This demands several receivers able not only to detect all kinds of emissions but also to analyse them with great rapidity. Incoming signals may be from a giant surveillance radar, or from a fighter radar, or from a ship SAM guidance system, or an army radio net, or any of thousands of other sources. All have to be almost instantly sorted into friendly and unfriendly. The former may be analysed to make sure, but in busy situations may be thereafter ignored. The unfriendly signals are analysed into wavelength (or frequency), waveform, pulse length, PRF and other characteristics, and then compared with known signals stored in a threat library. This enables the source to be identified, and this is stored along with the approximate direction, range and time. On the other hand, unlike the dedicated Elint aircraft, the system almost certainly cannot work full-time on each signal, but has to be time-multiplexed to switch rapidly from one to another according to various procedures.

As an example, the ALR-73 fitted to the E-2C was developed from the Litton ALR-59. This was a superhet D/F (direction finding) equipment, capable of simultaneous coverage over four wavebands between 500 MHz and 18 GHz, with automatic computer control of frequency scanning. D/F was achieved by phase interferometer and amplitude comparison techniques. Loral made the four-quadrant antenna system. The upgraded ALR-73 now in production uses 52 antennas in four groups of 13, each looking at a 90° sector. One group is in the nose, one in the tail and the lateral groups are in the ends of the tailplane. All receivers are controlled separately, so the thirteen wavebands are scanned simultaneously in the four azimuth sectors. Each antenna has dual processing channels feeding digital closed-loop rapid-tuned local

oscillators to give IFM (instantaneous frequency measurement) with great accuracy. Receiver outputs are collected at a signal pre-processor which performs pulse-train separation, D/F correlation, band tuning and timing, and BITE (built-in test equipment) tasks. Output data are then in a form suitable for the main GP computer which has overall control of ESM operations and can vary the coverage, dwell time and processing time. The technique adopted can also be varied by other on-board sensor data and by crew inputs. The output, sorted by the ALR-73 computer and then sent to the E-2C central processor, comprises signal DOA (direction of arrival), frequency, pulse width, pulse amplitude, PRF and special tags. Signals can be received from distances twice as far as the range limit of the E-2C's main surveillance radar, which suggests something like 400 miles.

Elint missions can also be flown by maritime patrol/ASW aircraft, transports, fighter/attack aircraft and even helicopters. Some have inbuilt systems, while others have external Elint pods. A very few aircraft combine internal Elint/ESM capability with other attack and reconnaissance payloads. One such is Tornado ECR. This contains an ELS (emitter locator system) which detects hostile emitters in a sector ahead of the aircraft, using receiving antennas in the leading edges of the wing gloves. Large LRUs in the fuselage (among other areas, occupying the former gun bays) analyse the signals, compare them with a threat library, identify them as to type and, using a triangulation method which automatically allows for source/sensor movement, pinpoint the positions. A computer then sorts all signals into a descending threat order, works out the lowest-risk attack profile, and if necessary arms and fires one or more HARM missiles at the most immediate threat(s) and, via the 1553B bus, displays everything to the crew, controls reconnaissance sensors, steers countermeasures and, via an Odin digital data link, transmits information to following attack forces and ground stations.

Of course, the performance of any passive receiver system depends crucially on the antennas. In the field of ESM one never has the luxury of knowing what hostile emissions may be encountered, so the antennas cannot be tailored to these signals in advance. A few installations use antennas precisely tailored to the most important known threats, but most have antennas with a fair

Left *Wingtip ESM pods can give perfect 360° surveillance. Loral supplied equipment for these Nimrod pods (British designation ARI. 18240/1). There are eight low-band antennas (big discs) and eight high-band (small), covering bands E to J. Pods themselves are made at Brough.* (British Aerospace).

Right *The STAR (system for tactical airborne reconnaissance) is a fully automatic podded package enabling fighters to fly ESM/ Elint missions. It outputs measurements for all kinds of hostile ground radar, sending the information by data link.* (Thomson-CSF).

performance in picking up anything. Certainly the most common type is the Archimedean spiral, a conductive spiral moulded into a dielectric base which can be a flat disc (for flush mounting in the sides of the fin, for example) but which, if possible, is a cone pointing towards the most likely source direction. Spiral cones give adequate reception over an enormous range of wavebands as well as an approximate DOA (direction of arrival).

ESM pods are so far quite rare. RAF Nimrod MR.2P aircraft have the Loral ARI.18240/1 system — amazingly, known by yet another acronym, EWSM, standing for 'early warning support measures'. The pods are mounted on each wingtip, because this has excellent all-round coverage and is a convenient way to fit equipment to existing aircraft. Each pod houses the superhet receivers and processors, fed by four antennas facing ahead and to the side and four identical antennas facing aft and to the side, covering 90° azimuth each. The sixteen antennas comprise eight high-band conical spirals under small domes and eight large low-band cavity-backed planar spirals, together covering the range 2-20 GHz around 360°. Such pods form a permanent part of the aircraft.

For fighter/attack aircraft one has the agonizing choice — repeated in the case of electronic-warfare equipment — of either making ESM internal and permanent, or packaged into a pod which can be fixed on or removed as easily as an item of ordnance. The choice is influenced by how often we are

going to need ESM capability. If such intelligence is seldom going to be thought to need updating it would be foolish to have an internal fit, and it is significant that even the dedicated Mirage F1-CR reconnaissance aircraft carries its ESM in the form of a quick-fit pod. Thomson-CSF make more kinds of ESM/ECM pod than any other company in the world. The original F1-CR pod was the Syrel, which oddly had a bluff radome at each end, the rear pair of planar spiral antennas looking aft — perhaps to collect from hostile emitters which were asleep until the fast jet passed overhead! Fast processing is claimed from thick-film and microwave circuits on ceramic substrates. Syrel led in 1987 to STAR (system for tactical airborne recon) which, though packaged in the same way and with a similar ram-air cooling system, differs in important respects. There are high-band, medium-band and low-band antennas (none looking to the rear) and a secure data link to a ground station where the powerful processors are located. STAR is expected later to feed a display in the aircraft, to help steer the best track between threats.

Chronologically the next type of reconnaissance avionics was radar. Early mapping radars such as H_2S were almost useless for the purpose, but with the development of the MIT/GE Project Cadillac radar in 1943 aircraft began to have much greater ability in the AEW (airborne early warning) role. This radar became the APS-20, which in 1944 was providing vital surveillance at 20,000 ft over US sur-

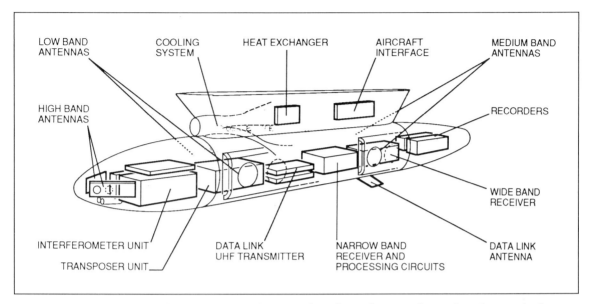

LOW BAND ANTENNAS

COOLING SYSTEM

HEAT EXCHANGER

AIRCRAFT INTERFACE

MEDIUM BAND ANTENNAS

HIGH BAND ANTENNAS

RECORDERS

WIDE BAND RECEIVER

INTERFEROMETER UNIT

TRANSPOSER UNIT

DATA LINK UHF TRANSMITTER

NARROW BAND RECEIVER AND PROCESSING CIRCUITS

DATA LINK ANTENNA

face fleets to warn of Kamikaze attacks. Almost unbelievably, the same radar in an improved form still provides Britain's AEW defence, in the Shackletons of RAF No 8 Squadron. The radars incorporate a digital AMTI and can detect large targets at about 100 miles, though operator skill goes some way to making up for the prehistoric equipment.

Subsequently General Electric moved on from APS-20 in the late 1950s to develop a family of AEW radars for the US Navy, the APS-96, 111, 120, 125, 138 and 139, fitted to the E-2 Hawkeye series. Using pulse compression, these radars operate at about 400 MHz and have been developed through early analog technology to all-digital forms with power of over 1 MW and outstanding signal processing. Many PD features have been incorporated, and in the APS-145, due after 1990, 'environmental processing' adjusts sensitivity cell by cell according to the traffic and clutter in each. A new feature is a choice of three PRFs to eliminate today's problem with blind speeds. One of the new PRFs will be a low value to enable large targets to be detected at up to 350 nm (403 miles), which in turn results in the rotordome antenna being slowed from 6 to 5 rpm. This antenna is one of the remaining problem areas. Weighing 2,000 lb, the 24 ft dish contains twelve complex Yagi antennas, each with a dipole, reflector and array of horizontal detector bars (as noted earlier, we are familiar with Yagi TV antennas on houses). If any element needs replac-

ing, the entire array has to be reharmonized.

Whereas the E-2C radar has to work over seas which may be stormy, and has often lost its targets amongst islands or over land, the US Air Force is concerned primarily with operations over land. Despite general replacement of bombers by ICBMs and SLBMs the USAF recognized in the 1960s that manned aircraft still represented a threat. The existing SAGE/BUIC defence network, backed up by a few piston-engined EC-121 Warning Stars, was clearly overdue for replacement (a cynic might say it was not much better then than Britain's electronic defences are thirty years later). Accordingly in 1965–67 ESD (Electronic Systems Division) conducted the ORT (Overland Radar Technology) programme, and this confirmed that PD (pulse doppler) radar could provide an answer to the need for a high-altitude overland downlook surveillance radar. Three brassboard (ie, with working parts, but not yet properly designed) radars were tested in the ventral position of an EC-121 in 1966. Raytheon provided a conventional radar derived from huge surface surveillance types. Hughes provided a PD with medium PRF. Westinghouse provided a PD with high PRF. Derived from the APQ-81, this had the second slotted-waveguide antenna to fly. Other new features included digital processing and dramatic reductions in sidelobes, essential for use involving looking down over land. In 1967 the two PD radars were picked for further development, and between March and August 1972 the resulting

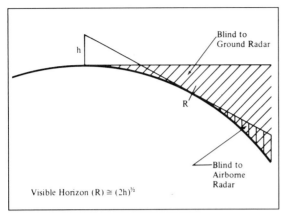

$$\text{Visible Horizon } (R) \cong (2h)^{\frac{1}{2}}$$

Airborne surveillance radar can see much further than ground radar. Using the formula for visible horizon, the limit for h = 30,000 ft is R = 245 miles. (Note: in the formula, R must be in feet or h in miles).

much more powerful radars, using giant 30 ft slotted-waveguide antennas mounted inside a rotodome [note, not 'rotordome'], were evaluated in a modified 707 called an EC-137D. In October 1972 the Westinghouse radar was chosen, and over

100 have since been delivered with the designation APY-2.

This is the radar of the AWACS (airborne warning and control system). The ACS part of the designation stemmed from the fact that, as repeatedly demonstrated in Vietnam, the USAF had no adequate surveillance or control capability in a tactical environment, resulting in a loss of battlefield effectiveness and unnecessarily high aircraft losses. At first very great command-post capability was demanded, but it was difficult to package both this and the radar into one aircraft and the E-4B, based on the 747, later took over the command function at the strategic level. The Boeing E-3 Sentry does house command authorities and communications, but its chief function is as a surveillance platform, normally at 29,000 ft, with the single continuously rotating antenna arranged back-to-back with antennas for IFF and a digital link. The 30 ft slotted waveguide antenna for the radar is mounted on a giant structural beam, carrying D-shaped dielectric fairings at front and rear to produce the circular shape. Operating rotational speed is 6 rpm.

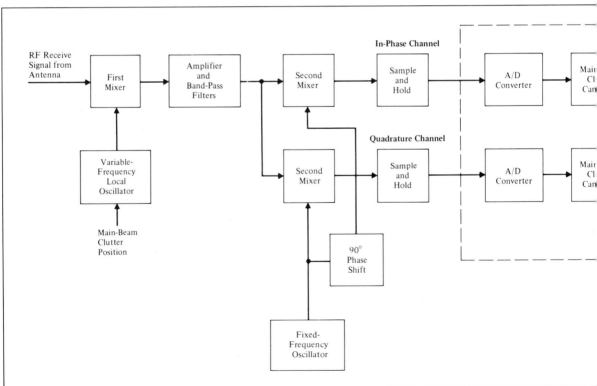

As shown in a block diagram, each incoming signal passes through a First Mixer where it is mixed with a local-oscillator frequency which continuously cycles between a minimum and a maximum according to the position of the rotodome, thus cancelling out the MBC (main-beam clutter) which varies through the entire spectrum on each 360° revolution. Bandpass filters reject unwanted mixer products. Then a second mixer translates the spectrum to baseband where the MBC and doppler spectrum of interest are centred at zero frequency. To preserve both amplitude and phase inputs two channels are used. The signal in each is divided into a number of range channels by a sample-and-hold circuit which divides the interval between successive transmit pulses into intervals equal to pulse width, representing ambiguous range. The samples are digitized in the A/D converter, and MBC is then cancelled by adding and subtracting successive pulses so that signals at exact multiples of PRF (and zero) are cancelled. This enormously reduces the number of bits necessary to describe the signal. FFTs then analyse each signal, and the output is passed through a CFAR which adaptively adjusts

Above *The antenna for the APY-2 (AWACS) radar is made up of 30 superimposed slotted waveguides, those about half-way down being 30 ft long. The waveguides and various major items on the back are mounted on a very strong structural beam which bears the loads.*

Left *Simplified block diagram of the AWACS radar (see text).* (Westinghouse)

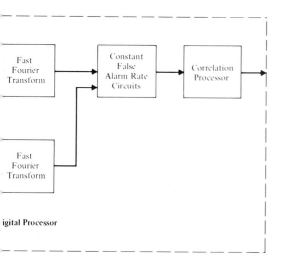

the detection threshold to match clutter or background noise variations. Signals that exceed the threshold are passed to the correlation processor for correlation over successive PRFs to give target report range, range rate, azimuth, elevation and S/N ratio.

APY-2 operates in S-band at around 10 cm. It comprises the transmitter in eight pressurized drums in the lower rear cargo bay, the receiver and signal processor in the centre of the cabin, and the pylon-mounted antenna. Total weight has risen from 7,571 lb in 1972 to 8,399 lb in 1989, one addition being an ability to operate over water (the 1972 requirement specified 'calm sea' only). The antenna face comprises thirty horizontal waveguide sticks each 24 ft to 30 ft long, the stacked assembly being 5 ft deep. Sidelobe reduction is achieved partly by computer-aided design, extremely precise milling of the radiating slots, and the effects of the Boeing-designed radome. Horizontal scanning is achieved solely by rotating the whole array. Vertical scanning and target heightfinding are achieved by electronic scanning using ferrite phase-shifters. These,

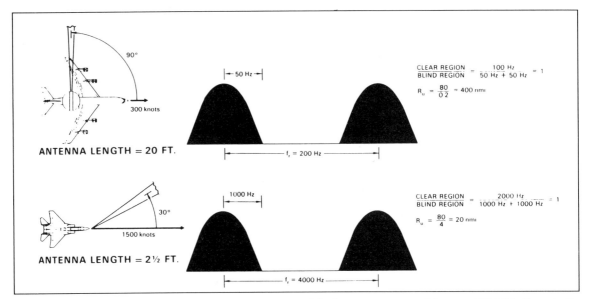

$$\frac{\text{CLEAR REGION}}{\text{BLIND REGION}} = \frac{100 \text{ Hz}}{50 \text{ Hz} + 50 \text{ Hz}} = 1$$

$$R_u = \frac{80}{0.2} = 400 \text{ nmi}$$

$$\frac{\text{CLEAR REGION}}{\text{BLIND REGION}} = \frac{2000 \text{ Hz}}{1000 \text{ Hz} + 1000 \text{ Hz}} = 1$$

$$R_u = \frac{80}{4} = 20 \text{ nmi}$$

together with the phase-control electronics, radioactive-igniter-powered receiver protectors and receiver paramplifiers, are mounted on the back of the antenna, the phase-shifters being on one end and the electronics on the other for balance. Also on the back are the IFF and Tadil-C digital link antennas.

The radar has seven modes of operation. PDES (PD elevation scan) measures target height by scanning the beam in the vertical plane. PDNES (PD non-elevation scan) enables aircraft to be detected and tracked down to ground level, though without height measurement. BTH (beyond the horizon) uses pulse radar without doppler for surveillance in the sky volume beyond the horizon, where ground clutter is in the horizon shadow. Passive is a mode in which the transmitter is shut down over one or more selected azimuth sectors, the receivers continuing to process emissions (such as countermeasures) within that sector, a single strobe line being displayed through each jamming source. Maritime surveillance, a mode added for operations outside the USA, uses very short pulses to reduce sea clutter and enhance detection of surface vessels. Standby is a mode with the receivers shut down but the whole radar ready for immediate use; in flight the rotodome turns at 0.25 rpm. Test maintenance is a mode placing the radar under control of test engineers. E-3 aircraft have been produced to nine different standards, and four more are planned, though by 1993 all USAF aircraft should be to a

Blind zones are no problem to AWACS. Even in the worst case (90°) the doppler-clear zone is as wide as the blind region even with a PRF as low as 200 Hz, which gives a theoretical range of 400 nm. In contrast the F-15 is forced to restrict look angle (say, 30°) and the high PRF restricts range to about 20 nm. (Hughes)

uniform (probably E-3D) standard, with export variants not greatly dissimilar.

A diagram shows the contrast in blind zones between an AWACS radar and a modern fighter radar. For the fighter we may have a V of 1,500 kt and the antenna aperture is limited to about 2.5 ft, so to get a 1:1 ratio of blind zones to clear zones we have to raise PRF to about 4 kHz and restrict the look (azimuth) angle to about 30°. This PRF limits range to about 20 nm, and raising PRF still further will make effective range even shorter. But the AWACS poses no problems. Even taking the antenna aperture as 20 ft (actually a minimum of 24 ft) and on-station orbit speed as 300 kt we can get a 1:1 clear/blind ratio at PRFs down to only 200 Hz (0.2 kHz), even in the worst case with the antenna in the 90° position. Obviously it follows that for surveillance missions the best answer is an aerostat (airship or tethered balloon). We can reduce velocity to very low values, and increase antenna size to 100 ft or more. The result would — or 'will' if the US Navy can find the funds — be really exciting new capability, always assuming we could get high enough.

So much for surveillance, but today radars are also used for reconnaissance. So too are IR and other sensors. There is much to be said regarding the information we can obtain about the land and sea, but first we have to return to the basic question of resolution. It was because of their poor resolution that early mapping radars, such as H₂S, were of hardly any use for reconnaissance. Resolution is the minimum distance between two sharply defined objects that the radar can discern separately. The resolution cell (which is sometimes, but not always, the same as a pixel or picture element) is a rectangle whose sides are d_a and d_r, the resolution distances in the azimuth direction and in the range direction. In a good recon radar we want both dimensions to be as small as possible, and we also would like them to be roughly equal so that each cell is almost a square.

A cell size of about 500 ft would be adequate if all we want to map are coastlines, rivers and cities. A useful recon radar must have a cell size not larger than 50 ft, and to resolve individual small buildings and vehicles it cannot be greater than 5 to 10 ft. Even this suffices merely to show that something is present. To identify objects by shape demands a cell size that is only a small fraction of the object size. For example, even with a cell size 1/5th the span of an aircraft we get a picture that could be almost anything. Not until the cell size is about 1/20th of the wingspan do we get an identifiable image, and even this can be sharply distorted by the fact that, as we saw in Chapter 4, real targets reflect very unevenly so that the actual image would be a moving pattern of bright patches which scintillate and fade as the look angle changes. To get a much better image we must map from different directions, with different frequencies and polarizations.

Of course, our cell size has to be a compromise between resolution on the one hand and rate of signal processing on the other. Obviously, the number of cells is roughly proportional not to the cell size (resolution distance) but to its square; thus, dividing the cell size by 4 multiplies the amount of signal processing by 16. To give an example, 100 days of reconnaissance by the Seasat satellite mapped 48 million square miles with a cell size of about 80 ft, resulting in the need to process about 200 billion cells. If the resolution had been improved to 10 ft the processor would have had to handle 12,800 billion cells. This raises factors of time and of cost. Seasat was a research satellite, so there would have been no crisis if analysing the images to extract the

information had taken months, or even years. On the other hand, single-seat attack aircraft flying at 600 kt at treetop height have to map areas of the terrain ahead in real time, so obviously there must be a severe compromise between resolution, area and time. Often individual frames are frozen for a second or two for the pilot to study.

How do we improve resolution? We use one approach for fine resolution in range and different methods for improving resolution in azimuth. We saw earlier that we can get a range resolution of about 500 ft per μs of pulse width. Thus, if we can live with a pulse width of 0.01 μs, we can obtain a resolution in range (d_r) of 5 ft. As pulse width is shortened, the required bandwidth has to increase (because, to pass most of the power in each pulse, the 3-dB bandwidth has to be approximately the reciprocal of the pulse width) and to use 0.01 μs pulses we have to use a bandwidth of not less than 100 MHz. We cannot do anything about this, but we can greatly ease some of the design and manufacturing problems by using pulse compres-

To get a meaningful picture a reconnaissance radar has to have a cell size much smaller than the objects of interest. Even 0.2 of the target size gives a meaningless image. (Hughes)

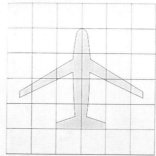

CELL SIZE: 1/5 MAJOR DIMENSION

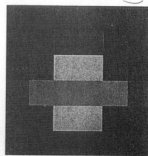

CORRESPONDING MAP

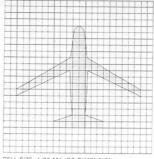

CELL SIZE: 1/20 MAJOR DIMENSION

CORRESPONDING MAP

sion. For example if we use a compression ratio of 1,000 we can transmit 10 μs pulses and still achieve range resolution of 5 ft.

Resolution in azimuth d_a is roughly equal to the 3-dB beamwidth of the antenna multiplied by the range. The 3-dB beamwidth, measured in radians, is approximately equal to wavelength divided by the length of the antenna (measured in the same units as we use for range, preferably m or ft). Thus, using a 10 ft antenna with a 0.1 ft wavelength at a range of 300,000 ft (50 nm) we get a resolution of about 3,000 ft. The answers are either to reduce the wavelength or increase the length of the antenna. Though millimetric radars are useful over short ranges, for helo obstacle warning and battlefield missile guidance, long-range mapping radars have to use much longer wavelength to avoid crippling attenuation by dust, water vapour and other matter; the bottom limit is X-band, about 3 cm (10 GHz). So we have to concentrate on making the antenna bigger.

Obviously we are limited in this respect by the size

The first SLAR was the British Red Drover, designed in 1954–56. A giant, it was 50 feet long and fitted along the underside of the fuselage of the Avro 730 Mach 2.5 reconnaissance aircraft, which was cancelled in 1957. Note in the side view the waveguide feeder passing under the pilot's seat. The antennas, looking out to left and right, were two-dimensional horns. (Avro)

of the aircraft. Today we can see many exciting possibilities with conformal radars, but for forty years the main method of making a long antenna compatible with 'normal-size' aircraft has been the SLAR (variously interpreted as sideways-looking airborne [or aircraft] radar, or side-looking array radar). We use a real-aperture array antenna 15 ft or more in length, arranged longitudinally so that it sends out a very narrow beam to the side. We can use one antenna looking out to one side, or two antennas looking out to both sides, or one antenna that scans about a longitudinal axis horizon-to-horizon. Among the first SLARs in service were EMI installations for RAF V-bombers, Westinghouse SLARs (notably APD-7 for the RA-5C Vigilante), the Motorola APS-94 for the OV-1D and Goodyear SLARs for RF-4s.

The traditional SLAR looks exactly sideways. Each pulse or scan illuminates a narrow rectangle of ground which typically extends from one to twelve miles from track; a few modern SLARs reach forty miles. The signal from the receiver is fed to a CRT to give a line-by-line TV output. This is recorded on film that moves past the CRT display at a rate proportional to the groundspeed. The radar is so arranged that the aircraft's forward movement exactly provides the necessary 'azimuth scan' so that successive strips cover the ground with no overlaps and no gaps. Typically the SLAR is arranged to give a film map with a scale of 250,000. The ratio of

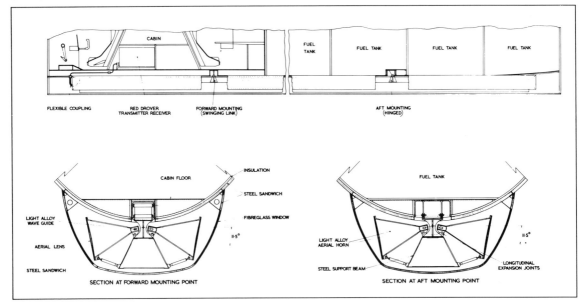

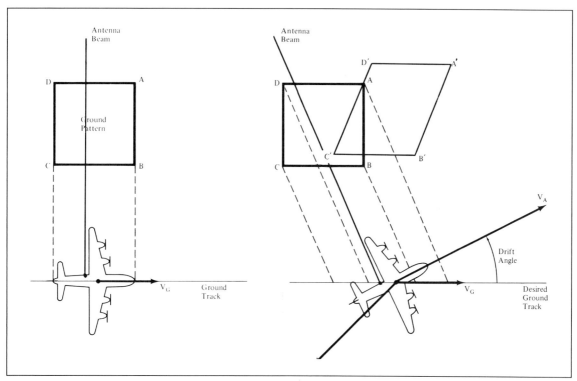

SLARs are fixed to the aircraft and look exactly sideways, film speed and aircraft groundspeed being synchronized. Invariably wind (V_w) causes drift, and without correction ABCD would appear on the film as A'B'C'D'. In modern SLARs all corrections are automatic. (Westinghouse)

lateral radar scan and film width give the correct transverse scale, and the film drive speed is arranged to give the same longitudinal scale; thus, a square on the ground appears as a square and not as a rectangle. SLARs can give a film map which appears to view each point from vertically above, without distortion due to varying incident angles on the terrain, but it is still no easy task to eliminate distortions due to major terrain variation, because the location of each point on the film depends on the arrival time of its echo, which is falsely short for echoes from mountains and falsely long for deep valleys.

Another problem is caused by drift. Strong crosswinds make the aircraft fly crabwise, heading into the wind. The author has never seen a SLAR that could be slewed to cancel drift. Instead the navigation avionics feed a drift signal to the CRT to slew the CRT trace to cancel out the distortion. The

reduced groundspeed due to the wind is fed in automatically, so that the output on the film retains the correct orthogonal scales both across and along.

SLARs can map large areas very quickly, in all weather conditions. To cover large areas requires the assembly of a mosaic from adjacent strips. At the end of each strip the antenna is switched to look

Many airshows have seen the Ericsson SLAR carried above the fuselage of a Swedish Fairchild Metro. 1, antenna aperture; 2, transmit/receive modules (200); 3, cooling air inlet.

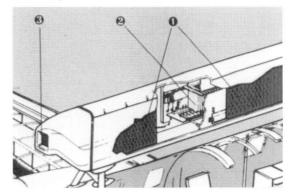

out on the other side of the aircraft, so that all radar shadows are in the same direction. If this were not done the image would appear inverted, with rivers running along ridges. In a few modes, such as ice reconnaissance for shipping, shadows are no problem and a single run can look out on both sides, though there is usually a blank blind-zone strip along the centre of the film. Ice mapping is one of many duties where it helps to broadcast the image information, so that users (in this case ships) can get a picture in real time. In overland reconnaissance a large dynamic range is needed so that strong targets do not mask weak ones close by, and MTI (moving-target indication) can be incorporated.

Returning to azimuth resolution — note, azimuth is parallel to direction of flight — we can calculate that an SLAR with a 16 ft antenna operating at 3 cm at a range of 5 nm might achieve a d_a of about 200 ft, which is adequate for seeing ships or oil slicks, and for most terrain mapping. Many customers, and certainly the military, want much better resolution than this, and we cannot make our antenna much bigger unless we use an airship. The answer is to create a huge antenna synthetically, in an SAR (synthetic array [or aperture] radar). This uses a combination of the aircraft's forward movement and signal processing — optical in early SARs, digital in the latest types — to produce the equivalent of an antenna array anything up to thousands of feet long, to give radar pictures of photographic quality. Broadly, SAR involves summing a number of returns from successive side-looking pulses, each sent out from a location a little further along the flight path.

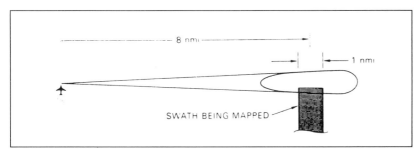

A simple SAR could begin with the side-looking antenna mapping a 1-mile swath at 8 nm. (Hughes)

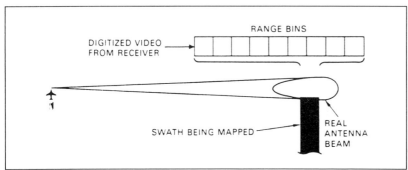

To form a 50 ft synthetic aperture we sum the returns of 50 pulses, each sent out 1 ft beyond its predecessor, in a bank of range bins just covering the swath width. (Hughes)

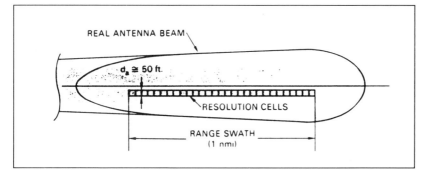

When the returns from the 50 pulses have been integrated, the contents of the range bins represent the returns from a single row of range/azimuth resolution cells. (Hughes)

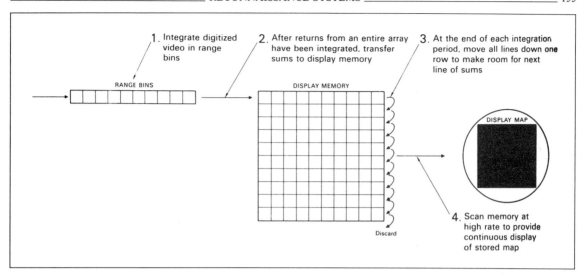

1. Integrate digitized video in range bins

2. After returns from an entire array have been integrated, transfer sums to display memory

3. At the end of each integration period, move all lines down one row to make room for next line of sums

RANGE BINS

DISPLAY MEMORY

DISPLAY MAP

Discard

4. Scan memory at high rate to provide continuous display of stored map

In the simplest case, consider an aircraft flying straight and level at 600 kt (1,000 ft/s) and using X-band radar pointing out at 90° to map a swath 1 nm wide at a range of 8 nm, with a required resolution of 50 ft. To achieve this resolution we must synthesize an antenna about 50 ft long. If we choose a PRF of 1 kHz then successive pulses are sent out 1 ft apart, so to synthesize our array we must sum the returns from every block of fifty consecutive transmitted pulses. Each pulse is transmitted from one of the fifty 'elements' making up the complete 50 ft synthetic antenna. We sum the returns received by successive elements in a bank of range bins which just span the 1 nm width of the swath. Because the range is much longer than the array length, the distance from any patch of ground on the boresight line (90° to flight path) is about the same to all fifty elements, so all have about the same RF phase and all add together. But for a patch off the boresight line, the echoes received by successive elements have progressively different phases which tend all to cancel out, so the result is a very narrow effective beam. When all fifty returns have been integrated, the sum built up in each range bin is extremely close to representing the total return from a single range/azimuth cell, so the contents of the whole bank of bins represents the returns from one row of cells spanning the swath being mapped.

When we have built up the fifty small picture elements they are transferred to corresponding locations in the memory, or scan converter, of the radar display. Simultaneously a new row of range bins is formed just ahead of and touching the last row,

How the output from the range bins is converted into an SAR picture. The memory is often called a scan converter. (Hughes)

which will be filled by returns from a new fifty-element array. Again at the same moment, the bottom line on the display memory is discarded. Thus, the display memory relatively slowly moves down, line-by-line, whilst being continuously scanned at a high rate in order to produce the continuous TV-type picture which is presented to the operator, or sent by data link or recorded on tape or film. This explains the simplest kind of SAR, called an unfocussed array because, like a pinhole camera, it is 'focussed' on infinity by assuming that incoming lines of sight are parallel. We could make the synthetic array longer. If it were twice as long, the first fifty returns would be summed in one memory position, the second in the next, and the sum of the two sums transferred to the memory. The first sum would then be dumped and the next fifty returns added instead, and so on. But we cannot increase array length beyond the point at which the actual range to a point on the boresight line becomes significantly less than the range from either the first or last of the synthetic elements. A small graph shows the maximum effective array length at a wavelength of 3 cm, and the corresponding minimum resolution distance, which is about 40% as great. If we want to obtain good resolution independent of range then we have to use a focussed array. All we need to do is apply an appropriate phase rotation correction to the return received by

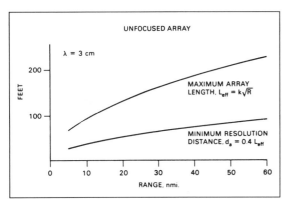

The maximum effective length of an unfocused array increases only as the square root of range, and resolution distance is about 40% of array length. These curves are for 3 cm wavelength. (Hughes)

each array element. This correction is proportional to the square of the linear distance of the array from the centre of the array.

With focussing, we can increase the length of the synthetic array in proportion to the range of the region being mapped. The processing load is increased because now, each time the aircraft moves forward d_a, we must read all the numbers in each bin serially, and then focus the array by phase-shifting and summing all the data, in a process called azimuth compression. Then the magnitude of the sum for each range bin can be entered in the appropriate position in the top row of the display memory to construct the picture. There are various ways in which computer load can be greatly reduced by doppler processing, which enables many lines of the map to be processed simultaneously. One apparent paradox is that, as the region being mapped must lie within the beam of the real antenna the whole time the synthetic array is being formed, the length of a synthetic array having a fixed look angle is limited to the width of the real antenna at the range being mapped. Hence, we can make a longer synthetic array (with better resolution) if we use a wider beam, which for a given wavelength means a shorter real antenna!

The modern SAR is a sensor of great versatility. It can look at things far away near the horizon and, irrespective of day/night, clouds, rain or smoke, produce a clear picture as seen from vertically overhead. As the synthetic array is formed in the signal processor, the radar can be adapted to meet varying demands. It can also operate in various

modes. It can be squinted to look diagonally ahead (or astern), by training the real beam forward and inserting the appropriate focussing correction and coordinate rotation. A simple SAR will notice moving targets, but will interpret their doppler shift as a change in location; thus, trucks may be pictured off the road, and a train off its track. The latest and most advanced SARs can interpret the doppler shifts correctly, and moving targets appear in the proper places.

The information contained in a radar map depends on the incident angle. When looking down almost vertically the return is very sensitive to slope of the ground; reflection is sufficiently mirror-like for differences in slope of only a degree or two to double or halve the strength of the echo. Far away at very shallow angles the slope has almost no effect, and instead the echo depends on texture and shadowing. Thus, map information can be enhanced by combining maps made from different angles, or with waves of different length or polarization. Such maps may contain too much information to be conveyed by monochromatic grey tones, and coded false colours must be added. Radar maps can see variations in height of the ocean surface, complex drainage networks buried under desert sand, and many other things impossible to detect by other means. By use of a multilook capability, using a real beam wide enough to map the same area several times without changing the look angle, scintillation can be reduced and a truer picture obtained.

Another mode, called spotlight, holds the real beam on a region of special interest for a considerable period. This requires that the look angle of the real antenna should progressively change with aircraft position, the processing simultaneously applying the appropriate changing phase corrections. Map quality is improved in two ways. First, as the beam is continuously trained on the area being mapped, the length of the synthetic array is no longer limited by the real antenna's beamwidth, so we can make the real antenna as big as we like. This increases mainlobe gain, and thus S/N ratio. Secondly, no matter whether the target is an aircraft or a field of grain, the effects of scintillation normally result in severe degradation into what can be an unrecognizable instantaneous image, but if we map it repeatedly from different directions; averaging successive returns from each resolution cell, we can get an almost perfect picture. Quality can be improved still further by auto-switching of RFs (by at least the pulse bandwidth) at points one or more array lengths apart, and/or by changing antenna polarization.

A particular SAR mode is DBS, doppler beam sharpening. This differs in that array length is not increased in proportion to range but remains constant. Thus, angular resolution is held constant, so azimuth resolution d_a increases with range. The map resembles one produced by a real antenna sending out a very narrow beam. DBS is a way of getting a fighter radar to act to some degree like an SAR. In DBS the radar scans the ground ahead through a chosen azimuth angle (a very narrow region dead ahead is usually blank because of the inadequate spread of doppler frequencies) to produce a map much finer than could be achieved by the real antenna. It falls short of SAR image quality because the integration time, or length of synthetic array, is limited to the length of time each ground patch is in the antenna beam, and at 600 kt at 200 ft this is not very long.

Over the past decade NATO countries have begun to develop advanced battlefield surveillance radar, and are even considering a limited amount of interoperability. They cover a wide spectrum of stand-off distances and operating heights. At the highest level, over 65,000 ft (20 km) is the Hughes ASARS-2 (advanced SAR system 2), carried by the TR-1. Launched as UPD-X in 1977, and first flown in a U-2R in 1981, ASARS-2 has two planar slotted-waveguide antennas looking sideways at an angle forming a V seen from the front. According to *Jane's Avionics* this is 'to enable the ground on either side of the aircraft's track to be surveyed without the aircraft having to manoeuvre'. In fact the TR-1 has no wish to study NATO territory, and the need for two antennas is so that potentially hostile territory can be looked at during both passes along the frontier, first in one direction and then in the other. In 1988 Hughes announced Pasars (Podded ASARS), which fits into external tanks down to 300 US gallon size, giving a very high-definition capability to fighters.

At the 33,000 ft (10 km) level will orbit the E-8As carrying the J-Stars (joint surveillance target attack radar system). Originally it had been thought Grumman's Melbourne Systems Division would merely bolt the Norden radar into ten ex-airline 707s, but the task is now seen as somewhat larger and Boeing will build 22 new E-8As to receive a more advanced radar. The latter is a Grumman design, with Grumman software totalling over 600,000 lines (much more than for AWACS) of new computer code, much of it of unprecedented complexity, with about 2 million lines running through each E-8A when on station. By comparison with the software the hardware seems almost simple, yet when Lieutenant-General Melvin Chubb, Commander of USAF Electronic Systems Division, was asked about the J-Stars antenna he replied 'It's ten orders of magnitude more complex than the E-3 AWACS antenna'. It has to look in one direction, with unprecedented precision, and study not targets in clear air but on the ground. The radar has 456 phase-shifters and no fewer than 228 LRUs which must all work in unison. The processing task may well be unprecedented. There are 27 major processors, including one for each display console. Each signal processor performs 625 MCOPS (million complex operations per second), about the

Installing the V-shaped left/right planar antennas of a Hughes ASARS-2 in the nose of a Lockheed TR-1. Its long-range imagery is less attenuated by the atmosphere than that at optical or IR wavelengths.

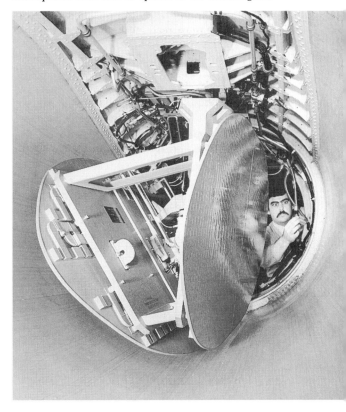

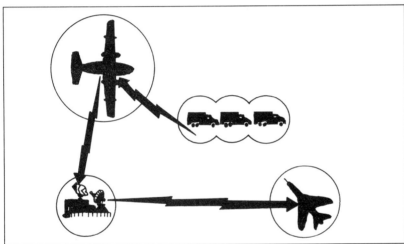

same as a Cray I computer! For the record, the J-Stars radar operates at 3 cm and has an antenna 24 ft long in a Boeing-built canoe radome under the forward fuselage. Each E-8A will have fifteen consoles for USAF and USA operators and controllers. The radar will operate in a wide-angle MTI mode, a narrow-field SAR mode, and a weapon-guidance mode. Eventually secure downlinks will enable an E-8A to task tactical aircraft in flight or correct missile trajectories, but we have yet to learn how the aircraft itself will survive. In January 1989 the vital ECCM had not even been ordered.

Between the TR-1 and E-8A in altitude the RAF may one day deploy the occasional Canberra fitted with Astor (airborne stand-off radar). Originally Castor, the C standing for Corps, Astor is a competitive programme involving Ferranti, Thorn-EMI and Marconi Defence Systems. But Astor could also be carried in a much cheaper light-twin Defender, and MEL are also involved in this alternative. Demonstrators of both the 50,000 ft Canberra and 10,000 ft Defender have been flying since 1982. It is conceivable that a broadly similar radar could be carried by either.

Astor is to be compatible with J-Stars and with the French Orchidée. Though French for Orchid, the name is an acronym. The LCTAR (Thomson) radar is an X-band PD with a planar array (but not SAR) antenna which swings down under a Super Puma II helicopter. From 10,000 ft Orchidée will stand off 31 miles behind the front line and look 62 miles beyond it, concentrating on hostile army activity. Data are sent to an ESD (Electronique Serge Dassault) ground station which will do all the processing. At even lower levels there are many other projects for surveillance systems to be carried in helicopters and fixed-wing aircraft, particularly in unmanned platforms.

So great is the ability of modern reconnaissance systems to acquire data that the humans become submerged under the sheer quantity of input. In 1967-72 the USAF used a unique system whose sensors were measured in thousands, but it proved a mixed blessing. Called Igloo White, its task was to detect and locate trucks, alone or in huge groups, moving by night along the Ho Chi Minh Trail (which was actually a complex road network, mainly in Laos). After racking their brains, the Institute for Defense Analyses in Washington came up with a novel answer. The entire Trail was to be repeatedly 'seeded' with sensors looking like bits of pipe, with fins and antennas. Adsid, the most widely used, penetrated soil leaving its antenna showing, to broadcast signals generated by vibration caused by heavy trucks. Spikebuoy did the same, but broadcast actual sounds picked up by a microphone. Acoubuoy was similar but dropped by parachute into trees, hanging from foliage. The millions of signals were relayed via special aircraft to a huge Infiltration Surveillance Center. By January 1972 Igloo White had cost $1.1 billion. It certainly helped, but the notion that it was the prototype for a huge NATO network for Europe (for example) has not been realized.

Today one of the new buzzword subjects is data fusion. Trying to correlate the inputs from different sensors, of different types, is far from simple. What are called AI (artificial intelligence) and ES (expert systems) are used, in techniques going under the names of Bayesian, Dempster-Shafer, fuzzy sets, cluster analysis and PDAF (probabilistic data association filtering)! As this was being written, Hughes and TI announced completion of a multisensor fusion demo linked to the USA LHX programme. The sensors were a thermal imager, a TV camera, a laser ranger and a millimetric radar. A computer integrates each sensor with a digital terrain map. Each sensor has advantages and weaknesses which vary with battle conditions, time of day, target range and many other variables. Merely superimposing all the pictures on one display, beyond which can be seen the real world, is likely to result in, at the best, a fuzzy picture; and of course we want to avoid emitting detectable radiation. Somewhere, future computers will provide complete answers.

Above *Strips from a reconnaissance photograph (top), an IR linescan image (8-14 μ) (centre) and a SLAR (90 GHz).* (Dornier)

Right *Printout from a very high resolution reconnaissance radar.* (Thomson-CSF)

9
ELECTRONIC WARFARE

From the dawn of history, the development of a weapon has spurred the development of a counter-weapon, or better protection, or both. This is certainly the case with avionics. No sooner had he outlined how radar could protect Britain against enemy bombers, in July 1935, than Sir Robert Watson Watt privately commented that future bombers would be what we today call 'stealth' designs. No sooner had the Luftwaffe begun to use radio beams to guide bombers over Britain than the British commandeered hospital diathermy equipment to jam the beams. No sooner had British bombers begun to use H_2S navigation radar than the Luftwaffe equipped its night fighters with a receiver that homed on to the H_2S. When Britain realized Germany had its own air-defence radars, RAF bombers were provided with bundles of 'Window' to smother the radar displays with false echoes; so in turn, the Luftwaffe changed the wavelength of its night-fighter radars to see through the chaff. It was all predictable. War is unquestionably futile.

What was not predictable is that EW (electronic warfare) appeared almost to be forgotten in 1945-75, perhaps because the wars in Korea and Vietnam were in general not against sophisticated enemies. This naturally led to a few unpleasant shocks, such as the discovery by Israel in 1973 that nobody had thought of a jammer to counter the CW radar of the SA-6 missile nor of the ZSU-23-4 flak. As recently as 1982 Britain at last noticed that it was sending Harriers and Sea Harriers into battle without even a simple chaff dispenser! Today EW is unlikely to be overlooked by anyone (but I'm always ready to be amazed).

Today EW is a big subject. It embraces almost every part of warfare, from the oceans to deep space, and covers the whole usable spread of EM radiation — though when we get to optical levels we run out of (unclassified) active devices, and the passive technique is called camouflage. Nobody would dream of going to war in a vehicle on land, sea or in the sky that was not properly equipped with EW devices. The basic EW suite comprises some form of passive warning, and some form of countermeasure. For example, at radar wavelengths the warning system comprises an RWR (radar warning receiver), which can go under various other names, and two types of ECM (electronic countermeasures), active jammers and expendables. The active jammer can be internal or housed in a clip-on pod, and the expendables consist of chaff and possibly cartridges containing aerosol clouds or even small active jammers.

In addition to EW suites added to all combat aircraft, we now also have various kinds of dedicated EW aircraft. Some are tasked solely with SEAD (suppression of enemy air defences), and have comprehensive wideband receivers, emitter locators and ARMs (anti-radar missiles). There are many dour pilots who say 'the best countermeasure is a thousand-pounder on the enemy radar'. Other EW aircraft have no ordnance, but carry comprehensive fits of receivers and jammers, to help friendly aircraft penetrate hostile airspace. Examples of these are the US Navy EA-6B and USAF EF-111A, which share almost the same tac/jam system, with the important difference that the Navy aircraft has a crew of four and jammers carried in external pods, while the USAF platform is more automated and needs only a pilot and EWO (electronic-warfare officer) to manage a system carried wholly internally. These aircraft will be described later.

In addition to the basic 'fit' or suite of RWR, jammer(s) and expendables, this chapter also deals with two other subjects which, amazingly, are still thought of as rather new ideas. One is encapsulated in the evocative word 'stealth', which should have become the norm fifty years ago. The other is what sixty years ago was called a death ray, and today has the more sober title of a DEW (directed-energy weapon).

Chronologically, EW began with the jamming of, or at least interference with, the Luftwaffe navigational beams in September 1940. Later the offensive shifted to RAF Bomber Command, and the EW battle was joined in earnest. By 1943 the Germans had retaliated by jamming the Gee navaid, while the RAF and British industry showed extraordinary (if sometimes misguided) skill in producing a whole string of EW devices. One of the first was Boozer, a passive RWR made possible by prior Elint which discovered the exact wavelength and waveform of Würzburg ground radar and Lichtenstein BC fighter radar. Boozer was in theory ideal: it ignored friendly aircraft but switched on an orange light in front of the pilot if its antenna received radiation from a Würzburg, and a red light if it detected a Lichtenstein. Its problems were that it frequently flashed false alarms, either through faults or from illumination by radars that were actually seeking a different target. Its successor was Monica, one of the most complete errors in the history of warfare. Monica was a small active radar which triggered off endless alarms by detecting other bombers in a Main Force stream (yet it often failed to spot deadly night fighters) and provided an ideal homing beacon for night fighters equipped with Flensburg receivers tuned to Monica's wavelength.

Tinsel was a simple noise broadcaster on frequencies used by Luftwaffe fighter controllers, fed from a microphone in an engine cowling. Mandrel broadcast jamming on frequencies of Würzburg and Freya ground radars. ABC (airborne cigar) monitored Luftwaffe fighter controller frequencies and immediately jammed on frequencies being used. Pipe-rack jammed night-fighter SN-2 radars. Corona was a powerful English radio station from which skilled RAF/WAAF personnel mimicked Luftwaffe controllers, broadcasting false instructions. Jostle was a giant 2.5 kW airborne noise jammer which obliterated Luftwaffe communications over a large area. Serrate enabled Mosquitoes to home on SN-2 radars, while Perfectos enabled them to interrogate Luftwaffe night-fighter IFFs and home on the responses.

On top of all these, chaff, called Window by the RAF and Düppel by the Luftwaffe, became a staple commodity dispensed by all aircraft penetrating enemy airspace. Chaff has to be correctly sized to have maximum effect on particular enemy radars, the length of each reflective strip often being half (or another exact fraction) of the wavelength. In general RAF Window of 1943 comprised narrow strips of aluminium foil while Luftwaffe Düppel was much wider and metallised paper, black on one side. By 1944 a typical RAF Bomber Command night operation involved numerous diversions, feint attacks, deliberate 'breakdowns' in particular EW devices (to reveal a previously hidden Main Force, that might in fact be just six aircraft twenty miles apart carefully dispensing Window) and all manner of other cunning deceptions. Certainly the dark art of EW reached a scale and maturity in the night sky over Germany in 1944 that has never since even been approached, though by modern standards the equipment was primitive.

In the late 1950s the technology began to move forward again. As the most basic form of ECM, chaff became improved in design. Today most chaff is aluminium, aluminium-backed Mylar or metallised glass-fibre. It is manufactured as continuous roving, in various widths. This is either precut in the factory for packaging into bundles or cartridges, or else supplied in continuous lengths for loading into a cutter/dispenser. The latter are loaded with roving packages which may contain several miles of folded raw material. This is then fed out through cutters which slice through multiple laminations to give astronomic numbers of dipoles. For example the Lundy ALE-43, which has been installed internally and in pods, can feed at up to 8.1 million dipole-inches (128 miles) per second for a maximum continuous dispense time of 660 s. The dipoles may be cut to a uniform length or to a combination of lengths, depending on the controlling processor which can either be preprogrammed or fed with real-time RWR information on the actual wavelengths of the hostile threats encountered. All chaff is surface treated so that the clouds of dipoles do not stick together (forming what are descriptively called birdsnests), but when ejected into a deliberately turbulent airflow bloom rapidly to give the maximum RCS (radar cross-section) within about 1 s.

Probably 90 per cent of today's chaff is dispensed in the form of cartridges. Like roving, cartridges are standard in size and design. Many look like giant shotgun cartridges, two of the most common sizes being 36 mm (1.4 in) diameter and 147 mm (5.79 in)

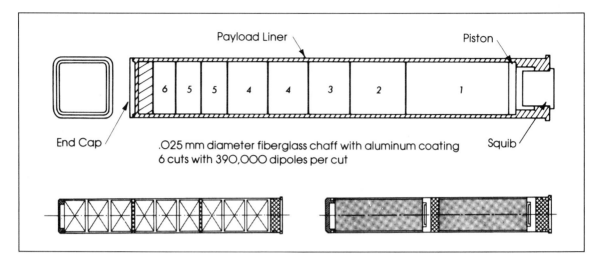

Payload Liner   Piston

End Cap   .025 mm diameter fiberglass chaff with aluminum coating   Squib
                    6 cuts with 390,000 dipoles per cut

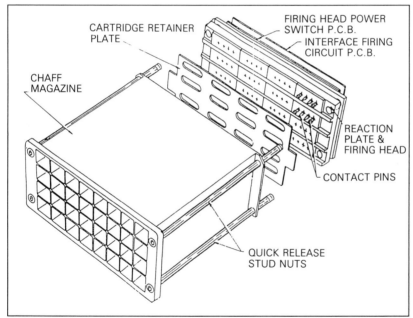

CARTRIDGE RETAINER PLATE

FIRING HEAD POWER SWITCH P.C.B.

INTERFACE FIRING CIRCUIT P.C.B.

CHAFF MAGAZINE

REACTION PLATE & FIRING HEAD

CONTACT PINS

QUICK RELEASE STUD NUTS

Above *Longitudinal sections of common ECM cartridges. The larger drawing shows Tracor RR-170A/AL 'smart chaff'. To a smaller scale are two Lacroix cartridges, the Chaff 651 (three units each containing three subpayloads with length cut to user's specification) and the Flare 407 (two identical and independent IR sources). These French products are circular, 55 mm in diameter.*

Left *Computer's perspective drawing of a typical chaff dispenser, the Vicon 78 Series 203. Of course, it could also be loaded with IR flares, provided they fit the 1 in-square cross section. Note the electronic PCBs at the rear. (Vinten Military Systems)*

long and (RR-170) a square section 1 in (25.4 mm) across and 210 mm (8.3 in) long. It would seem logical to make dispensers fire like machine guns, but so far virtually all are like crude egg-boxes, each cell being loaded by hand with a single cartridge which usually contains chaff precut to a range of lengths. The mathematics of RBC (rapid-bloom chaff) clouds are very complex; a British firm, Chemring, has identified fourteen different types of motion of individual dipoles as they slowly fall through the sky. Each dipole is many times finer than a human hair — most of it is so fine that

several hundred fibres could pass through the eye of a needle — so it is not difficult to understand the dispense rates quoted earlier. Such fine filaments, especially of glassfibre, have a very low sinking speed, and even dispensed at a height of 200 ft can form an electronically effective cloud for several minutes. RCS of a single cartridge is typically about 220 sq ft (20 m^2).

Chaff can be sized to cover almost the whole spectrum of radio/radar wavelengths. At shorter wavelengths we have to use even smaller particulate matter, and the traditional answer at optical wavelengths is smoke. So far as the author is aware, smokescreens have never been used to protect fast jets, but they are very important for battlefield helicopters. Today specially formulated smokes can be dispensed to give protection over the whole band of wavelengths from UV to IR, with especial emphasis on the latter. For example the Swedish FFV company markets smoke dispensers tailored to the range 0.4–14 μ. Dispensing systems include methods of injecting smoke material into engine jet-pipes, and self-screening launchers for smoke rockets which in 2 s can create a wall of smoke covering a 120° arc some 330 ft ahead of the helicopter from ground level to 33 ft above it. In typical breeze conditions the screen would last at least 30 s.

Smoke is one of several OCMs (optical countermeasures). At IR wavelengths there are several specific IRCMs, but first we should look at TWSs (threat warning systems). These have been developed in great profusion by dozens of companies, some tailored precisely to particular types of aircraft and others much simpler and often carried externally in clip-on pods. For each aircraft in the inventory we have to ask: what threats is it likely to meet; what are the wavelengths to be countered, and in what order of priority; where will the threats be located, relative to the aircraft; what are the problems and drawbacks of totally integrated internal warnings, linked to the countermeasures; and what are the problems and drawbacks of packaging everything externally? In addition, a crucial decision has to be made on the extent to which the total EW installation should be automated. Countermeasures of all kinds are wanted at the times of highest pilot stress and cockpit workload. Accordingly it is sensible to make them as self-contained as possible, but in the past this policy has often had unfortunate results. Just as we are approaching the target, keeping as quiet as possible, our aft-facing RWR can be triggered by the radar of our wingman, automatically triggering clouds of chaff, bright flares and maybe an active jammer! Or our equally automated ARM (anti-radar missile) decides it prefers the strident smart jammer of our wingman to the enemy SAM radar that we intended. To some extent, the best systems are the ones we don't possess.

The earliest TWSs, such as Boozer, looked astern only, and were tuned to a single radar wavelength. By the 1960s fast attack aircraft were much more interested in threats on the ground in front of them, and it became common to see RWR antennas looking both ahead and astern from near the top of the fin. With the rapid growth in IR technology many attack aircraft also took on board an IRWR. For example F-111s have the Cincinnati Electronics AAR-34, whose fore- and aft-facing hemispherical detection heads occupy a tube on top of the fin which also houses the associated cryogenic cooling system. Like all IRWRs it attempts to detect the

Later versions of Mirage 2000 have an ICMS (integrated countermeasures suite) by Thomson-CSF. It comprises (a) a passive warning system with Serval antennas at the wingtips and tail (and, not shown, a Matra IRWR), (b) self-managed active jammers (the HF part provided by Electronique Serge Dassault), and (c) Matra Spirale chaff/flare cartridge dispensers.

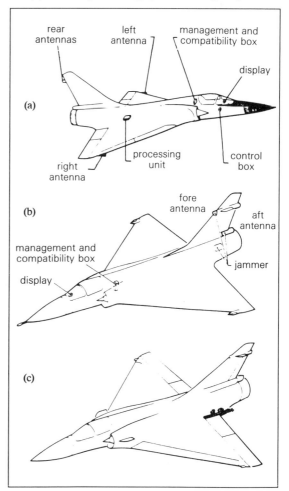

spectral signatures in hydrocarbon exhausts, such as would be left by a SAM, AAM or hostile fighter, whilst ignoring all other IR sources. FOV is selectable, but AAR-34 merely gives a warning without indication of direction. A later IRWR, in this case called an MWS (missile warning set), is the AAR-47 by Honeywell. This uses later electronic technology to give 360° coverage with less system weight. Honeywell is working on a DMMWS (dual-mode MWS) which adds a small PD radar for accurate determination of threat range, the basic AAR-47 already giving an indication of bearing.

An unusual installation called an MDS (missile detection system) is the ALQ-156 produced by Sanders Associates. This is a pure PD radar, intended for use by helicopters to warn of any oncoming missile. The radar is specially designed for 'immunity to battlefield clutter' even in NOE (nap of the Earth) flight, yet to spot a small missile approaching from any direction, and to do so early enough for an appropriate countermeasures response. ALQ-156 is now also used by fixed-wing aircraft. Another advanced system is SAWS (silent attack warning system) being developed by Texas Instruments. This uses IR search/track 'to detect and classify attacking missiles by their IR

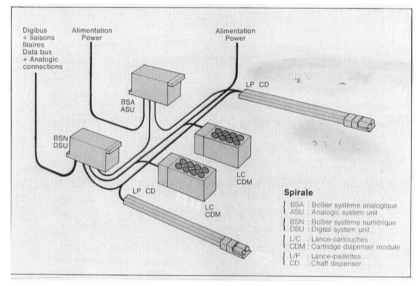

Schematic diagram of the French Matra Spirale chaff/flare dispenser system being developed for the Mirage 2000. The dispensers are at the trailing edge of the wing roots.

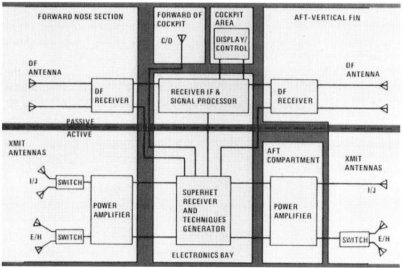

Loral's Rapport was the first reprogrammable internal ECM system to find a wide market, the first version equipping Belgian Mirage 5s. With smart noise it can engage 14 threats simultaneously, with angle and range-denial programs used in combination.

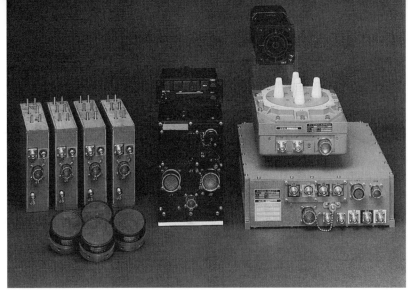

Typical of today's RWRs is the Litton ALR-67, used in the newest US Navy and Marines combat aircraft. The four spiral receiver antennas are at lower left and the cockpit indicator at upper right.

signature'. Again, countermeasure action can be pilot-controlled or automatic.

This leads to the vast subject of ECM (electronic countermeasures), IRCM (IR) and OCM (optical). Countermeasures are central to EW, and their different forms occupy the bulk of this chapter.

The complexity of modern ECM installations can be considerable. The most comprehensive are tailored to the aircraft and housed internally but the vast majority of ECM systems are packaged into externally carried pods. Some of these are hung like any other store, for example on NATO 14 in (356 mm) twin lugs, while others are scabbed on flush with the skin to reduce drag. The latter mode of carriage can restrict angular coverage; Wild Weasel F-105Gs had an ECM pod scabbed on each side of the fuselage. In all cases we have only a limited amount of energy we can pump out, though some pods are self-contained by having an integral windmill-driven generator. When an EA-6B has five pods with windmills running its speed at sea level is reduced from 651 to 610 mph. In any case, we want to use all our energy effectively; we do not want to waste it, and advertise our presence, by pumping out high-power emissions either on the wrong wavelength or in the wrong direction. Accordingly, our ECM must be linked with an effective TWS, either automatically or by telling the pilot as much as possible about each threat and letting him take decisions. As we have seen, automation can be dangerous.

The basic active ECM at RF wavelengths is the jammer. The simplest jammers, often called barrage jammers, merely blast out high power on selected wavelengths. They broadcast the energy, typically over the entire forward or rear hemisphere. Stand-off jammers (SOJ) are carried in dedicated EW aircraft and, together with Wild Weasel SEAD aircraft, do their best to neutralize the enemy defences. Deception jamming, or DECM (also interpreted as defensive ECM) which was coming into use in 1945, is the cleverest kind of RF ECM. Instead of being a 'brute force and ignorance' technique, it uses the available energy very carefully to create the maximum confusion. There is not room to describe the techniques — such as range-gate pull-off, velocity-gate pull-off, inverse conical scan, swept square wave and main-lobe blanking, but all are designed to offer the most effective interference with individual hostile radars. Each jamming transmission is 'set on' to the enemy emitter in timing, in angular direction and in wavelength and waveform. Different modes can counter CW, monopulse, PD or other radars, and most can give a false indication of target location, speed or track. You could write a massive book about it.

Pods hung on standard store carriers have many advantages. They are independent of the aircraft and so can be carried or left behind, replaced in minutes if faulty, removed for major modification or even, in some recent types, reconfigured very quickly to meet different threats whilst hung on the aircraft. Almost all incorporate their own digital processor whose software can be reprogrammed on the flightline. Virtually every pod incorporates its own cooling system. Some operate only in preset modes, but the majority can also operate in a power-managed mode to use the available electrical power to the greatest effect in dense electronic environments. Almost all are so-called dual-mode jammers (ie, noise or deception), and a surprising number are of the Janus or double-ended type, able to jam just as well to the rear as ahead.

One of the first mass-produced ECM pods was the Westinghouse ALQ-101, designed in 1969 to

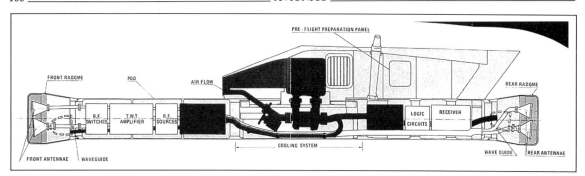

jam all known RF threats in South-East Asia. This was naturally progressively developed into successive configurations each identified by a (V) version number. The original small ventral gondola for the receiver antennas was extended until in 101(V)8 it extended the entire length of the pod. This gave a significant increase in internal volume with minimal effect on cross-section and drag. This arrangement was adopted from the start with the next-generation ALQ-119, and in today's ALQ-131 it has been combined with a high degree of modularity. The structure of the 131 is a deep I-beam carrying a supporting tray along the bottom. Along the top are the ram-air ducts for the Freon liquid cooling system, which consumes no power. The pod volume can accommodate 'full canisters' each 42 in long and

The French Remora active jammer is packaged in a very slim pod, with transmitting antennas at both ends. The weight is 386 lb. (Thomson-CSF)

'half canisters' 21 in long, each housing up to three equipment modules and enabling line crews to arrange the pod in any of sixteen configurations to match any mission requirement or profile. Underneath is the C/I (control and interface) module, with an MLV (memory loader verifier) with which the digital processor can quickly be reprogrammed. The C/I module also contains the high-speed waveform generator capable of supply-

The ALQ-131 was the first jammer pod to be filled with quickly replaceable modules (see text). (Westinghouse)

1. RF Module – Transmitter No. 3
2. Transmitter control module – Transmitter No. 1
3. RF Module – Transmitter No. 1
4. High voltage power supply – Transmitter No. 1
5. Structure cooling system
6. Aft transmitter module
7. Transmit/control module – Transmitter No. 3
8. High voltage power supply – Transmitter No. 3
9. Covers
10. High voltage power supply – Transmitter No. 2
11. RF Module – Transmitter No. 2
12. Transmitter control module – Transmitter No. 2
13. Receiver antenna
14. Interface control module
15. Forward transmitter module
16. Transition module

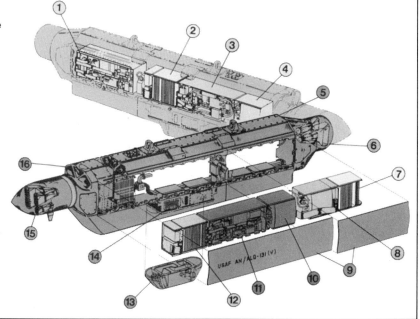

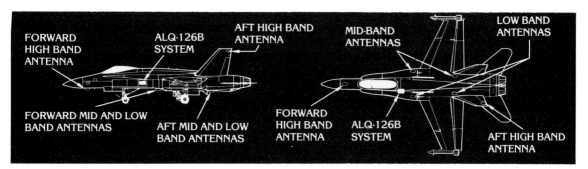

Above *Location of major elements of the Sanders ALQ-126B in the F/A-18A Hornet. Operating alone or integrated with the ALR-67 RWR (see photo, p. 165), this is a programmable power-managed DECM (defensive ECM) system housed in two LRUs, total weight 190 lb.*

Right *Block diagram of an integrated airborne self-protection system, the SPS-65. It covers all frequencies from low band to 18 GHz, managing the outputs in direction and power.* (Elisra)

ing up to 40 waveforms simultaneously. Receivers are in a small gondola, and the three sizes of horn antennas are grouped in radomes at front and rear. This pod, probably the most important in Western air forces today, weighs around 570 lb.

Many modern combat aircraft, including Soviet fighters and the A-6, F-14, F-15, F/A-18, Mirage 2000 and F-111, have internal ECM self-protection systems. All have gone through various upgrades, none more so than the F-15, whose current F-15E multirole version has numerous changes. The antennas under the nose are replaced by flush antennas in the wing-root leading edges, similar to those seen on Soviet aircraft for twenty years, while to make room for the second cockpit the original Band 1 and Band 2 jammers are replaced by a broadband 'Band 1.5' installation. Thus, in this aircraft there are two RWR antennas and two jammer antennas facing aft and two RWR and two jammer antennas facing forward. For the immediate future the most important Western ECM system (by far) will be the ITT/Westinghouse ALQ-165 ASPJ (airborne self-protection jammer). Except in the

AV-8B, where there is considered to be no room, the ALQ-165 will be installed internally, in all new US Navy/Marines aircraft and in many USAF types beginning with the F-16. The system started production in 1988 weighing 237 lb and with frequency coverage 0.7-18 GHz. The A-6F/G, if produced, and F-14D will have an extra 85-lb augmentation set extending cover up to 35 GHz, and up to 140 GHz is a long-term goal.

For the period after 1995 Congress has directed that all US forces should jointly sponsor INEWS/ICNIA (integrated EW system, integrated CNI avionics). ICNIA is primarily a scheme for integrating all the com/nav/ident systems into one compact group which should be roughly half the weight and bulk of current equipment. INEWS, initially for the YF-22, YF-23 and A-12, has been developed since 1983 by teams representing almost the whole of the US EW industry. The objective is an all-can-do system able to operate 'from DC to light', in other words at every kind of EM frequency. Its technology will include MMICs (monolithic microwave ICs) requiring voltage about one-

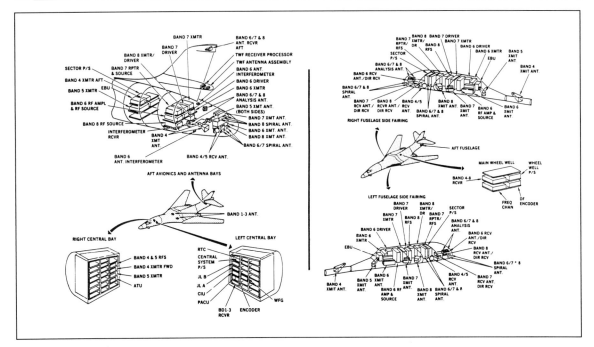

thousandth that of current TWT amplifiers, yet able to put out an effective radiated power of more than 10 kW through advanced array antennas. A typical INEWS weight is guessed at 550 lb, and the programme cost estimates range up to $50 billion by 2005, with initial production due in 1993.

The capability of INEWS will in almost all respects handsomely surpass that of the Eaton ALQ-161A installed in the B-1B. This is easily the biggest, and in many respects the most capable, of all known airborne EW systems actually in service, though it has already cost about $3 billion and is still in need of modification in order to attain the specified performance. The main system comprises 108 LRUs weighing, exclusive of about a ton of cables, over 5,400 lb and consuming 120 kW when in full operation. There are four main segments: the RFS/ECMS (RF surveillance and ECM system); the TWF (tail warning function); the ASQ-184 OAS/DMS (offensive avionics system, defensive management system); and the EXCM (expendable countermeasures). Thanks to the sheer volume and electric power available, this vast system has almost total coverage, in all directions, from 0.5-10 GHz. The entire TWF and EW system is integrated via 1553B buses, with batteries of high-speed computers in overall management. Line drawings give some idea of the all-round cover of the receivers and

The Rockwell B-1B has by far the biggest and most comprehensive defensive avionics system ever put into service. These diagrams show location of major elements of the RFS/ECMS. Despite a multitude of contractors, there were still problems in 1989.

transmitters. So fast are the processors that, in a split second, dozens of new hostile emissions can be detected, analysed, located and then jammed in the most energy-efficient manner. Thus, the response to each threat is virtually real-time. Jamming in the higher bands is transmitted from phased-array antennas in the left and right wing roots and tailcone; each is electronically steerable through 120° in azimuth and 90° in elevation. Alongside are mounted the quadrantal-horn antennas used for lower-band jamming. The TWF, in the upper tailcone aft of the fin/tailplane junction, is a PD radar which detects, identifies and locates hostile aircraft or missiles approaching from astern, and keeps the DSO (defensive systems officer) continuously informed on the situation. The DSO chooses which EXCM to fire from the eight dispensers, each of which can be loaded with twelve large flares or up to 120 chaff cartridges. (It is surprising that the B-1B should not have a bulk chaff cutter/dispenser.)

For many years industry has worked on dispensed active jammers, but it is only since 1980 that microelectronics has made possible small payloads with an attractive combination of bulk/weight, performance and cost. So far as the author knows, the only expendable jammer in widespread service is the Sanders AM-6988A POET (primed oscillator expendable transponder), which is contained in a standard 36-mm-diameter cartridge compatible with many dispensers including the ALE-29 and -39. After being fired from its tube POET uses a single antenna to receive the hostile signal of interest and broadcast a greatly amplified return, thus diverting attention from our aircraft. POET's successor is Gen-X (generic expendable), a Texas Instruments product ($117 million R&D contract in August 1987) notable for having three flick-open airbrakes. Compared with POET, Gen-X has greater power and much wider frequency-band coverage.

So far I have hardly mentioned the homing method used by about 90 per cent of the world's AAMs: IR. Obviously, IRCM has to consist of some form of heat source, more attractive to the missile than our own aircraft, which can be ejected overboard. But it has also been found that an IR seeker in a missile can be countered by sending out intense IR pulses with a PRF carefully chosen to confuse the seeker and make it 'break lock'. Such a

EXCM (expendable countermeasures) in the B-1B are entirely housed in cartridges, fired upwards from two quadruple groups of dispensers.

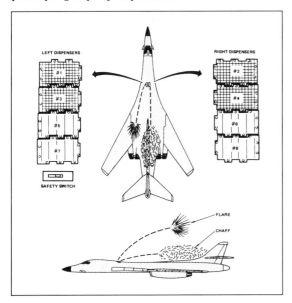

POET, seen here in production at Sanders, is one of a rare species: the expendable jammer. Output reached 25,000 annually.

pulsed IRCM jammer does not attract the missile — quite the opposite — so it can be mounted on our own aircraft.

Early IRCM jammers, in the Vietnam period, almost all used the so-called 'hot brick' type of IR source. In this a block of ceramic, such as alumina (Al_2O_3) would be heated to incandescence, usually by a propane burner. In the Sanders ALQ-147, carried by the OV-1D, fuel from the aircraft's tanks is burned with ram air; the hot-source emission is then modulated mechanically to produce the jamming signal, a covert filter being added to eliminate visible light. This IRCM jammer can be mounted on the aft end of an external tank. IRCMs for helicopters usually resemble small lighthouses, giving a 360° output and mounted either on the top or bottom of the fuselage. Some are hot-brick type, while BAe produce one with an intense electric lamp, a graphite element in a sapphire envelope, spun at high speed to direct the beam successively through the 16 surrounding windows. Of course, electrically heated IRCMs need a very heavy current.

By far the most common type of IRCM is the

The Sanders ALQ-147(A) was designed to provide IRCM protection to aircraft without high-power electric supplies. The nose is streamlined, ram air coming in underneath to leave through the filter emitter (right).

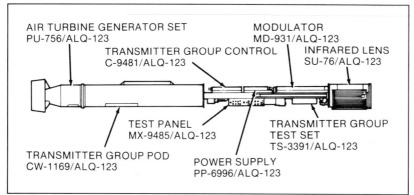

AIR TURBINE GENERATOR SET
PU-756/ALQ-123

MODULATOR
MD-931/ALQ-123

TRANSMITTER GROUP CONTROL
C-9481/ALQ-123

INFRARED LENS
SU-76/ALQ-123

TEST PANEL
MX-9485/ALQ-123

TRANSMITTER GROUP
TEST SET
TS-3391/ALQ-123

TRANSMITTER GROUP POD
CW-1169/ALQ-123

POWER SUPPLY
PP-6996/ALQ-123

Loral's ALQ-123 is an electric IRCM pod, but to avoid the heavy drain on the host aircraft it has its own generator driven by a shrouded ram-air turbine on the nose. Here the internals have been withdrawn from the pod.

flare. Most look and behave like fireworks, though their packaging has to fit standard countermeasure dispensers, the flares often being loaded in a mix alongside chaff and even active jammers. Usually a cockpit indicator shows what type of payload is in each cell, in case the crew wish to dispense manually; alternatively cells can be fired automatically by the TWS. Publicity pictures and videos have shown flares being fired from both sides of aircraft at a very rapid rate. This looks impressive, but gets through the self-protection EXCM in a few seconds. In a real war all we have to do is fire one flare at a time, and have the next one ready when the first burns out.

Flares are made in such numbers that their performance is closely repeatable. On being fired, the propulsion charge ejects the priming composition and flare pellet from the case so that the bright flare follows an exact trajectory. Full spectral brilliance is achieved in about 0.4 s, the radiant intensity thereafter falling by half in 2–3 s and to near zero in 4–6 s. Ignition and build-up has to be very rapid to ensure that the bright source is still well within the hostile seeker's FOV. The flare has to generate a

new power centroid (geometric centre of all IR sources 'seen' by the missile) in comparison with which radiation from the aircraft is feeble. This centroid progressively moves away from the aircraft, luring the missile with it. Flare ejection direction must be such that, when the missile hits the flare or the flare burns out, the aircraft is no longer in the missile FOV, or the missile would simply reacquire its true target. For a missile approaching at the same level this normally means ejection downwards, and it is interesting to find such aircraft as the F-14, MiG-29 and B-1B ejecting flares upwards. In flight at minimum altitude you have little option.

Flare radiance varies to some degree with airspeed, altitude and other factors. Typical grains, for example a composition of magnesium and tetrafluorethylene, burn at about 2,000°C. This gives a peak emission intensity at 1.5μ or less, whereas that of typical jetpipes is somewhere over 4μ. Missile designers naturally try to incorporate ECCM or IRCCM, and the most modern heat-seeking missiles continuously sample two wavebands, one at around 2μ and the other at around $3-5\mu$. If the intensity in the short-

Left *Sanders have delivered over 1,400 ALQ-144 IRCM self-protection systems for helicopters. They resemble an omni-directional beacon with a modulated output.*

Below *Typical performance of an IR flare (decoy 1 in × 1 in). Of course the fine detail would vary from one flare to another, but all would give exactly the same gross outline. Vertical scale is measured in kilowatts per steradian of solid angle. Horizontal scale in seconds. (Pains-Wessex (Schermuly))*

Bottom *Typical flare spectra, contrasted with that from a non-afterburning fast jet. The difference is a key to an important IRCCM (counter-counter-measure) method.*

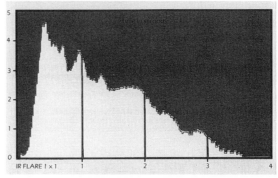

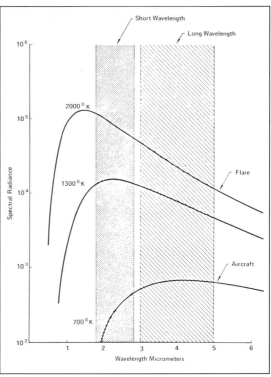

wavelength band suddenly becomes much higher than that in the LW band the missile ceases to home on the source and goes into a 'coast' mode for (typically) 5 s.

Though today every military aircraft, fixed-wing or helicopter, must be fully equipped with EW devices in order to survive, many aircraft are now flying whose sole purpose is EW. They fall into various categories. The most diverse are the Elint platforms (also see Chapter 8), which can range from small fast jets through large turboprop transports to small piston-engined machines. In the Soviet Union the vast efforts being made in the field of what that country calls Radio Electronic Combat have resulted in the conversion of over 1,000 large aircraft — about half jet bombers and the other half turboprop transports — to carry heavy, varied and powerful loads of receivers, D/F receivers, analysers, locators, recorders and other devices to ensure that intelligence on NATO, Chinese, Israeli and other electronics is updated daily.

In contrast, a few aircraft combine Elint receivers with attack, and especially with anti-radar, capability. The latest is the Luftwaffe Tornado ECR (electronic combat and reconnaissance), which replaces the guns and certain other items with a FLIR, IIS (IR imaging system) and ELS (emitter locator system), whilst at the same time carrying AGM-88 HARM anti-radar missiles. Only two of the latter can be carried, whereas Tornados can carry nine of the newer and much more compact Alarms, as selected by the RAF. The latter service has not ordered dedicated EW Tornados, but instead is upgrading regular Tornado GR.1 aircraft with a 1553B bus and 128K computer for instant response to threats and the ability to reprogram Alarms after launch, for example while they are in a para-suspended search mode. The advantage of the

Left *Two antenna groups and a processor comprise the HLWE (helicopter laser warning equipment) produced in West Germany by Standard Elektrik Lorenz. It detects, identifies and pinpoints laser threats.*

Below *Greatly simplified block diagram of the ALQ-99 stand-off tactical jamming system installed in the EA-6B Prowler. Receiver antennas (left) are in the fin pod, while the active jammers are housed in up to five externally hung pods (below).* (Eaton AIL)

RAF's policy, partly made possible by the greater sophistication of the Alarm missile, is that the Tornados remain available for normal attack missions.

Among Western dedicated EW aircraft the leaders are the EA-6B Prowler and EF-111A Raven. As noted earlier, these both carry versions of the same tactical jamming system, the Eaton ALQ-99. This is a large integrated system which receives almost every kind of hostile RF and, automatically or under crew command, counters it by various forms of deception or barrage jamming. Most of the receiver antennas are in a large pod at the top of the fin. In the US Navy EA-6B a crew of four is carried, three of whom are ECM Officers. One is tasked with navigation, communications, defensive ECM and chaff dispensing, and the other

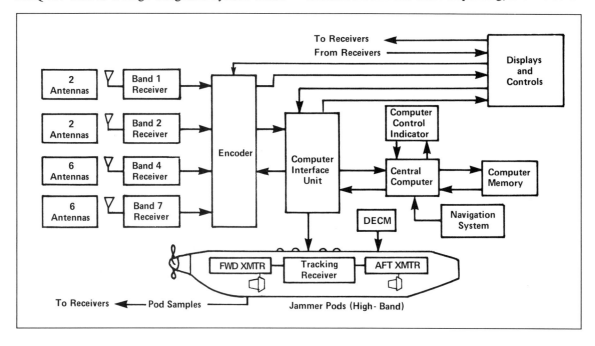

two (in the rear) with management of the ALQ-99, whose jamming assets are housed in detachable external pods each with its own windmill-driven generator. Originally each pod jammed on one waveband, but since 1984 each pod has been able to jam in two bands simultaneously. EA-6Bs are being further upgraded with larger fin-cap antenna groups and extra receivers under the rear fuselage. The USAF EF-111A has the later ALQ-99E which, because of its high degree of automation needs no extra crew. The main jammer transmitters and antennas are grouped in a pallet in what was previously the weapon bay and in a canoe radome along the underside of the fuselage. Upgrades for this big system were cancelled in May 1988, and the USAF is now studying the addition of external pods and/or expendable decoys.

The interference with Luftwaffe ground/air communications 45 years ago has gradually developed into C³CM: command, control and communications counter-measures. Like most aspects of EW, the chief nations (in the West, at least) appear to harbour the strange belief that their own C³ are secure, whereas they can interfere as they please with any potential enemy's. So far as is known, the RAF no longer has a capability in this field. The chief USAF platform is the EC-130H Compass Call, which has the necessary enormous jamming power to be effective from long stand-off distances. The longer wavelengths are jammed from antennas surrounding the tail. For short-range jamming over the battlefield the US Army uses the EH-60A and EH-1H helicopters carrying different generations of Quick Fix (such as ALQ-151), able to interfere with SAM guidance as well as C³.

This leaves to be discussed two of the most exciting aspects of EW, about which little could usefully be reported until recently: 'stealth' and 'directed-energy' weapons. Oddly, both have long histories. When in 1935 Sir Robert Watson Watt outlined the principles of radar, he did so in response to an Air Ministry enquiry about whether directed-energy weapons were possible. At the same time he suggested that the designers of future bombers would do their best to design for minimum RCS (radar cross section). Perhaps one day we shall learn how it came about that 'the designers of future bombers' did no such thing, so that the concept of an LO (low observables) aircraft seems to have been ignored until the late 1970s!

Stealth technology is widely associated in the public mind with RCS. Certainly, when the aircraft is far away, beyond visual range, RCS is the most important single factor. As it gets closer its IR signature becomes important, and perhaps more important than RCS. Within a range of perhaps five miles visual signature (appearance) and aural signature (what it sounds like) must also be taken into account. One has only to think of a fast flypast at full throttle by any modern combat jet to appreciate that merely reducing (even eliminating) its RCS would be pointless. We have to make it silent, invisible and the same temperature as the sky background. In the present state of the art all these objectives are unattainable; we just have to do the best we can.

Like all objectives in all branches of technology, you can do what you can pay for, and in achieving it you invariably pay penalties elsewhere. For many years it has been blindingly obvious that there is little point in trying to develop *any* military aircraft that might possibly encounter the enemy unless it is a totally stealth design with powered-lift STOVL performance. Both requirements exact penalties in complexity, cost, performance and — at least in the case of stealth — in reliability and maintainability. Stealth design almost certainly rules out supersonic performance, is bound to increase basic airframe weight, and makes the whole aircraft extremely complex. The fact that it is worth striving for shows its overwhelming importance.

The author cannot explain why probably 90 per cent of the unclassified column-inches devoted to stealth design have addressed the reduction of RCS, which is (relatively) the easy part. Maybe it is simply because making aircraft silent, invisible and devoid of hot parts is so difficult that nobody has much to say about it.

For the fullest unclassified treatment of RCS the reader is referred to *Radar Cross Section* by E.F. Knott and others, published by Artech House, Massachusetts; as an indication, the chapter in this book most relevant to stealth, on Radar Absorbers, lists 47 references to further reading. The first RAM (radar absorbent material) was devised in Germany very quickly in late 1942, and applied to U-boat snorkels and periscopes. RAM can be broadband or resonant, and can obtain its properties by mechanical design or by surface layers or coatings. Basically we try to minimize reflections and absorb the waves into the material, and this is usually achieved by providing a lossy matching network —

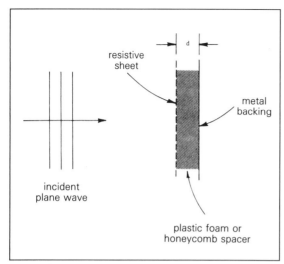

A Salisbury screen, one of the fundamentals of RAM construction.

a volume whose size is related to expected enemy wavelengths — between free space and an inner conductive surface. Probably the oldest and simplest form is the Salisbury screen, comprising a thin dielectric outer skin spaced distance d away from a perfectly reflective inner skin, where d is an odd multiple of one-quarter wavelength of the expected radar. The space between the two skins is filled with a honeycomb or low-density foam. We can see at once that aircraft made like this would easily be damaged by 600-knot hailstones or hob-nailed boots.

Other RAMs include multilayer dielectrics, hair mats, magnetic types and circuit-analog forms. The multilayers have conductivity varying from layer to layer, and though overall thickness ideally should be about 0.3 wavelength (which against big surveillance radars means several inches) the AN series of graded dielectrics marketed by Emerson & Cuming, probably No 1 among specialized RAM manufacturers, are mostly only about 30 mm (1.2 in) thick, because they are tailored to short-wavelength fighter radars. Hair mats are just what the name suggests: thick, almost felt-like sheet made of plastic netting with a conductive coating, conductivity increasing from the outer to the inner surface. Magnetic RAM combines dielectric with magnetic losses, almost always using ferrites or carbonyl iron, a fine pure powder. The extremely finely divided magnetic material can be bonded on in

the form of tiles, usually glued on in flexible (often rubber based) sheets. Though flexible they are difficult to bond to lumpy or irregular surfaces, and their use partly explains the fact that so much of the Lockheed F-117A exterior surface is single-curvature (straight lines). A large and growing number of firms are marketing sprayed-on magnetic RAM, often called 'iron paint'. The heavy magnetic dust is suspended in an epoxy vehicle which after spraying mainly evaporates, to leave a tightly bonded surface to reduce travelling and creeping waves and give large non-specular reductions. One problem, at least in the past, has been more or less rapid and permanent degradation in performance caused by rain and subsequent rusting, typical iron oxides being non-magnetic. Many recent Eccosorb NZ series at least partly overcome this problem. Circuit-analog sheets comprise meshes, millions of repeated dipoles, slots, crosses and many other kinds of repetitive pattern, which are usually inserted between structural skins.

Apart from RAM, RCS can be very greatly reduced by suitably adjusting the aircraft's gross shape. The designer must eliminate large flat surfaces which might be 'square on' to a radar, and especially junctions between vertical sides and the undersurfaces of wings or horizontal tails. If a radar can look up an inlet duct and see the engines's fan or first-stage compressor the echo is likely to be outstanding. And we naturally must avoid helping the enemy by using a highly radar-reflective paint, such as the anti-flash white so thoughtlessly sprayed on RAF V-bombers thirty years ago.

Lo-RCS structure reaches by far its highest level to date in the Northrop B-2. This has an external shape only slightly compromised by stealth considerations, the chief area of conflict being the leading edge of the wing (and head-on the B-2 is virtually all leading edge). The wing profile is most unusual, with a flattish undersurface meeting a down-curved upper surface along a sharp edge with no radius giving echoes. The upper skin from this sharp edge to a point 3 ft aft, and from the tip to a point 6 ft inboard, is shiny black, contrasting with the low-vis blue/grey elsewhere. This leading edge must be one of the most complex structures in any airframe yet built.

As other aspects of stealth are non-avionic, this leaves just DE weapons. Directed-energy is what fiction writers eighty years ago called death rays — in other words, beams of energy that can kill or

Sintered ferrite materials are often very good at absorbing EM radiation over certain specific bands of frequency. We are still seeking the dream material. (Emerson & Cuming)

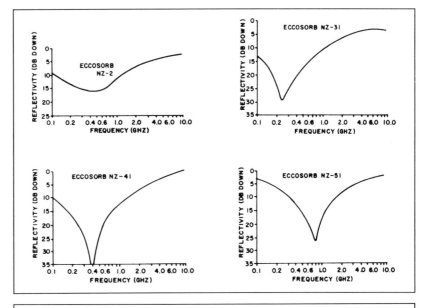

Circuit-analog RAM can be positive or negative; ie, the strips, for example, could be actual strips or gaps cut from a sheet.

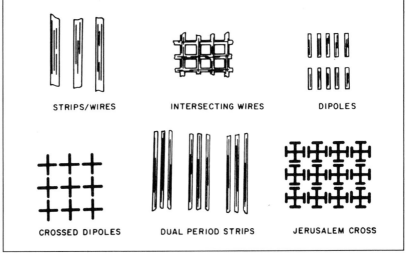

Section through a hypothetical wing showing possible RAM structures. The profile is rather traditional, but the B-2 has an even stranger section with a sharp edge at the junction of the leading edge and undersurface. (Rockwell International)

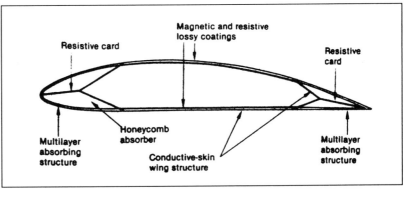

cause material damage at a distance. In the twenty years between the World Wars the British Air Ministry received 31 letters from inventors claiming to have such a device. An official requirement was therefore written: to be acceptable the ray has to kill a sheep at 300 ft. An official history records 'No sheep was so much as singed'. But when Dr T.H. Maiman of Hughes switched on the first laser on 15 May 1960 we entered a world of new possibilities. Because laser light is coherent, it can be sent out in a narrow beam which retains its intensity for thousands of kilometres. Lasers could form a communications link between Earth and Moon, for example. Thus, the technology for a death ray was at last to hand. All that was needed was the construction of lasers with about the same power as Niagara Falls.

The USAF began working with lasers in 1961, and by September 1963 its Weapons Lab Laser Division had a team working on possible laser weapons. At first carbon-dioxide lasers showed the greatest promise, and in 1965 a 500-W example burned through a firebrick in 5 s; trouble was, this laser was 44 ft long. But the technology developed rapidly. By 1971 a much more compact GDL (gas dynamic laser) had been built at the Weapons Lab with an output of over 100 kW. Its operation involved laser action between mirrors on each side of a nozzle passing a supersonic flow of white-hot nitrogen and carbon dioxide. By 1973 the lab, and many others — notably including the Soviet Union — had lasers of the GDL, shock tube and other types with powers up to 0.5 MW. Several were tested from a dorsal turret in an NKC-135A (55-3123).

A big spurt to DE weapons came with the SDI (Strategic Defense Initiative) in 1983. New types of laser were tested, including such dual-gas systems as hydrogen/fluorine, deuterium/fluorine and oxygen/iodine, and eximer (excited dimer), free-electron and X-ray patterns. Relatively conventional chemical lasers have been built with output up to at least 25 MW power. Meanwhile, particle-beam and KE weapons have been added. In the former, beams of particles are used, shot out with fantastic energy such as 50 MeV (million electron volts) from giant accelerators. KE (kinetic energy) weapons use actual pellets of material, shot from a novel electromagnetic gun at a speed of about 27,800 ft/s. The immediate objective is a gun firing sixty 'bullets' per second at a speed of 62 miles per second.

10
AVIONICS FOR SAFETY

Probably the earliest and most widespread use of a radar technique, at least in civil aircraft, was the radio altimeter. This can just as accurately be called a radar altimeter. This is one of the few radar applications that is technically simple. The altimeter has merely to measure the range looking straight down at the Earth's surface. There may only be a single point at the shortest range (it might be the tip of a tree leaf) but within a range spread of a few hundred feet the echoing area may be two or three square miles, so the strength of the return is tremendous. Consequently the radar can be very small, of low power, with a broad beam. There is no need for high antenna directivity; all we want is the range to the nearest source of strong return.

Clearly, the accuracy increases as height is reduced, which is just what we want. Almost invariably, radio altimeters use CW in the C-band (4–8 GHz). This waveband was originally selected because the altimeter could use a cheap triode transmitter valve (tube). Such waves have no problem with atmospheric attenuation, and as directivity is unimportant the antenna can be very small. The ranging is achieved by pulse methods or alternatively by FM, in which transmitter frequency rises at a uniform rate, falls back to the start value and then repeats, giving a sawtooth output. Length of slope is much greater than the round-trip time. In most FM radars the slope has to be shallow, but in an altimeter the slope can be very steep, which means accuracy can be excellent. The fact that altimeters look straight down at very low power means that their emissions are unlikely to be detected by enemies. Of course, whereas barometric altimeters merely measure atmospheric pressure outside the aircraft, which gives a good general idea of height above the datum to which the instrument is set, a radio altimeter measures the actual clearance between the ground and the aircraft, which among mountains is a totally different measurement. But such altimeters are used mainly at very low levels, as for example during the landing approach.

Next to altimeters, the oldest use of radar techniques in civil aircraft, dating from 1946, is to look straight ahead and warn of storms, cloud turbulence, precipitation and, usually, mountains and other hazards. Today such equipments are usually simply called weather radars, abbreviated to WXR. Until now we have wanted our radar to ignore precipitation (rain, snow and hail) and see through clouds and fog in order to detect various kinds of target. In contrast, a weather radar's first task is to 'see' different kinds of weather, so we choose a pulsed radar with a wavelength carefully selected to give the best picture of the weather ahead. If our radar has no other role we can insert an MTI circuit to suppress any returns from the ground, but most such radars, and 100 per cent of those in commercial transports, can operate in ground map and terrain avoidance modes. Thanks to the ceaseless improvement in microelectronics it is possible today for a privately owned light twin to have a much more versatile radar, with far superior picture clarity, than the biggest commercial jets of the 1950s.

Weather radars are almost always designed primarily to detect raindrops, even when seen through 100 miles of cloud. In general, the size of raindrops or hailstones gives an accurate measure of the vertical velocity of the air around them, in other words of the gust velocity and turbulence. This is what we are interested in; nobody bothers much about 'weather', but aircraft structures can be catastrophically broken by flying at high speed through violent vertical gusts (which have to be alternately upwards and downwards). In the days of piston engines weather radars helped prevent airsickness; today this malady is almost unknown, but a WXR can prevent a wing from coming off.

Above *Surely the neatest radar ever — the Collins TWR-850 turbulence detection set is a low-power solid-state package (no magnetron) weighing less than 20 lb.*

Below *A typical WXR display (Collins WXR-700), showing a clear storm band about 20 nm ahead. Digital doppler shows the most severe turbulence as spots of pink, which are sometimes nowhere near the main red storm areas. Maximum range of this radar is 320 nm.*

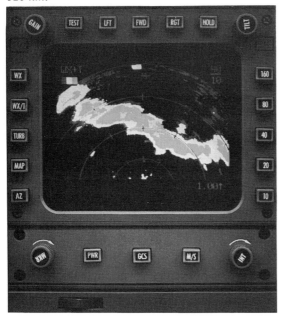

Accordingly, we pick a wavelength suited to the job. We have to do more than merely detect the rain or hail. The precipitation is a function of droplet or stone size and their density (how many there are in a given sky volume). Together these give the strength of the radar return, and we must design the radar to sense the gradient of this return, in other words the rate of change of the return with look angle and range. Thus we can generate a picture which indicates which areas are clear and where there is intense precipitation, and especially the contours along which there are abrupt changes in precipitation rate, where we may expect to find violent windshear and vertical gusts.

Almost all modern weather radars operate in X-band at such frequencies as 9,345 or 9,375 MHz. Slotted waveguide flat-plate antennas are virtually universal, scanning at about sixteen looks/min over a chosen azimuth, such as 45° or 60° to either side of dead ahead. The antenna is usually stabilized within the kind of manoeuvre limits to be expected of civil aircraft, and can be deliberately aimed vertically through an elevation range of about ± 40°. Sidelobes are suppressed as far as possible. The operating frequency is partly a compromise between penetrating too far through a storm (and failing to notice it), and getting such high returns from the near precipitation that the beam fails to penetrate any further. It is also partly a compromise between antenna size and the space available. C-band used to be favoured for large aircraft, but today this is usually just an option; for example the Collins WXR-700 series offer C-band 5.44 GHz as an alternative to X-band 9.33 (9,330 MHz).

Since 1970 a growing proportion of WXRs have been provided with multicolour displays. Usually a shadow-mask tube (Chapter 13) is used, with three electron guns, green for harmless precipitation, yellow for significant areas, and red for severe turbulence. In the WXR-700, the Bendix RDR-4A and several other WXRs, a new method of using a doppler technique to measure not rainfall but changes in rainfall velocity makes possible a direct measurement of turbulence, which is presented in magenta. Instead of requiring the pilot to interpret radar echoes by shape, intensity and gradient, this actually shows regions to be avoided, which are often in unexpected places. The popular (2,600 sold 1979-89) WXR-700 airline radar has an unusual number of other features. PAC (path attenuation compensation) automatically compensates the return signal to allow for attenuation by intervening precipitation, in order to maintain calibration and correct signal colours. A yellow arc is displayed at a particular range and over a particular azimuth spread beyond which attenuation is so severe that no further compensation is possible. A low-noise pre-amp RF receiver can give improved long-range performance and tilt management. The doppler processing can be switched to eliminate all ground clutter, which would otherwise mask light precipitation. A sector scan feature enables the operator to switch the antenna to scan a 90° sector ahead (45° left/right), or all to the left or right of the flight path, for faster updating of areas of interest. Alien interference, caused by other aircraft radars within the scanned band of sky, can be eliminated by an AI rejection mode. On the other hand, rejecting alien echoes could eliminate the important ability of a WXR to warn of impending collisions. This subject is addressed later in this chapter.

Radar is by no means the only method of detecting regions of dangerous turbulence. CAT (clear-air turbulence) almost never shows up on a WXR, but can be sustained and extremely uncomfortable. Normally encountered at jet cruising heights, especially near the boundaries of jet streams, CAT can impose quite severe and erratic vertical and lateral accelerations which eat into fatigue life and upset passengers. Research into detection of CAT

began in about 1962, and concentrated on lasers, electrostatic-field detectors and IR radiometers. Lasers have shown correlation between CAT and discontinuities in populations of micron-sized aerosols and particles, and have also proved to have some capability in mapping the area of turbulence in the wake of large aircraft carriers, but at present the only real hope for CAT detection appears to be the radiometer. There are significant differences in temperature between severe turbulence and surrounding atmosphere, and the difficulty is measuring it with sufficient reliability and definition several miles ahead, so that if necessary a 747 could take gentle avoiding action.

Another completely different method of detecting storm turbulence is the Stormscope. These are four related systems which all rely on the fact that the shearing action between intense convective air currents generate electrical discharges — a form of localized lightning — which in turn broadcast RF energy. Stormscopes are passive D/F receivers which detect and analyse each discharge. Azimuth is determined as for a radio beacon, and range 'by fingerprinting in accord with the behaviour of lightning discharges'. The result is a bright green dot on the display (which can be 60° left/right or 360°). Each dot is held 4 min, the population of dots showing severity of activity. When the 257th dot appears, the first dot is erased, and so on. 3M has developed

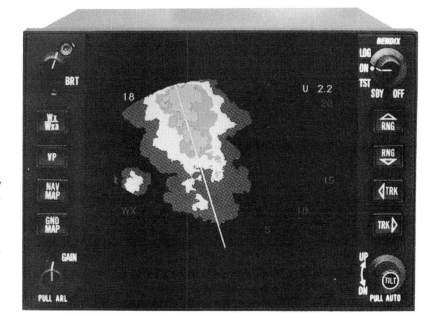

Bendix/King have introduced a neat colour radar with a useful new feature. By pressing the button VP you convert the plan display shown here to a vertical profile, a vertical slice through whatever is of interest. Probably all general-aviation radars will have this feature.

an interface which puts the dots on Sperry colour radars. As the received signals are LF, a Stormscope works just as well before take-off — which may be delayed in consequence.

Another important safety task of avionics is the avoidance of collisions. Clearly, we may be liable to two types of collision: with other aerial traffic and with the ground. Other aerial traffic includes birds, and, though these constitute a severe hazard to all kinds of aircraft from 747s to low-level attackers, the author knows of no efforts to avoid collisions apart from trying to scare birds away from airfields. In the case of the 747 the problem is principally on take-off; here a mere warning would be useless, unless the engine inlets featured some kind of emergency anti-ingestion option. Even at cruising height however many big jets have suffered severe damage at heights as high as FL395 from kites, whistling swans, geese and other large species. On no occasion did the crew have any warning. In the low-level attack mission the problem is much more severe and frequent. In the author's view, though the software must be assembled with exceptional care, this problem is amenable to avionic attack, and single or multiple birdstrikes could be significantly reduced and might become almost a thing of the past. Though target RCS is small, target V is relatively low.

Avoiding actually flying into the ground has been covered in earlier sections on TFRs and TARs. The point was made that masts and supporting guy wires are a major hazard which, despite their small reflective area, must be detected well in advance. Since 1972 a vast amount of work has been done on dedicated sensors to protect battlefield helicopters against such collisions in particular, and all obstacle impacts in general. The system designer is faced with a wish to use a non-emissive passive system, but has concluded usually that an active system is essential. One of only two passive ones known to the author is Martin Marietta's Fulvision, a commercial product developed from the Apache's TADS/PNVS and using a sensitive thermal imager. Martin claims this 'sees wires and poles at night better than the eye can see them during the day'. This is interesting, because the wire presents an extremely narrow target — either near horizontal or near vertical — at almost the same temperature as the background.

Every obstacle-warning radar known to the author operates in the millimetric range, the usual

frequency being 94 GHz. This is a compromise between atmospheric attenuation, the effect of rain, and target discrimination. After a lot of work at 60 GHz, MBB appears to have settled on 94, and this is also the frequency of the Thomson-CSF Romeo (*radar ondes millimetriques d'evitement d'obstacles*). This uses CW at only 1 W power, too weak for most enemy receivers to detect, but still capable of reliably sensing cables at 1,640 ft (500 m).

Several important authorities, including the USA Avionics Lab at Ft Monmouth and United Technologies Research Center (for Sikorsky), consider lidar (laser radar) to be the best bet, and progress is being made at near-optical wavelengths. Two major programmes are Cotaws (collision and obstacle/terrain avoidance warning system) and Lotaws (L for laser), the most common lasers being YAG and CO_2. The first Ft Monmouth study concluded that PRF had to be 500 KHz, but such a rate poses many problems. Almost all today's lasers use a PRF from 40 to 60 KHz, and in several installations the laser is made to look ahead for wires and also project a second beam down and ahead for doppler navigation and hover control. In generally adverse weather today's systems have to detect power cables at a mile (1,600 m) and a field telephone line at 1,640 ft (500 m). The GEC Avionics Locus is packaged in a pod suitable for fast jets. It is being added to RAF Tornado GR.Is in the MLU (mid-life update).

Curiously, helicopters are never fitted with simple cable-cutters such as were standard on RAF bombers in World War 2, though a few have primitive knives above, and occasionally also below, the nose. The lifesaving warning systems for helicopters are of recent origin, almost all having been designed since 1984. In contrast, the GPWS (ground proximity warning system) for fixed-wing machines, and especially for commercial transport and executive aircraft, has a history going back at least to 1954. Indeed, more models were on the market twenty years ago than today, when comprehensive flight systems are expected to take care of 'ground proximity' along with dangerously low airspeed, windshear, departure from an ILS glidepath and everything else.

A GPWS has to measure the aircraft's trajectory in relation to the terrain ahead. In other words it measures the rate at which aircraft/ground separation distance decreases. Sophisticated systems do not just measure vertical radar-height clearance but

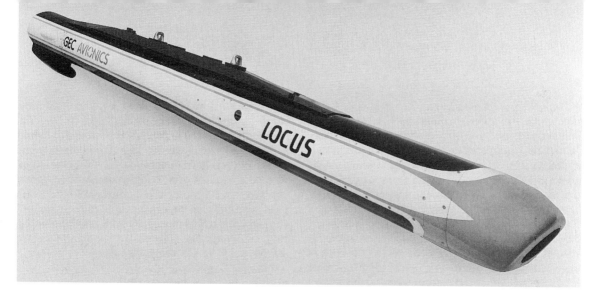

gain information on future trend by scanning the terrain ahead and taking account of changes in range rate. A few also take into account airspeed/AOA (angle of attack), and warn if the aircraft enters a high-AOA regime from which a sudden pull-up manoeuvre is impossible. One of the simpler systems is the Kollsman radio/barometric altimeter with voice terrain advisory. This can serve many functions, giving voice warnings on descending below decision height, or below the ILS glidepath, or if the ground clearance is 2,500 ft or less and continuing to fall. One of the latest systems is the GCAS (ground collision avoidance system) by Cubic, which monitors radar height and airspeed and attempts to predict future ground clearance of low-flying tactical aircraft. Sundstrand has marketed seven generations of GPWS, the most advanced having seven operating modes: excessive sinkrate, excessive terrain-closure rate, significant altitude loss after takeoff, insufficient terrain clearance (three sub-modes, terrain, gear and flap), excessive descent below glideslope, altitude callouts

A totally new species of pod for fast attacking jets, Locus (laser obstacle cable unmask system) scans ahead for unmapped power lines and other obstructions. Successful trials were carried out with a US Navy A-6 Intruder.

(alert 'minimums') and windshear. Each mode triggers repeated visual and voice warnings.

Windshear, the existence of large and rapid changes in wind, is extremely dangerous when an aircraft on landing approach encounters a headwind whose velocity falls rapidly or even reverses into a tailwind. At least thirteen companies have studied the problem. One of the few commercially available WSW (windshear warning) systems is by Safe Flight. It senses the two orthogonal components of a wind gradient (horizontal and vertical)

The four elements of the Safe Flight enhanced performance and safety package, used mainly on business jets. From left: autopower amplifier, SCAT (speed command of attitude and thrust) and windshear computer; performance computer; and control/display unit.

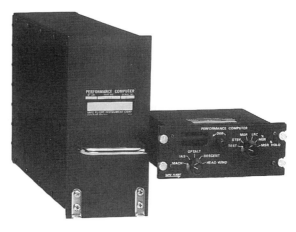

and provides a threshold alert in time to avoid a potentially hazardous situation. An optional enhancement is a recovery guidance input to the flight-director pitch command bars. Horizontal windshear is derived by subtracting groundspeed acceleration from airspeed rate (rate of change). The latter is obtained by passing airspeed (from the ASI or ADC) through a high-pass filter. Longitudinal acceleration is sensed by a computer integral accelerometer, whose output is summed with a pitch-attitude gyro to correct for any acceleration component due to the fuselage not being horizontal. This circuit has a dead band equivalent to $0.2°$ pitch, preventing correction for airspeed rates below 0.1 kt/s. The vertical acceleration, or downdraught drift angle, acts by determining flightpath angle by subtracting the pitch-attitude signal from an AOA signal sensed by the stall-warning system. This is fed to a high-pass filter and multiplier to which the airspeed signal has been applied. The output is the flightpath angle rate, which, when compared with the output of a normal computer integral accelerometer, should give near-zero output. Failure of the two values to measure is an indication of acceleration due to downdraught. When integrated, the acceleration gives vertical wind velocity, and this divided by airspeed gives the downdraught angle. The system is based solely on atmospheric conditions, and ignores manoeuvres that do not increase the aircraft's total energy. Thus, actions by the crew to anticipate windshear cannot mask the condition and prevent a warning. The warning circuit is triggered by a horizontal shear threshold of 3 kt/s and downdraught angle of 0.15 rad, or a combination giving an equivalent signal level. By 1990 this system was expected to be standard on Boeing commercial jets.

Since 1956, and possibly earlier, various teams have been working on systems for eliminating mid-air collisions. Oddly, the first ever to go into regular use was developed by a fighter manufacturer (McDonnell) to avoid problems with intensive F-4 test flying in busy St Louis airspace. Called Eros (eliminate range-zero system) it was a combined radar which sensed rate of change of its sightline and a computer which integrated an unvarying sightline with range and range rate, the whole being packaged into a pod with a deep blade antenna fitting into a Sparrow missile bay.

Nearly all the collision-avoidance and conflict-warning systems have fallen by the wayside, but surviving systems likely to be FAA-approved and become industry standards go by the name TCAS II (threat-alert/collision-avoidance system). While Bendix thrust ahead with the full-blown system, Sperry and Dalmo Victor in 1983 formed a joint venture company to develop a simpler and much less expensive system called Minimum TCAS II. This is broadly an airborne interrogator transmitting signals in the horizontal plane around the aircraft. It detects other aircraft (which may or may not have TCAS equipment), determines azimuth within $10°$, range and range closure rate, and altitude and vertical-separation closure rate, displaying on the weather radar all potential conflicts. Any risk that continues to increase eventually commands an evasive manoeuvre in pitch on a modified VSI. The Bendix Enhanced TCAS II is similar, but computes collision-avoidance commands in both horizontal and vertical planes. This is partly the result of using a phased-array antenna which, emitting a very narrow beam, interrogates only a few aircraft at a time, reducing confusion in high-density terminal areas, and giving much more accurate azimuth bearing and rate of change of bearing. Logic circuits sort potential conflicts in order of increasing risk, so that the greatest threats are interrogated the most frequently. Special software generates the avoidance manoeuvre commands. A Mode-S transponder enables TCAS-equipped aircraft to co-ordinate their avoidance manoeuvres. A Florida company, Gables Engineering, is marketing Mode S TCAS cockpit instrumentation, and yet another TCAS II was in 1989 to be available from Rockwell's Collins division (see photograph), under a joint agreement with the original developer, Toyocom of Japan. After 15 years the Tokyo company perfected the receiver/transmitter, antenna and beam-steering units.

Airlines are in much the same position over TCAS as they are over MLS: don't let's rush things. The US Congress, conscious of public (ie, voters') concern, has passed legislation requiring TCAS in all 30-plus seat aircraft by December 1991. This legislation cannot, it appears, be enforced on non-US aircraft. The airlines are bothered at the cost, the problem of false warnings, and compatibility of hardware and, especially, software with TCAS III and later systems not yet invented. Several countries are running TCAS trials, but the only large-scale adoption is by US carriers, including Northwest's entire fleet, using Honeywell TCAS II.

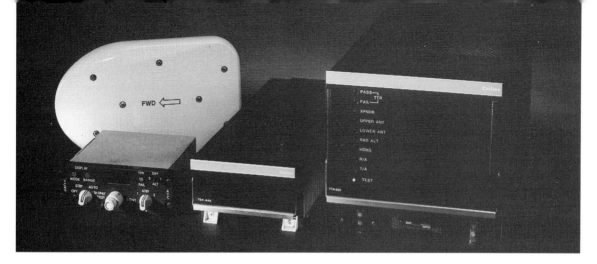

Introduced in October 1988, the Collins TCAS-94 meets the TCAS II requirements. At left are the directional antenna and control panel. Centre, Mode S transponder, which interrogates all surrounding aircraft. Right, R/T processor which determines conflicts and determines advisories. Complete traffic pictures can be displayed on an EFIS.

A close relative of rendezvous radar — which is used, for example, by both tanker and receiver aircraft to find but not collide with each other in cloud or other bad weather — SKE (station keeping equipment) is an important aid for military transports. Such aircraft often have to maintain formation in order to pass over a DZ (dropping zone) or pick-up point at precise intervals, which may be in the order of 30 s. Thus, precise formation may have to be held several hundred feet or metres apart, and in IMC or at night this needs SKE. The standard USAF set is LTVs APN-169, the antenna of which is visible as a 'pillbox' above tactical airlifters. It comprises a short-range radar plus proximity warning, and a cockpit display showing the relative positions of all participating aircraft.

There are many other avionics systems which improve flight safety. Some are concerned with fire and overheat warnings. A few fire warnings are triggered by optical surveillance detectors tuned to be triggered only by the UV wavelengths in the incandescent part of a kerosine fire. The vast majority, such as Graviner Firewire, are of the thermistor or thermocouple type in which a continuous thin-tube sensing element, routed along places where flames would travel (such as a powerplant zone extractor duct), suffers either a sharp change in electrical resistivity or in output voltage. The sensed signal is passed through an amplifier to the flight deck where it typically sounds an alarm bell and illuminates a flashing red light in the handle of the relevant engine fire-extinguisher lever. After immediately shutting down the engine the pilot pulls

the handle up and turns it to fire one extinguisher bottle. If necessary, he can later turn the handle 180° in the opposite direction to fire the remaining bottle. Smoke detectors are usually optical. Several systems aim a hollow tubular beam of light at a detector which, being in the centre, receives no light. Smoke diffuses light, so that some is received by the detector. Typically, an LED source and photocell detector are pulsed in unison, and if light falls on the detector for ten consecutive pulses, showing continuous obscuration of 10 per cent or more, the alarm is sounded.

There are several related systems. Smiths Industries produce various engine overheat warn-

A typical TCAS display, seen in the TA (traffic alert) mode. Traffic is seen at 11 o'clock, 1,200 ft above at 4 nm and climbing. Traffic advisory at 4 o'clock at 3 nm, 400 ft above and climbing. The resolution advisory square commands a climb greater than 1,500 ft/min. (Smiths)

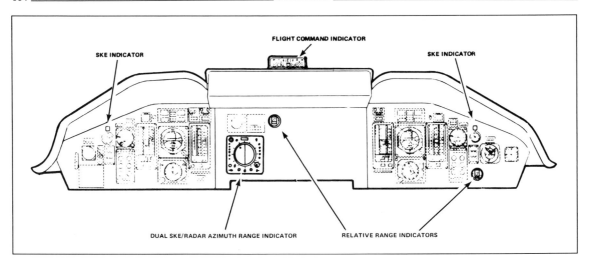

ings which trigger an alarm if chosen locations, typically near the HP turbine, should exceed a given limit during the starting cycle or at any other time, or if the turbine cooling airflow should fall below a critical level. GEC Avionics produce tyre temperature sensors mounted on the main landing gear, which aim an IR radiometer at a point on each tyre carcass most prone to heating from the brakes. Actual temperature is displayed in the cockpit, and exceeding a safe threshold sounds an alarm, calling for a reduction in airspeed and temporary gear extension.

Some of the oldest avionics safety systems warn of severe icing. Today these exist in fascinating variety. Some use a sensing head containing a very small cylinder which slowly rotates against a knife-edge. Build-up of ice is detected by measuring the increased drive torque needed to scrape the ice off. Another method uses a fine cantilever probe which is magnetostrictively vibrated at its resonant frequency, which varies as even a very small mass of ice is accreted. This type can indicate a given thickness or accretion rate. One of the most sensitive detectors uses a resonant surface waveguide, whose frequency again varies with ice thickness. Several such detectors can be linked to a single microprocessor and display, giving numerical or pictorial thickness and rate. One of the newest systems operates in a cyclic fashion, alternately being electrically heated and then left to collect ice, whose thermal characteristics, and heat released by the latent heat of fusion as the water freezes, provide data giving the thickness indication. All these later sensors are triggered by as little as 0.003–0.005

in (0.076–0.12 mm), a sensitivity which could lead to anticing systems being switched on unnecessarily.

In addition to fire and overheat warnings, engines need vibration indicators. Virtually every engine in today's jet aircraft is protected by a system which senses and warns of unusual vibration. The usual method is to bond small piezo-electric accelerometers to places (usually near a bearing or on the exterior) where vibration would be a maximum, and feed the output through a narrow-band digital filter controlled by the tachometer (rpm sensor) output to isolate the vibration frequency. The system has to have very rapid response and good software in order to sense any vibration instantly, even when an engine with three different shaft speeds is undergoing slam acceleration. Some vibration detectors can give inflight indication of the exact mass and mounting position needed to balance a rotating system more accurately. The British Aerospace Views (vibration indicator engine warning system) feeds a panel instrument displaying vibration level of each engine by illuminating small lamps numbered 1 to 10.

At least four companies have developed systems which measure aircraft weight and CG (centre of gravity) position. All rely on some form of sensor on the landing gear. Sfena of France, for example, measures shear stress in the axle or bogie beam and axle torque as an additional measure of tyre deflection (giving an output of pressure, distress and incipient blowout). The Honeywell WBS (weight and balance system) is somewhat similar but continues to operate in flight, fed by fuel-flow and quantity measures to manage CG position.

Left *SKE items in the cockpit of a USAF C-141B. The flight command indicator is used to insert desired changes in aircraft relative position. The large indicator shows the whole formation in plan view and gives proximity warnings. The RRIs give pilot and copilot a quick picture of range to the next aircraft.*

Right *Typical sensors for angle of attack (right) and ice (vibrating probe type, far right).* (Rosemount)

Sfena sensor on a bogie main landing gear for determination of aircraft gross weight and CG position.

11
LANDING AIDS

Any pilot will confirm that, no matter what happens in the rest of each flight, you earn your keep on each landing. Even with a STOVL aircraft or helicopter — which has it a thousand times easier in being able to stop and then land, instead of having to land and then hope to stop — it is no easy task in bad weather to find the correct landing place. With CTOLs (conventional takeoff and landing aircraft) you have to position yourself several miles downwind of a single narrow runway, and then make an approach at exactly the right slope (usually 3°), at the correct airspeed and rate of descent, and exactly along the projected centreline of the runway so that you hit the runway just beyond the threshold with near-zero rate of descent and close to the stalling speed. All this serves as an indictment, underlining how crazy modern aeroplanes are. But we have to live with them, so our very lives depend on electronic help in getting back on terra firma.

Until the 1930s pilots had virtually no help in landing in fog. Airline pilots, at least, did by this time have radio, and with skill and experience could fly near to the airport, where the controller would tell the pilot his rough position based on the sound of his engines. This was usually enough for a pattern to be flown, ending in a landing somewhere on the grass airfield. By about 1931 radio range stations were being used routinely as landing aids, the dot/dash transmission giving azimuth guidance and two extra beacons being added to indicate linear position along the approach. A diagram shows the first such station in Britain, at Liverpool Speke. The pilot attempted to pass over the outer marker, with three miles to go, at 650 ft. He then let down so that he passed over the inner marker at 100 ft. The inner marker was on the airport boundary 4,800 ft from the main (dot/dash) beacon, which was on the bank of the Mersey at the far end of the field. Such facilities were thought fantastic.

Throughout Europe the best that could be done was the ZZ system. This relied on voice radio, using the Q-code in which three-letter groups denote particular messages, and on the noise of the aircraft as heard by an observer on the ground. The pilot had to fly an accurate pattern, with altimeter set to airfield pressure, relying entirely on his own skill and that of the observer (in fog, a mere listener) on the ground. This crude system was introduced to Britain at Heston as late as 8 November 1938! In total contrast, the American Hegenberger system required that the aircraft carry radio, a radio compass, marker-beacon receiver and a distance (tuning) meter. Each landing was preceded by complex and precise manoeuvres, each carefully timed and letting down to lower altitudes on each, with frequent retuning. The airport transmitted from what could be called outer and inner markers, each broadcasting around 360° for the radio compass and a narrow vertical fan as a beacon.

Hegenberger recognized in a complex way that radio can provide positive guidance. In about 1927 Conrad Lorenz AG, in Berlin, began development of a much better system which provided such guidance throughout the approach. The drawback was that, in an age when a radio was thought a luxury, it needed a special receiver and a special panel instrument. The ground station broadcast a two-component beam, dots one side of the runway extended centreline and dashes on the other, with a continuous note along the central equisignal zone. Range was about thirty miles. The big new feature was that the beams were also coded vertically to give a further equisignal zone along the ideal glide path. The pilot listened to the equisignal note and also watched his indicator. This had a horizontal and a vertical scale, both traversed by small white pointers. By keeping these centred the pilot knew he was on the correct approach path. Lamps in the indicator flashed as markers were overflown, twice per second for the outer marker and six per second for the inner marker. Not least, by using VHF at 28 to 35 MHz Lorenz eliminated static and greatly reduced errors caused by refraction and reflection. This system was widely adopted during World War 2, the British name being SBA (Standard Beam Approach). As noted earlier the Luftwaffe used a specially sensitive Lorenz receiver as a long-range navaid, in conjuction with Knickebein and X-Gerät beams.

During World War 2 the US Army Air Force concluded that the Lorenz system was the way to go, but that it was far from perfect. Cutting a very long story short, the result was SCS-51 (Signal Corps Set No 51), which was exhaustively tested at the end of the war and was coming into wide service at the time of the Berlin airlift in 1948. ICAO named it the Instrument Landing System in 1949. Like most US products, it then became the world standard — for a change, an excellent choice — and ILS is fitted to at least one runway of virtually every

Before World War 2 pilots thought themselves fortunate to arrive at a major airport equipped with marker beacons. There was no guidance of lateral position or height, but primitive (equisignal zone) guidance on the QDM, in Liverpool's case 259°.

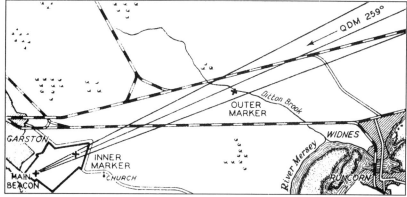

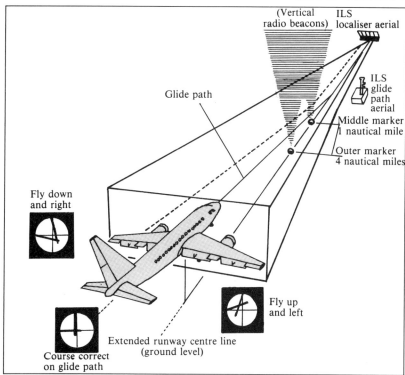

Taken from a UK CAA brochure, this gives a good general idea of an ILS approach.

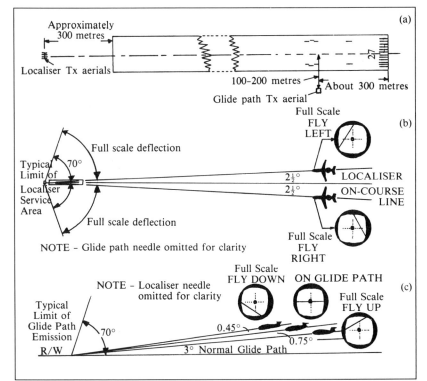

Diagrams showing (a) locations of the LOC and G/S antennas (the term glide path is used here); (b) service area of the localizer; and (c) service area of the G/S (glide path), showing full-scale deflection if the pilot wanders either 0.45° above the 3° line or 0.75° below it. (Oxford Air Training School)

civil airport and almost every military airbase in the world. Such runways are called instrument runways. All 'autoland' or blind landing systems are based entirely on ILS.

In concept, ILS continues the tradition of using overlapping pairs of radio beams to define a line along which aircraft can be guided. Each ILS installation comprises two distinct pairs of beams. One pair, called the localizer (LOC), provides azimuth or directional guidance in the horizontal plane. The other, called the glide path or glide slope (G/S) provides guidance in the vertical plane. The localizer transmitting antenna is a giant horizontal array at the far end of the runway, facing the distant landing aircraft. It sends out precisely defined beams along the runway and out to a distance of 25–30 miles. One covers the left side of the runway and the other the right; of course, the beams get bigger and bigger as distance from the antenna increases, but they always intersect along the extended runway centreline. Both have the same frequency, which is between 108 and 112 MHz (at London Heathrow, for example, most installations are 109.5 or 110.3), but the left beam (as seen by a landing aircraft) is modulated by a tone at 90 Hz,

while the right beam is modulated by a tone at 150 Hz. The ILS receiver continuously compares the difference in depth of modulation (DDM), and the pilot flies to make DDM zero. When DDM is zero, ie, when the 90 and 150 Hz tones are equal, the aircraft is on the runway centreline. Vertical guidance is given by the upper and lower beams sent out by the G/S transmitter, whose antenna comprises a pattern of groups of dipoles arranged on (usually two) towers abeam of the runway touchdown point. The glideslope beams are at UHF frequencies of 300–330 MHz. These, like the LOC beams, are modulated by superimposed tones, 90 MHz above and 150 MHz below.

The airborne ILS receiver, which is usually duplicated — as is the case with most major avionics on which safety depends — is tuned to the installation at the destination airport. It receives the signals in the four beams, and the demodulated tones are separated by filters, rectified and compared differentially. The sum of the rectified tones is fed to a warning circuit which, should the transmitters or receiver malfunction, causes a bright flag to appear on the cockpit indicator. The difference signals are fed to the indicator's crossed pointers, one giving left/right and the other up/down guidance. If the LOC needle is over to the right, the pilot turns to the right until it returns to the centre; if the G/S needle is displaced to the bottom of the instrument, the pilot reduces power or lowers the nose until the needle is horizontal. Alternatively, the difference signals can be fed to the autopilot so that the aircraft can make an automatic 'coupled approach', the pilot adopting a passive monitoring role.

This system alone can provide landing guidance, the pilot being able to see his progress towards the threshold from the radio altimeter, or from an accurately set barometric instrument. To give further linear guidance, marker beacons are usually still provided. These are often called fan markers, because their signal is broadcast in the shape of a narrow vertical fan lying across the glidepath. About 4 to 5 miles from touchdown the outer marker will be heard as two Morse dashes per second, and a purple panel light will flash at the same rate. About 3,000–5,500 ft (say, up to a mile) from touchdown the MM (middle marker) will be heard as a dash-dot-dash each second, with a sychronized amber light. Finally, some airfields still have an IM, about 1,000 ft from touchdown, emitting six dots per second and flashing a white light at the same rate.

Like VOR, ILS is essentially the same all over the world. It has removed the terrors of having to land in fog, though this needs some additions as described later. It has many shortcomings, mostly minor. One is that the G/S beams come from antennas displaced to one side of the runway, and also continue in an approximately linear fashion to the height of the antennas, whereas the pilot has to start his landing flare to arrest rate of descent purely by reference to radio height, unless he can see the approach lights. Another problem is that, like all radio beams, the ILS beams are always distorted by the ground, and especially by hills and large buildings. The original Lorenz beam at Heston worked well until a new hangar was erected; then there were near-crashes until a way was found to realign the beam in the correct direction. Today many airports are in valleys with steep mountains close on one side, or even on both, and this makes an accurate ILS installation a big challenge. Even on easier terrain it often costs more than the ILS hardware to level the ground in front of the G/S antenna, and aircraft queuing for takeoff may have to be hived off to remote taxiways to avoid in-

terference. Moreover, it has been found that totally unrelated transmissions (from buildings or aircraft) with radiated power as low as 1 mW (0.001 W) can cause serious ILS interference.

To overcome interference problems the RAE at Farnborough developed CPILS, correlation protected ILS. This uses duplicated transmitters for both LOC and G/S. Unlike the conventional arrangement, the two LOC antennas are placed on each side of the runway near the mid-point, and the G/S antennas on both sides at opposite ends. This gives a straddle-type radiation pattern, with zero DDM along the runway centreline. The signals, which are C-band at around 5 GHz, interact in such a way that the beams curve gently in a hyperbola, which has been found preferable to a straight-line

Below *A neat ILS receiver and tuning unit (Cossor CILS 75/76). The output would be fed to a primary flight instrument or EFIS display.*

Bottom *Typical of private-owner avionics, the Narco Centreline II includes the NAV 825 for radio, VOR and ILS, and the associated ID 825 instrument. The radio is set to 113.5 MHz (knobs at right set MHz outer and kHz inner) active, and VOR 180° 'TO' on standby. The cross-pointer instrument can be used on VOR or ILS.*

approach. The four transmissions are correlated in the aircraft in such a way that position information is determined not by field strengths but by time-differences. Accuracy is thus that of well-proven hyperbolic navaids (a matter of a metre or so), and integrity is enhanced by the very high frequencies, which facilitate precise beam tailoring. The correlation process itself almost eliminates errors caused by reflected signals.

Such protection was essential to enable more runways to be cleared for landings in very poor visibility. In the 1960s, while US airports were proudly being cleared for Cat II (decision heights down to 100 ft, visual range 400 m/1,300 ft), British teams were pioneering the Autoland concept which, in theory, works in Cat IIIc (no external visibility whatever). On 22 May 1972 BEA received CAA approval for Trident (Smiths Autoland) operations in Cat IIIa (blind down to and along the runway with external visibility near touchdown of 200 m (656 ft). For such operations it was established by British authorities in 1961 that equipment failure causing a catastrophic accident should occur not more frequently than once in 10^7 landings. This was the basis to which Hawker Siddeley and BAC, Smiths and Elliott, and BEA and BOAC worked. While Air Inter in France cunningly modified the Sud-Lear autopilots of their Caravelles to operate by 1968 down to DH (decision height) of 15 m and vis of 150 m, the British teams did it 'the hard way' with the Trident having triplexed systems giving 'majority voting' to nullify a failed channel and the

VC10 having a hybrid system with a quad-actuator giving at least equal integrity.

The Autoland effort was pioneering on a major scale (but, like many British efforts, it was not rewarded by any commercial success, either to the planemakers or the airlines). It involved such new features as elimination of unwanted stick activity due to ILS beam noise, development of new flight-control laws, autothrottle throughout the approach, auto kick-off drift during the autoflare, auto runway guidance by rudder down to 75 kt and by head-up guidance thereafter, and runway speed and distance-to-go indication. The latter was dialled-in prior to the landing, so that the available distance wound down to zero with a safe margin. The runway guidance involved a buried leader cable along the centreline and a 'barber pole' cockpit-coaming indicator called a PVD (paravisual display), operative only on take-off or landing with oleos compressed, and deriving azimuth from the LOC beam.

Only brief mention need be made of GCA, PAR, VASIs, PAPI and other wholly ground-based landing aids. A GCA (ground-controlled approach) is a landing made, usually in very bad weather, by a pilot who is continuously 'talked down' by a controller watching his aircraft on the display screens of a ground surveillance radar. The bright blip moves down a glidepath marked on displays showing height errors and lateral errors, and no new avionics are required. Again, a PAR (precision approach radar) is similar to a GCA radar but the ground

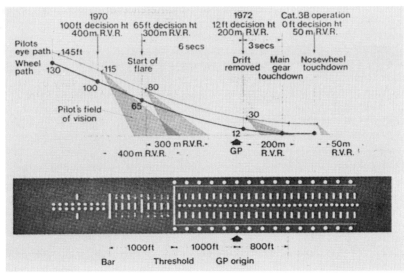

Main features of the pioneer Autoland procedure certificated on BEA Tridents in 1970 and 1972. RVR = runway visual range.

A representation of the US Navy C-Scan system, in this case shore-based (TRN–28 is similar to SPN–41 except that it does not need the stabilization elements of the shipboard system). The ARA–63 drives a crosspointer display on the HUD.

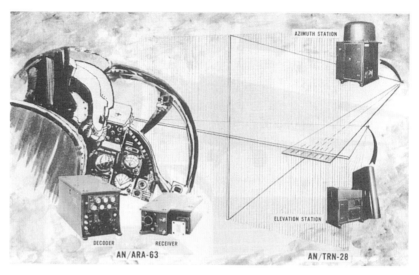

observer has a monitoring function only. If necessary, for example on detecting a dangerous excursion below the glidepath, he can warn the pilot. VASIs (visual approach slope indicators) are groups of lights beside the touchdown end of the runway giving white, white/red or red/red indications, depending on whether the approaching aircraft is high, on the glidepath, or too low. PAPIs (precision approach path indicators) are groups of lights which progressively change, one by one, from all white (too high) to all red (too low). Litas (low-intensity two-colour approach system) is a simple, cheap and extremely useful Vasi for general aviation. All these are ground aids.

In 1971 noise at major airports was so severe that there was discussion of adopting a 6° approach, joining the 3° glidepath at 300–500 ft about 1–2 miles from the runway. This was not adopted, but today glideslopes angled at 6°–9° are in use at STOLports for use exclusively by aircraft which have good control at low airspeeds. Again, on-board avionics are unchanged.

For General Aviation various types of VOR/LOC (or Vorloc) are on the market. These are what the FAA terms an SDF (simplified directional facility), giving azimuth guidance only. Usually directional guidance is given, on front or back course, from a final-approach fix. Most resemble a VOR but with the same 90/150 MHz left/right modulation as an ILS. The pilot flies on the indication of any VOR or LOC needle. In Germany, Becker market a Vorloc 'for gliders and balloons'!

Since 1956 many groups have worked on various forms of microwave landing aid, using principles (usually) different from the overlapping beams of ILS. One which in 1971 was adopted as the NATO standard portable tactical landing aid, produced by MEL, is Madge (microwave aircraft digital guidance equipment). The ground station, easily erected in 15 min in any convenient location (for helos or fixed-wing), is interrogated by each aircraft and, having satisfied the interrogation and ident functions, automatically responds with the caller's azimuth and elevation, the elapsed time of each interrogation giving range and range-rate. The az-el information is compared with selected approach path data, and the difference drives a conventional ILS instrument or flight director.

Another early MLS (microwave landing system), and in 1960 a pioneer of the scanning system, is C-scan (carrier system for controlled approach of naval aircraft), produced for the US Navy by AIL division of Cutler-Hammer. It comprises SPN-41 on the ship, with an azimuth station, an elevation station and a control centre, and the ARA-63 receiver/decoder in the aircraft. The shipboard set operates on any of twenty channels between 15.5–15.7 GHz. The azimuth and elevation beams are scanned to sweep out the approach region of sky and pulse-coded to distinguish elevation, az left and az right. The signals received at the aircraft drive a cross-pointer (ILS, attitude-director indicator or flight director) or guidance on the HUD.

By 1971 the need for a replacement for ILS was considered to be urgent, and the US Radio

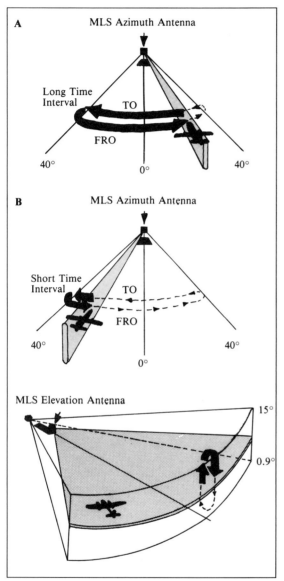

A MLS Azimuth Antenna

Long Time Interval

TO

FRO

40° 0° 40°

B MLS Azimuth Antenna

Short Time Interval

TO

FRO

40° 0° 40°

MLS Elevation Antenna

15°

0.9°

The MLS azimuth beam and elevation beam both sweep rapidly to and fro, the former 40° left and 40° right and the elevation beam between 0.9° and 15°. The aircraft receiver measures time intervals. (Micronav/Ferranti)

Technical Commission for Aeronautics set up Special Committee 117 to study the problem. Among other objectives, the new system was to eliminate the problems of ILS (for example, costly preparation of flat areas in front of the G/S antenna, and the need to make departures queue for take-off in remote areas where they did not cause interference). It had to serve CTOL, STOL and VTOL. It had to offer guidance over a broad azimuth arc, making possible curved and/or segmented flight paths. It had to reduce noise on the ground, and make possible channelling of traffic from left and right on to close parallel runways. About fifty schemes were proposed, and fairly soon (1971–72) all were rejected except two forms of MLS, the CD (commutated doppler) and the TRSB (time-referenced scanning beam). To a lesser degree, it was 1958 over again. The doppler MLS, invented by Charles Earp at STL in Britain, seemed to the author superior in almost every respect (his assessment was 28 out of 32) to the rival TRSB. Yet, predictably, the final choice became a 'UK versus the rest' situation, so TRSB was naturally selected by the USA unilaterally in 1975. In 1978 this US choice was rubber-stamped by ICAO. Six years then elapsed before the FAA placed a contract for 178 pre-production MLS installations, and in the subsequent six years (1984–90) the MLS saga has been punctuated by politics, delays and a general cooling of enthusiasm — partly due to choosing TRSB. Part of the antipathy is due to the high cost, to airports and to airlines, while the delays (at least thirty months, at the time of writing) are put down to customer indecision, management problems and financial problems. Now (mid-1989) MLS at last seems to be making progress again.

An MLS comprises an azimuth antenna at the far end of the runway, and an elevation antenna beside the runway near the touchdown point; thus, in these respects, it resembles ILS. The differences are considerable. The linear phased-array antennas transmit extremely narrow beams on frequencies of 5–5.25 GHz. The azimuth antenna puts out a beam 2° wide which sweeps rapidly between 40° left and 40° right of the runway centreline (these angles can be adjusted to suit local terrain). To determine its lateral position, the aircraft MLS receiver measures the time intervals between successive sweeps. As the diagrams show, the time interval shows whether it is L or R of the extended centreline. The elevation antenna puts out a horizontal fan-shaped beam with a beamwidth of 1.5°. This sweeps rapidly up and down through the sky volume already swept by the azimuth beam, between the angles of 0.9° and 15°. Again, the aircraft's receiver measures the time between sweeps to determine the aircraft's glidepath angle.

Above *A typical airborne MLS receiver, the white disc being the antenna. Total weight of the Canadian Marconi CMA-2000 is under 19 lb (8 kg).*

Right *Pilots making MLS landings receive distance-to-go information from a DME-P (precision DME) at the far end of the runway. In Germany SEL (Standard Elektrik Lorenz) is producing DME-Ps, this being the airborne unit which was based on a Bendix product.*

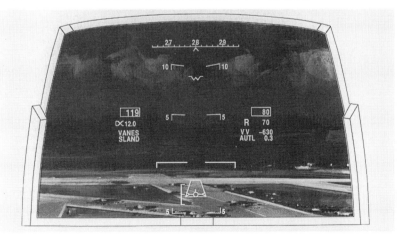

Steering symbology on the final approach with the F-15S/MTD. Azimuth/elevation guidance is provided for (it is hoped) precision landings 'between the craters'.

Thus, the pilot first sets up the appropriate az/el inbound approach angles to his MLS receiver. Having flown into the MLS beams, he thereafter receives extremely precise L/R, up/down steering guidance from any cross-pointer instrument. He also receives continuous distance-to-go information from a P-DME (precision DME) located near the MLS azimuth antenna. Some MLS installations include a back-az transmitter to provide guidance during overshoots (missed approaches or go-arounds). All transmitters on any one runway transmit in continuous rapid sequence on the single channel assigned to that approach or overshoot.

Collins and Canadian Marconi are working on the MMLSA (military MLS avionics) programme for the USAF. The number of aircraft receivers required is over 10,000. The USAF said it would 'gradually transition to MLS as part of the worldwide changeover from ILS during the next decade'. Some observers have calculated that the last ILS will not be switched off until after 2015.

To conclude this chapter, the F-15S/MTD (STOL and maneuver technology demonstrator) is already exploring ALG (autonomous landing guidance). This is intended to facilitate short landings 'between craters' on bombed runways. The rather optimistic idea is that the airfield should be studied 'from great distances' by the APG-70 radar in the hi-resolution ground map mode, supplemented (certainly at night) as the range closes by the FLIR of the Lantirn nav pod. The pilot is guided to his designated touchdown point by symbols superimposed over the IR image displayed on the HUD. Flight simulations have shown that 'pilots can easily interpret the symbols and follow their guidance to precision landings without active ground-based navigational assistance'.

12
MONITORING AND RECORDING

Nothing better exemplifies the growth of avionics, and indeed the overall progress of technology, than the recording of data aboard aircraft. At first nobody appreciated the need for it. Then rather clumsy devices recorded a small number of parameters, perhaps taking measurements once per second. Gradually recorders became smaller, lighter and so much more capable that they could record up to 100 different things, taking measurements at the rate of millions per second. They diversified into different families, some for replay after a crash, others to assist maintenance and reduce unreliability and cost, and others (for example) to help train fighter pilots. Then it was realized that we do not need the torrent of routine information, so recorders became cleverer, and now record only the things that matter, such as unexpected changes or excursions outside defined limits. Today integrated data systems cover the whole aircraft, just as our nervous system extends throughout the body, and recorders can claim (along with computers) to be the brain, or at least the memory part of it.

The earliest flight recorders comprised pencil and paper, and some test pilots were still faithful to this method in the 1960s. In 1942 the music firm of Boosey & Hawkes began supplying RAF Bomber and Coastal Commands with simple voice recorders, and these gradually became reliable and gave a clear output. In the early 1950s new types of recorder were developed using such recording media as scratching on thin metal foil or variably magnetizing a fine stainless-steel wire. Leaving groups of fine scratched traces on foil sounds extremely crude, but it was easy to understand and relatively easy to make the foil survive severe crashes; a drawback was that not much information could be recorded, and the foil could not be reused. Scratch-foil crash recorders began to come into use on airlines in 1957, soon to be joined by wire recorders. For some reason the media began to call crash recorders 'black boxes', though they were usually Day-Glo red or some other bright colour. They have from the start been required to meet severe standards of acceleration (eg 1,000 g for a brief period), crushing and impact load, and intense heat applied for (typically) 30 min.

By 1966 many countries required that all transport aircraft of over 12,500 lb or 5,000 kg MTOW should be fitted with a crash recorder having five tracks: heading, pressure altitude, airspeed, g and pitch attitude. By this time the number of recorder manufacturers had proliferated, especially in Britain where much of the pioneering was done. Most of the new recorders used magnetic tape, either thin (0.0005 in) stainless steel or, increasingly, Mylar. This was the dawn of the vast worldwide audio tape industry, and the technology moved very fast. Mylar gave better recordings but needed greater protection, especially against distortion due to high temperature. Probably the biggest advance was that more information could be stored in a smaller space, somewhat paralleling the audio industry's progress from vulcanite cylinder to '78' record to 'long-play' Hi-Fi record to tape and to CD. Early wire recorders typically contained fifty miles of wire, spooled past at high speed to record 64 10-bit words per second. Second-generation tape was not much better: the important Penny & Giles equipment of 1972 contained 1,400 ft of stainless tape to get a mandatory 25-h record. This, like most of its rivals, had eight tracks. Some recorders drove the medium alternately first in one direction and then back in the other, while some used a medium that was recycled continuously in the same direction.

By the early 1970s several trends were marked. Most of the hopeful manufacturers had gone broke or merged. The mandatory number of channels

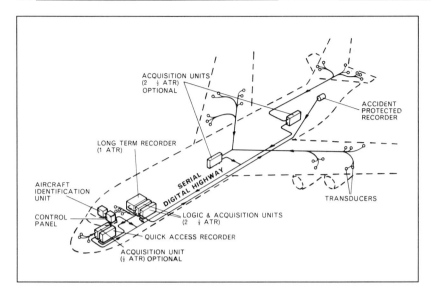

went up to sixteen, with new equipments able to record (for example) 64. From late 1969 Aircraft Supplies of Bournemouth offered an excellent recorder which, instead of recording everything as an analog voltage, was totally digital. This recorded sixteen sequentially switched tracks on 900 ft of Mylar tape, enough at 1.75 in/s for 26 h of recording. By 1972 this had become the basis of a slightly improved recorder by NGL (Normalair Garrett), who survive to this day. Despite improved performance, this recorder weighed about half as much as earlier 'black boxes' at 26 lb (11.79 kg), not including a tiny location beacon able to send out signals for thirty days at ocean depths to 20,000 ft.

By the 1970s different sorts of recorder were giving rise to even more different names. The original crash recorder was also being called a crash-protected flight recorder or an ADR (accident data recorder). Alongside these had grown up a range of generally larger, but unprotected, recorders normally called FDRs (flight data recorders), but often called FDASs (flight-data acquisition systems), and normally forming with the crash recorder an AIDS (airborne, or aircraft, integrated data system). Gradually, as civil and military operators realized it made financial sense, the AIDS was enlarged to monitor and record not just eight or sixteen parameters but hundreds. Almost every important facet of aircraft operation became the object of close scrutiny throughout each flight, not so much with the possibility of a crash in mind but because it was discovered that the knowledge could have far-reaching implications.

For example, by 1970 United Air Lines was routinely monitoring and recording the following for each engine of its wide-bodies: EPR, EGT, N_1, N_2, IAS, TAT, fuel flow, fuel used, vibration, altitude, Mach, oil pressure, oil temperature, oil quantity, nacelle temperature and breather pressure. During the 1970s United and most other major operators added: variable stator angle, fan pressure ratio, LP and HP compressor delivery P_t and T_t, LP turbine inlet P_t and T_t, fuel tank temperature, fuel filter pressure drop, scavenge oil temperature, scavenge oil filter pressure drop, bleed flow T_t and P_t, pressure drop and valve position, anti-ice valve positions and, increasingly, hot-end temperatures (eg, by a pyrometer or radiometer) and the readouts of SOA (spectrographic oil analysis). Similar measures were increasingly taken for all powered items and systems throughout the aircraft, several hundred in all.

Thus, especially during the 1970s, the notion of recording just five parameters was multiplied by perhaps 1,000. This multiplication was made possible entirely by digital techniques managed by modern microelectronics, which can handle bit rates thousands or millions of times greater than the mechanical sampling methods of 1960. We have come far beyond the idea of a narrow-band crash recorder, and today's advanced aircraft have one or more 1553B or Arinc 429 buses along which are fed signals from anything up to 250 originating sensors, which are often some kind of transducer. The measurement may be a pressure, temperature, mechanical position, voltage, vibration or (for example) a count by size groupings of small solid particles in lubricating oil. The torrent of signals are managed at all times, and many are 'conditioned' to put them in a more usable form. Some may be fed direct to an indicator in the cockpit (or rather, today, to be available should the pilot choose to call up the information on a display). Most are channelled to a recorder, which can be called an AIDS, an FDR, a HUMS (health and usage monitoring system), an FIR (flight incident recorder), an MDR (maintenance data recorder) or even, in the case of Smiths Industries AYQ-8(V), a Ulaids (universal locator AIDS).

Why do we do all this? Certainly not because we all love avionics, though the power it gives us does make it hard to resist measuring everything (Stealth aircraft record the resistivity of the exterior paint). We do it for hard commercial reasons, which apply just as much to air forces as to airlines. There is not the slightest doubt that health monitoring will quite rapidly percolate down through general aviation to the level of the simplest private aircraft, and this process will automatically lead to mass-produced systems suitable for cars and HGVs. Already today dozens (at least) of engine faults every day are caught before they happen. There is not room to go into detail, but modern HUMS measures are so detailed they immediately establish a 'signature' for every engine. Any significant change in the signature can be worth investigating, no matter whether it is sudden or a gradual deterioration. Experienced engineers can interpret the records with assurance, and unfailingly spot the signs that might have led (for example) to bearing failure. The result is greater safety, uninterrupted schedules, and — because of the tight and continuous control — maintenance credits. For example, instead of 'pulling' engines at, say, 2,000 hours, we now enjoy OCM (on-condition monitoring) which means we leave the engines alone unless something shows up in a changed signature.

This is not just good for airlines. I happened to visit an F-15C unit on the day they were celebrating their ability to rig F100 engines and then leave them

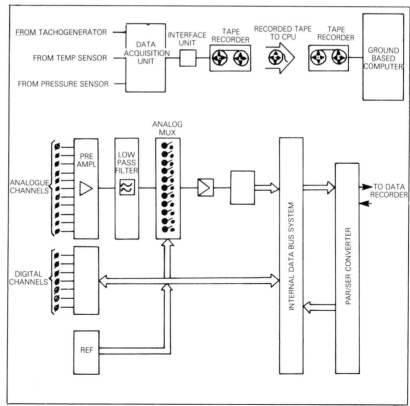

Every major airline and air force uses trend monitoring systems to stop trouble before it happens. Viggens of the Swedish AF use the SATT DAU (data acquisition unit). It actually measures seven engine parameters, all analog.

alone. Thanks to digital control and continuous monitoring it had become possible to know in advance precisely what power would be obtained from a given pilot demand, ie. throttle position. This meant the elimination of many hours of ground running for each engine, extending into full afterburner. I will leave it to the reader to think what this means in terms of fuel cost saved and environmental disturbance eliminated.

Health monitoring began in 1962 when Smiths supplied data acquisition units for the BEA fleet of Trident 1s. They interrogated thirteen items, which were digitized prior to recording on tape which was then physically downloaded and analysed on the ground. By 1972 microprocessors were making possible previously undreamed-of inflight computation. One of the first new capabilities to result was to count LCF (low-cycle fatigue). Whereas HCF (high-cycle fatigue) is that caused by very rapid stress reversals in such parts as turbine drive shafts occurring at the rotational speed of the part, LCF is caused by the major but slower changes in stress and temperature which occur only a few times on each flight. Thus LCF could be accrued by: start engines and taxi; takeoff; cut back for noise-abatement climb; cruise; letdown; full reverse; taxi

The British Negretti EMS is a more complex system which records just about every significant parameter in an engine that can be measured, as well as air data (which can be bussed in from the ADC). It can give immediate warnings in flight.

and shutdown. It needs a processor to translate the measures into cycles of LCF.

To look a little more closely at engine monitoring, the EMS (engine monitoring system) by Negretti Aviation provides six outputs. The ESC (engine start recorder) records the cumulative number of times the engine is started. The RTR (running time recorder) is self-explanatory. The LER (limit exceedance recorder) records running time during which any of eight datum values are exceeded. The LCFC (LCF counter) records damage accumulated by critical components due to cyclic rotational stress; the engine maker supplies an algorithm for this purpose, usually using a modified rainflow technique which makes various assumptions to assist the calculation. The CDM (creep damage monitor) again uses an algorithm supplied by the engine manufacturer in calculating turbine-blade creep damage accumulated from combined high temperature and high stress. Finally, the TFM (thermal fatigue monitor) uses an engine-company algorithm to calculate turbine-blade thermal fatigue damage resulting from thermally induced mechanical stresses.

Similar instrumentation can record other operative systems. Clearly, we have to be concerned with fatigue damage, which goes on accruing all the time, and the concept of exceedances, parameters which, for whatever reason, gradually or suddenly go outside the established limits. We are now able to collect data so fast that since 1980 designers have been standing back a little and

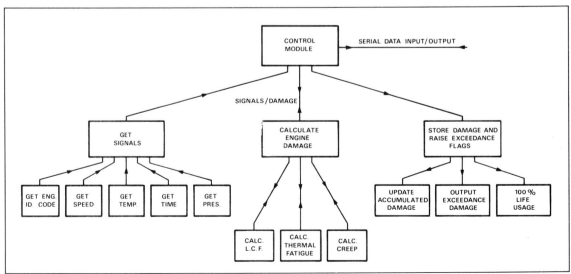

developing recording systems that are more useful. In this they parallel what has happened in the cockpit. Traditionally the pilot has had to sit facing dozens or hundreds of instruments looking like clocks. He does not need to know what most are telling him, and there is nothing to warn him that (perhaps) one is giving a reading that spells oncoming danger. Today's more fortunate pilot is told nothing (as explained in the next chapter) except information of possible interest. In the same way, there is no point in pouring in ever-greater floods of data just to fill up our recorder memory. We are now being carefully selective, in various ways. We ignore all routine data unless the reading goes above or below a chosen threshold. We ignore (for example) the first two digits of a number which do not vary, and record only the third. And we automatically take account of what is happening in order to bias the data. Taxiing out, we record fatigue damage to landing gear and wing spars, but let the engine parameters tick over. Arrived at the runway, the engine channels go into high gear to get full details of the spool-up and full-power performance, but we don't bother to record longitudinal attitude and AOA until we get to ROTATE. In maybe twenty hours of cruising flight we slow down almost everything, but might need quite rapid g measurements in order not to miss cobblestones and the quite vicious hammer-blows that soothing captains call 'light chop'. We certainly record airbrake and spoiler position, but nothing like as often as on letdown and approach. And so on.

All airliners from the A320 onwards are likely to have a CFDS (centralized fault-display system). Such a system highlights the difficulty of structuring this book, because the whole system is totally computerized (Chapter 15) and the human interface to the CFDS is via the two keyboard/display units on the cockpit console which also double as part of the flight management guidance system (Chapter 14). This, however, is the best place to mention CFDS developments, because they are the latest expression of maintenance recording. In the photograph the ground engineer in an A320 is reading through a hard-copy printout after a flight to see if there are any malfunctions. Tapping keys can isolate a problem not just to one LRU but to a single circuit. A CFDS eliminates unnecessary component removals, and saves maintenance time and cost. It can include an air/ground Acars (Arinc communications addressing and reporting system) to alert

Above *The A320 is the first commercial transport to have a CFDS. Every maintenance task is either eliminated or printed out on the flight deck after each flight.* (Airbus)

Below *Schematic of an airborne monitoring system for 1st, 2nd and 3rd-line maintenance. The ACARS alerts engineers before the aircraft arrives. The DTU is held in the hand.*

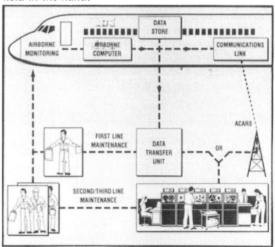

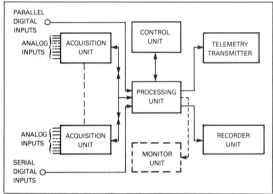

The Plessey Modas (modular data acquisition system) is widely used in many forms, but the block diagram is typical. The photograph shows (from left) the monitor unit, control unit, recorder unit and processing unit.

maintenance staff awaiting aircraft arrival.

One of the drivers towards selective recording and data compression is that, increasingly since 1980, the traditional tape recorder has given way to the solid-state device, storing digital bits in microscopic pieces of semiconductor (or, rarely, ferrite cores, see final chapter). Today's RAMs, ROMs, EAROMs and EEPROMs have come to stay, but it needs careful design in order to use them to store the mandatory 25-h continuous record (which was no problem with tape, you simply made it long enough). We need 25-h non-stop because of the ability of such aircraft as the 747–400 and A340 to fly non-stop over the longest airline sectors.

On the whole the move towards all-solid-state recorders has improved their ability to survive crashes, immersion in the sea and similar adverse environments. Certainly the vibration of most helicopters posed problems with tape drives, but has virtually no effect on solid-state chips. One of the first such installations to go into production is the

Lear Siegler Model 6213, which won a USAF/Tri-Service competition in January 1984, initially aimed at the F-16. This comprises a big cube and a little one. The big one, about 7 in (178 mm) along an edge, with a finned exterior, is the SAU/AMU (signal acquisition unit, auxiliary memory unit), while the small (3 in, 76 mm) cube is the CSMU (crash survivable memory unit). The SAU/AMU is packed with eight PCBs (plus a spare slot for a future board), which include a microprocessor, elapsed-time clock, 16K program memory, 2K scratchpad memory, 2K non-volatile memory (see final chapter) and an AMU of 256K with growth to 512K (512K means it can store 512,000 bits of information). The CSMU stores 28K (growth to 64K) of non-volatile memory in devices mounted on a ceramic substrate housed in a triple shell of protective enclosures.

Tape recorders are by no means obsolete. One that has gained wide acceptance is Lockheed's 209-F DFDR (digital flight data recorder), which shows how far we have come by storing 25 h of extremely accurate data at the rate of 2,076 bits/in despite a tape speed of only 0.37 in/s. This recorder is noteworthy for its data verification and BITE (built-in test equipment) provisions. The BITE examines the recording function, by checking for tape motion and recording head current, and for data recoverability. The latter is checked by always comparing playback data with recorded data. The

Right *This maker's sketch gives an indication of the triple protective enclosure needed to meet requirements for the CSMU part of the USAF solid-state data recorder (Lear Siegler 6213).*

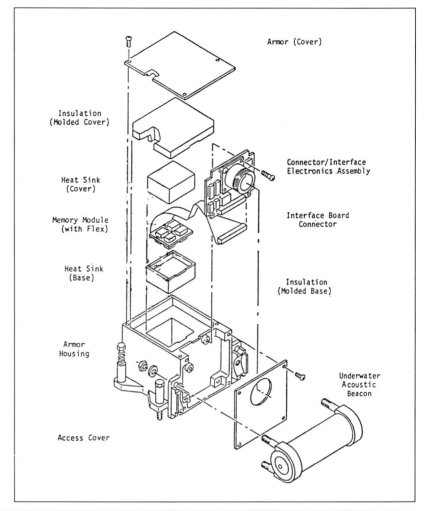

Armor (Cover)

Insulation (Molded Cover)

Heat Sink (Cover)

Memory Module (with Flex)

Heat Sink (Base)

Connector/Interface Electronics Assembly

Interface Board Connector

Insulation (Molded Base)

Armor Housing

Underwater Acoustic Beacon

Access Cover

Below *Lockheed's Model 209 is one of the surviving examples of a tape recorder, but it is a modern digital product.*

analysis circuit decodes sync words, and verifies the presence of 63 words between them. An improper number of intervening bits, or a wrong sync word, is flagged as an error. Two checks are made to ensure the data are new, not old. First, a comparison is made with the sync word recorded about twelve records earlier, which is the time-lapse from record to playback head. Second, a portion of a data word is compared. The word selected gradually propagates through the subframes so that different words are tested each time, ensuring a progressive check of all words recorded. Should the errors reach the level of four dropouts in any sequence of 10^6 bits, the flag output goes to open-circuit. The MTBF is a guaranteed 8,000 h, and the MTBO 15,000 h.

Today most airborne recorders, of whatever species, are left in the aircraft and 'milked' at intervals to obtain the data. The latter can be downloaded in various ways, for analysis, playback or merely storage. A big airline can easily achieve 1,000 revenue sectors a day, and nobody wants to conduct detailed analyses on 1,000 recordings a day, so most are (typically) just stored for six months. Immediate attention is paid to any parameter that shows up in the record as being off-limits or progressively deteriorating, and in the case of older recorders — less full of BITE than the Lockheed DFDR — careful checks have to be made to ensure that the recorder itself is working properly. Even modern solid-stage digital recorders tend to be defeated by the cleverness of the system. Bus management buffers the input to the recorder to prevent transient overloading and present data in a uniform stream, and occasionally this helpful process can get bits

displaced in timing (milliseconds can be vital in crash investigation) and even transposed in sequence.

This shows that even getting the data on the record can be fraught with difficulty, and so can the process of reading it. Modern fighters have multiple parallel redundant buses, and there have been several instances in which, through oversight by the system designers, different lanes have fought each other at interfaces with recorders, causing either no data or corrupted data. The recorder(s) must be protected against any corruption from feedback by the 'milking' or interrogation unit, and particular care is always taken after a serious accident, when the likelihood of corruption of the record is greatly increased, even in cases where the recorder has been physically severed from the aircraft.

Some recorders, or at least beacons, are especially designed to separate from the aircraft to facilitate recovery after a crash. S.Davall developed various ADRs, including the famous Red Egg series, which were mounted on aircraft externally (one formed the tailcone tip on the One-Eleven). During flight testing of the Concorde the ADR was an ML Aviation device which could be fired underwater by a giant 15 in (381 mm) cartridge. Today many combat aircraft routinely carry a CPI (crash position indicator) in the form of a quickly deployed beacon — often called an ELT (emergency locator transmitter) — in a shockproof housing which can also contain a flight data recorder. One example, carried by AWACS and many Tornados, is the Leigh Instruments CPI, which can be separated from the aircraft by various manual or automatic means, thereafter zooming as an aerofoil away

These Leigh CPIs proclaim, in English and German, 'No danger, please bring to nearest police station, or inform Luftwaffenamt....' They could explain the crash of a Tornado.

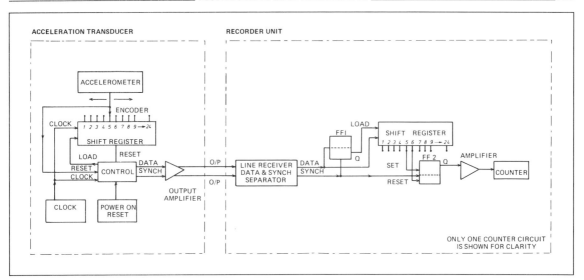

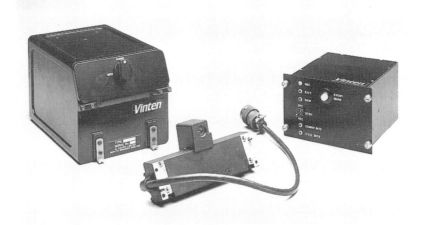

Above *Block diagram of a Negretti airframe fatigue meter. The split type is shown, with accelerometer near the CG and the recorder elsewhere.*

The HUD colour video recording system selected by British Aerospace for Hawk 100 and 200 and by Smiths Industries for F-5E retrofit. From left, Series 2768 video cassette recorder, Series 3150 camera, and camera control unit. (Vinten Military Systems)

from the immediate crash vicinity to transmit within a 30,000 sq mile area for 48 h.

One of the simpler types of recorder is the CVR (cockpit voice recorder), today's descendant of the wartime speech recorders and often, at least in the 1960s, the means by which unprofessional and even outrageous flight-deck behaviour was brought to light. Today's CVRs can be very compact, recording on one or several channels between 300 Hz and 15 kHz, occasionally adding digital data such as a single channel for helicopter rotor rpm (small helicopters normally having no other recorder). There are still arguments over how far it is a good idea to combine all recorders into one package. Long ago Smiths Industries made a neat job of combining an ADR and a HUMS, and there are a

few combined DFR/CVR packages, but, though we can gain in compactness and efficiency, we can lose in having the aircraft grounded because of a failure in a non-mandatory portion of the package.

One type of recorder not previously mentioned is the video recorder, which is a compact colour camera. Usually its function is to record everything seen by the pilot, either on the HUD, or through the windscreen. Occasionally a video recorder is required to look at head-down displays and instruments (and of course this is always the case in test flying). Most NATO combat aircraft do not yet have video recorders, though they are sometimes specially added at armament practice camps or on visits to air-combat ranges. It was therefore educational to find that every MiG-29A has two, one on each side of the seat. RAF Tornados will get one in the MLU (mid-life update), the GEC Avionics product using Super-VHS giving better quality than domestic TV. For the forthcoming EFA Ferranti and West German partner BKT are offering the first combined VVR (video and voice recorder). This will record not only the HUD and cockpit audio but also the three big HDDs (MFDs), enabling the whole sortie to be replayed in real time, with quick-search for any specific event. Such an aid would be really useful in debriefing. There are also a few airborne radar recorders, used mainly by large aircraft such as maritime patrol and ASW platforms, where it helps to have a record not only of radar displays but also of the whole tactical picture including sono-buoy outputs and other sensors.

Back in the 1950s when airborne recording was in its infancy a few people, including what was then Negretti & Zambra, produced so-called V-g recorders to keep a record of aircraft speed and vertical acceleration. This work was greatly accelerated by the belated recognition in 1960 that bombers could no longer avoid being shot down just by flying higher, and everyone began learning how to attack 'under the radar'. This gave airframes a very hard time, and today Negretti Aviation sell what are now called fatigue meters. They come in two families, composite meters where the whole package can be installed on the aircraft centre of gravity, and split systems where congestion at the CG precludes putting the counter box there and it has to be linked to the accelerometer by cables. The output is almost always fed to a series of counters which record the number of times particular accelerations have been exceeded. Each counter operates in two steps, a lock followed by (at reduced acceleration) a release, this constituting one count. The difference between lock and release levels is called the threshold. Like the absolute values of g, the thresholds are chosen according to whether the aircraft is a fighter, attack aircraft, transport, trainer or whatever. A threshold of 0.1 g is adequate for a transport, but on a fighter, or any aircraft with severe wing/fuselage resonances, 0.1 g would be triggered perhaps several times per second; in one high-altitude fighter the threshold for the various g levels varies from 1.5 to 3.5. As well as batteries of veeder-counter readouts the acceleration measures can also be fed to RAMs, a ROM and EAROM to give a non-volatile memory which effectively is the life-story of the airframe.

13
DISPLAYS

The first type of avionic display was the CRT, and devices of this family are still absolutely dominant in the field of big 'multipurpose' displays giving a TV-type picture. CRTs have been discussed in earlier chapters, but there is still a lot to be said about how they work. In addition, the cockpit designer has an increasing wealth of other types of display, such as the LED, liquid-crystal, plasma, EL and other species. Moreover, various types of traditional 'instrument' have over the years become so complex that they undoubtedly must be considered avionic in nature, and these will be dealt with first.

As late as the 1950s aircraft had two primary flight instruments giving spatial information: the compass for the horizontal plane and the artificial horizon for the vertical (or attitude) picture. Neither could be called an avionic item, but by the 1960s they had been replaced by, respectively, the HSI (horizontal situation indicator) and ADI (attitude director indicator). These were electronic and rapidly grew in both complexity and in what they could indicate. Today the HSI can be 4 in square but is usually 5 in square, and always displays a miniature aeroplane (for helicopters the symbol is often stylized into a three-line cross) at the centre of a 360° compass card. Information is today fed in digitally, and a typical HSI of the 1970s is illustrated, with a key to its features. Its range display, which is usually to a Tacan or DME, is electronic of a type described later. In most HSIs it is a mechanical veeder counter, and there are other forms such as the LED dot matrix.

Sometimes one encounters a 'heading and attitude indicator' (there are many other names) in which a horizon is mounted in a 360° dial free to rotate on the outside of the pitch/roll sphere. This is unusual, and the common panel matches an HSI with an ADI in which a sphere or barrel painted in

contrasting colours, such as black or brown for land, and white, pale blue, grey or yellow for sky, is free to rotate in pitch and roll with presentation exactly as in a traditional horizon. In 1957 Britain

An HSI of the 1970 period, designed by Smiths Industries for Tornado: 1, range display dimmer; 2, range display in nm; 3, glide flag (G/S failure); 4, heading index; 5, fixed lubber; 6, actual track pointer; 7, command track counter; 8, azimuth flag; 9, heading index knob (sets 4); 10, elevation angle deviation bar; 11, display flag; 12, command track pointer (gives command trks and x-trk errors); 13, to/from flag; 14, compass card (mag or true); 15, mode indicator (NAV, TAC, APP or ADF); and 16, command track knob (sets runway hdg in APP).

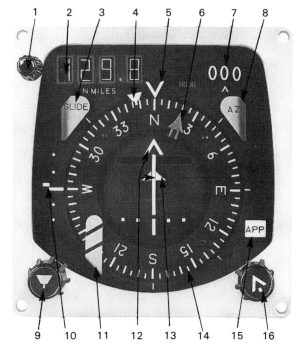

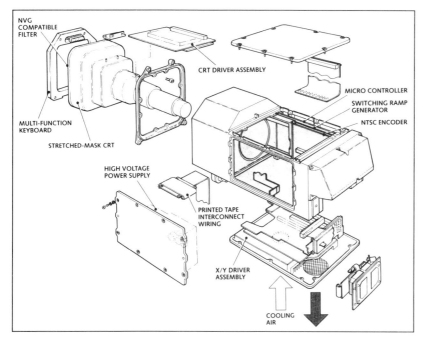

pioneered the roller-blind horizon, and this kind of flat presentation was obviously preferred when in the 1970s manufacturers began designing electronic ADIs. Such instruments are the primary source of pitch/roll steering information in all non-HUD aircraft, and their clear command indications enable the pilot to stay in the control loop even without external visual cues. Nevertheless, the progressive introduction of digital microelectronics from about 1980 onwards brought about a revolution in all except the simplest aircraft, and it has not yet run its full course. Modern avionics can measure and process information on such a vast scale that traditional methods of cockpit presentation are completely outclassed. Even the complex HSI and ADI cannot accept the available information, nor present it clearly to the pilot.

In this situation these basic flight instruments are merely affording yet another example of the power of modern avionics. Not only can we now offer the pilot tens or even hundreds of times more information, but we can do it far more effectively, by eliminating nearly all of it except when it is needed. We can also reduce costs. At the time when the changeover was beginning, in 1981, EFIS (electronic flight instrument system) displays were relatively heavy, only just acceptably reliable, very costly and not very obviously an advance. The

revolution did not happen in a vacuum but in a world peopled by professional pilots who had to earn their living, who had to be led by the hand, and who belonged to trade unions eager to pounce on anything construed as a threat. Accordingly the first generation of EFIS displays had to be electronic clones of existing electromechanical HSI/ADI instruments. Even today some important aircraft, such as the 737, are only just making the changeover. A pilot in a 737 airline fleet may have to fly a traditional aircraft one day and an EFIS one the next, so the differences have to be minimal. But we are now well into the revolution, and in newer aircraft the displays are larger, many times more capable, and much more flexible and unfettered than anything seen previously. This is purely because the first generation of pilots to have tasted electronic displays — even primitive ones — in the early 1980s have found them wonderful. As for the lower costs, these are becoming more apparent every day. Modern displays are lighter, consume less power, run cooler and are better in every way than early patterns, and their reliability is outstanding. Whereas in 1982 one 'expert' predicted 'No airline will be able to afford these displays. They would mean millions of dollars tied up in spares at every airport on the network', today cockpit maintenance costs are a fraction of what

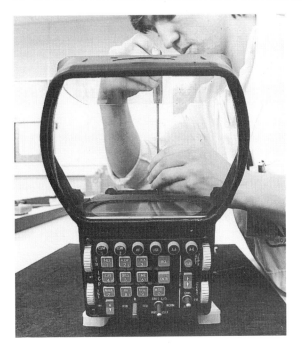

they were in the days of complex watch-like electromechanical instruments, laboriously stripped and reset by craftsmen.

As the revolution is still in progress, we distinguish modern aircraft with all-electronic displays by saying they have 'glass cockpits'. But military aircraft have had flexible electronic 'glass' displays since 1967, in the form of the HUD (head-up display). Already briefly referred to, the HUD ought to be dealt with before returning to the glass-cockpit revolution.

All HUDs — which the author often writes as the 'word' is pronounced, Hud — are fed with information on aircraft trajectory, navigation and, for combat aircraft, weapon-aiming. This is translated into visual symbols and projected on the face of a CRT, whose display is then collimated (guided as a beam) by mirrors and lenses and projected on to a 'combiner glass' in front of the pilot near the windscreen. The display seen on the glass is focussed at infinity, so that the pilot can study it whilst at the same time looking through it at the external world ahead. Any HUD makes a dramatic difference to pilot workload, especially in any attack on a surface target, or in combat missions at low level in bad weather. Today the HUD is much more than just a sight; it is a primary flight and navigational instrument on which can be presented not only the steer-

ing and command symbology but also a moving-map display, or pictures supplied by a sensor such as a radar or FLIR.

To the pilot new to the idea a HUD is great, but soon he will become irritated by its limitations. It has to be mounted right in front of his face, so it has to be as compact as possible. In particular, its opaque box must not obtrude above the level of the cockpit coaming, or external objects — such as a taxiway or a ground target — would pass out of view at a significantly greater distance. This need for a small HUD is in direct conflict with the wish for the largest possible HUD field of view. The IFOV (instantaneous FOV) is what the pilot can see without moving his head; the TFOV (total), gained by moving the head within the limits imposed by seat, harness and helmet, is a function of the HUD's optical design. Traditional HUDs with refractive optics typically have IFOV of 12° in elevation and 18° in azimuth. TFOV might be as much as 25°, but this is still less than an attacking or air-combat pilot would like. Moreover, there are problems in reconciling the need for high transmissivity in the combiner (sometimes called the combining glass), for a clear view ahead, with the need for high reflectance to give a bright HUD display. Clearly, you can have one at the expense of the other. Typically, ignoring scatter and absorption, refractive HUDs are designed for about 70% transmissivity and 25% reflectance. To get a sufficiently bright display requires operating the CRT at maximum brightness (say, 10,000 ft-Lamberts), which shortens its life.

Two variations on the traditional refractive HUD which increase the IFOV are the multicombiner and the Perihud. In the former the combiner is a glass block made up of four plates each with different reflectance in order to produce almost constant outside-world transmissivity and display brightness. In the Perihud a wide periscopic combiner containing beam-splitting surfaces allows the pilot to 'look around' the optics. Both extend IFOV in the vertical plane to about 17°, helping the pilot see into turns. But the breakthrough, again a British development, was the reflective HUD. The crucial reason for the limited IFOV of traditional HUDs is the small size and forward location of the exit pupil, the lens through which the beam emerges from the HUD box. In the reflective HUD the combiner is also the collimating element, and large IFOVs are possible, but it proved extremely difficult to make the large aspheric (ie, not quite spherical) collimator/com-

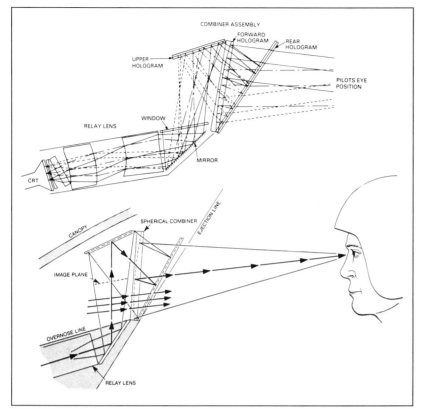

Below *One way of outlining the three scanning techniques used in HUDs, CRTs and many other displays. Stroke writing is virtually like handwriting with electronics. Mixed scanning (centre) requires two inputs, synthetic (stroke) symbology signals plus a video input. Full raster scanning (right) is like TV, with a single (video) input. (Sfena)*

biner, with a reflective coating, and this precluded such devices, at least as commercial products. Then in 1982–3 GEC Avionics achieved a breakthrough with reflective HUDs in which the combiner reflective elements are holograms.

Holograms come in various forms, but all are uniquely capable. They are made photographically by exposing sensitive material to the interfering wavefronts of monochromatic laser light arriving by two routes, one direct and the other via some more complex route. The holograms in modern HUDs are in essence diffraction gratings, with the remarkable property of being almost perfectly transparent to all light except that within an extremely narrow band of wavelengths. We pick as the chosen wavelength the bluish-green phosphor of the HUD CRT. This is reflected very efficiently (about 90%) by each hologram surface, all other

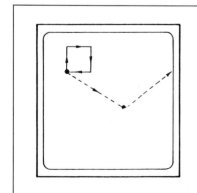
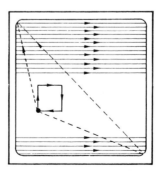
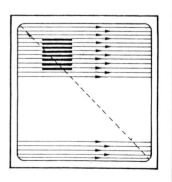

light passing straight through. Diffractive, or holographic, HUDs can be arranged in various ways. The first to go into production, for the F-16C/Lantirn, is of the quasi-axial type. This provides the greatest possible IFOV whilst allowing the HUD body to fit back in its recess in the coaming. Aberrational performance, display brightness and combiner transmissivity are of a wholly new order. IFOV of these brilliant new HUDs is around 19° by 30°.

This is an appropriate point at which to explain the two forms of symbology that are presented to the pilot on a HUD: raster and cursive. Raster systems scan the CRT display area line-by-line as in TV, sometimes in a straight sequence L-R-L- etc, sometimes L-R-fast flyback to L-R-, and sometimes with some form of interlacing (as we saw in fighter radars in scanning airspace). To form a character in such a display requires a character generator able to translate the shape into a pattern of dots on a checkerboard matrix. We call L/R columns X and up/down lines Y. Each character has its own unique X count and Y count, and when these are passed to X and Y shift registers we get the dots which generate that character. Typically we need a video bandwidth of 10 MHz, but a lot depends on the perfection of resolution demanded. Compromise is needed in creating curved or diagonal lines, which of necessity have to be rather jagged. In contrast, cursive writing is also know as stroke (or stroke-generated) writing, and it creates each letter in an electronic approximation of the way we ourselves write. We create each symbol by assembling strokes culled from a repertoire which has to be large enough to produce clearly read characters. If we do not mind rather crude stylized characters we can use a cartesian (two axes at 90°) matrix in which the available deflections are ±X and ±Y, giving eight directions and two lengths, but if we have enough processing power we can go to ±2X and ±2Y to give a 24-stroke repertoire. Even so, the required diode matrix and waveforms for even a single sequential-stroke character are truly formidable, and of course in a real display there are likely to have to be dozens or even hundreds of characters, each in its exact place.

Further complications are added by the different spectral signatures (colours) of the symbology or alphanumeric characters, their contrast or otherwise with the background, the enormous variation in cockpit illumination and the fact that the pilot may be wearing NVGs. Whereas on a clear day the pilot has no problem seeing the ground ahead through the HUD glasses, at night it is a different story. Then he needs a synthetic picture, for example created by a FLIR, superimposed on the real one; but the colour has to contrast with the (usually bluish green) phosphor used for the overlaid symbology, both to the naked eye and to the scene as viewed through NVGs. And whereas the symbology is almost bound to stand out well against the background at night, what about the contrast with the unnaturally brilliant sunlight of high altitude falling direct on the combiner glass?

These are by no means the only ways of displaying alphanumerics. We can do it without needing a CRT at all. Historically, various kinds of EL (electroluminescence), such as AC or DC powder and AC or DC film, have been around longest, and the Sigmatron LEF (light-emitting film) has been on the market over fifteen years; but the author has never come across an avionic application other than of an experimental nature. ELDs (EL displays) can be light, robust, bright, consume low power and give a generally good picture, but their driving circuitry is incredibly complex, and it is very difficult to achieve a display that is both bright and large.

Certainly the most common types of alphanumeric display are the LED and LCD, the former

A typical example of a colour video display (the main picture) on which are overlaid both stroke-written symbology (centre) and raster-written symbology (edges). (Collins)

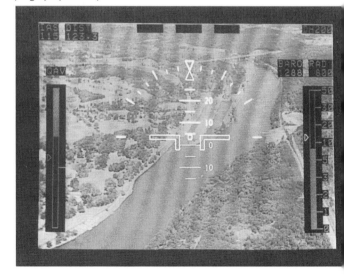

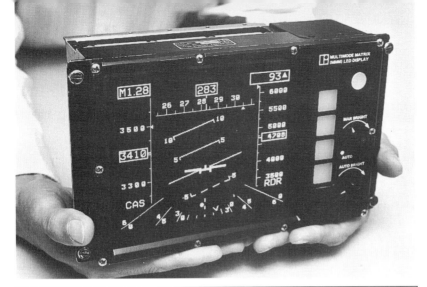

A demo LED flat-panel display arranged as a PFD (primary flight display). It comprises three 1 in modules, each with a 64 × 64 matrix (thus, 4,096 LEDs per square inch). A display using this density is in production for the UFC (up front control) of the F–16C/D. It is hoped to achieve a 90 × 90 density, or 8,100 per sq in, giving a remarkable combination of resolution, brightness and real-time response. (Litton Systems Canada)

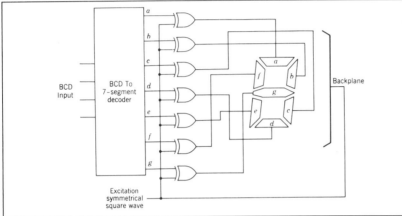

By far the most common alphanumeric digit display is the seven-segment font, also called (for obvious reasons) the double-hung window. This shows how each character is controlled. The seven segments can be LEDs, often bright green or red, or LCDs (usually black).

referred to in chapter 1. The light-emitting diode is, in fact, an application of EL, but in a new way. We need not examine it in much detail, other than to note it is a true solid-state diode which usually has p-type material recessed into a substrate of n-type, in which case application of a sufficient voltage can cause the emission of photons from the conduction band to the valence band, accompanied by large hole migration in the valence band. Many arrangements are possible, with different materials, so that we can have LEDs that are bright red, orange, yellow, green or blue. Most manufacturers use LEDs in the form of dot-matrix diodes. The most common is the 5 × 7, in other words each character is formed in a rectangle containing 35 dots, any one of which may not be illuminated. For example, an L would be formed by illuminating all those down the left side and along the bottom. There are 77 standard alphanumeric forms commonly used in English-language aircraft, including the alphabet, ten numbers (zero being distinguished from O by having a diagonal stroke through it) and various other items, many of which are found on a

typewriter. A few items of cockpit equipment use a different matrix, notably the 7 × 9 which gives arguably better clarity.

As LEDs can be switched in nanoseconds, we can change quite complex displays extremely rapidly. Normally the display makes simple demands. For example, most modern instruments with a pointer (needle) and a numerical (veeder) readout can effectively replace both by LEDs, without any pilot learning needed. Sometimes a mechanical pointer is retained, but accompanied by a rolling-digit numerical display which simulates a veeder counter. Sometimes the pointer is replaced by a radial line which appears to rotate around — or around the outside or inside of — a circular, or part-circular, ring made up of (typically) green, amber and red segments. Alternatively, LEDs may be used to generate stroke-written (cursive) characters. By far the most common of this big species is the seven-segment font, or double-hung window, the whole 'window' being used to create figure 8. Such a display is common in the home in digital clock/radios. Rather unusually the SI standby engine

In 1982 this LCD engine display was considered remarkable, especially as it provided the readouts of eight traditional indicators in a single 3ATI case. Behind it are hundreds of microelectronic circuits, with BCD (binary coded decimal) inputs and decoders to control each of the seven 'bars' forming each numeral. (US General Electric)

display for the 757 and 767 uses a 14-segment font (without any apparent advantage) with inserted decimal points. The 24-stroke repertoire has already been mentioned, and another common species is the 14- or 16-stroke starburst, which increases the possible range of strokes, including diagonal ones, though the author has never been enamoured of the result.

Most liquid-crystal displays use the twisted nematic type of crystal, in which (in the absence of a field, left) the crystals progressively change their orientation 90° through the depth of the cell. Depending on the polarization of the light (here we show it at 90° to the paper going in and in the plane of the paper coming out) we can make an LCD display dark-on-light or vice versa. In a typical matrix display (right) each element is addressed by two electrodes at 90°; thus we can control M × N pixels (image elements) with only M + N electrodes. (Eurodisplay)

Stroke-written alphanumerics can equally well be generated by LCDs (liquid-crystal displays). Unlike CRTs, LEDs, EL and other displays, the LCD emits no light. A separate light source is needed, and the display is created by placing the LC cell in the path of that light, to modulate the light's transmission or reflection. LCs are intriguing, in that you can pour them out of a bottle (at least over

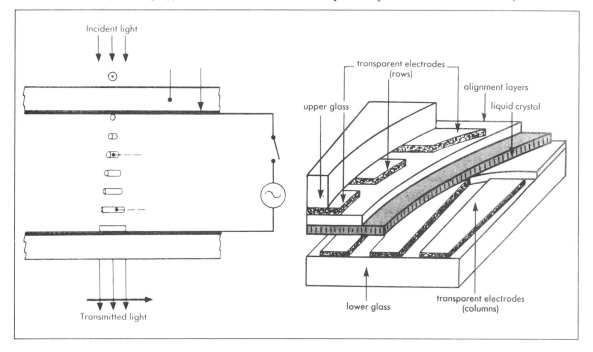

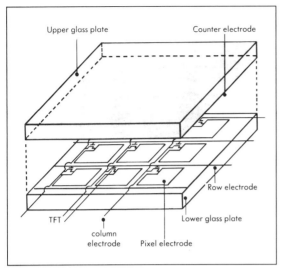

Above *In the active matrix type of LCD, every cell is individually controlled by a thin-film transistor (TFT). They are each addressed by applying a video voltage to the column (containing the pixel) corresponding to the signal to be displayed, and applying to the row a voltage that turns on the TFT.* (Eurodisplay)

Below *Among unexpected uses for LCDs are Airvision's screens for inflight entertainment. In an alternative scheme they are recessed into the backs of the seats. Passengers use credit cards not only to get films or TV but to call up route maps from the aircraft's flight management computer, or even scan a mail-order catalogue.*

their normal operating range of temperature) yet they have a precisely ordered structure, like other crystals. We do not really need to know that there are three families, the nematic (all molecules exactly parallel), the smectic (arranged in parallel layers like plies in plywood, all with a constant preferred direction) and cholesteric (arranged in layers, the orientation in each layer being rotated, so that in passing through all the layers the orientation forms a helix).

To make an LCD we pour the crystal material between transparent glass plates provided with electrodes through which we can apply a voltage. We can control the LC in several ways, but the most common one in cockpit displays is the twisted-nematic field effect. Here the LC has nematic molecules which are aligned homogenously (parallel to the plane of the display) but with a 90° twist from the top layer to the bottom, in the absence of an electric field. When a signal voltage is applied, the molecules are untwisted and line up with the applied field. Thus, if we put the LC in the path of polarized light, depending on whether we put the polarizer and analyser (output polarizer) parallel to each other or displaced by 90°, we can obtain a light-on-dark or a dark-on-light display. Twisted-nematic displays work at a mere 3 to 10 V, consume tiny currents (so need no cooling), are tough, cheap and reliable, and have a response time of around 0.01 s, which is adequate for most purposes.

Twisted-nematic LCDs can have any chosen background colour but are monochromatic in nature. Today other forms of LCD are coming into use with various degrees of colour. The usual type is the DAP (distortion of aligned phases), in which incoming white light is progressively changed in colour as a function of applied voltage. It is still not easy to get precisely a specified colour for a specified applied voltage, but for most pictorial display purposes this is of no consequence. Smiths Industries use LCDs in a totally synthetic Mach/airspeed 'instrument', complete with 'pointers' and a numerical readout of both functions, all created in a flat LCD about as thick as a newspaper. Another SI product is a vertical display of N_1 and EGT in which white bars climb up green borders towards amber and red. Such a display would have been difficult to produce as a commercial product as recently as 1980.

To show how fast the technology of avionics is moving, when in 1974 Ferranti built the prototype COMED, or Co-med, it was 'probably the most advanced multifunction inflight display currently being developed in the world', whereas in comparison with the colour LCDs it now seems like good old traditional technology. This is not to deny its very important role in many military aircraft, however. It contains optics which project on to the display a moving map and whatever appears on a CRT, the two being geographically synchronized. The map display is simply ciné film projected from a selected map cassette. The CRT display may be radar, FLIR, command tracks, waypoints or (round the edge) various kinds of useful data. Map cassettes covering an area the size of Europe can be projected, and if necessary the pilot can correct the map position and orientation to bring it into exact coincidence with the radar or FLIR picture.

We can now return to the mainstream subject of the cockpit revolution. It is perhaps predictable that there has been no shortage of people who — not because of ignorance, but because they have large axes to grind — have pretended that the new cockpits are in some way undesirable, or unreliable, or a threat to established aircrew trades. So far they have had some success, to the extent that Australian passengers have to pay for a third man on almost every jet flight deck. In the rest of the world the two-man cockpit has come hand-in-hand with dramatically reduced workload, in either routine flying or an emergency, with elimination of misreading of instruments (I wrote this before the M1 crash report) and a wonderful feeling of calm engendered by what is often called 'the dark cockpit'. If almost everything is switched off, with no need to tell the pilot much, that means everything is working normally.

Of course, the cockpit is not really wholly dark. In front of the pilots we find (typically) six displays, each completely flat, brilliantly clear, and — depending on mode selected — presenting various beautiful coloured pictures on a black background. Their versatility is amazing; in contrast to the rudely uncompliant presentation of traditional 'instruments', the new glass cockpit can be transformed at the touch of a button, though each display usually continues to present the same basic kind of information. In the case of combat aircraft we usually have a single pilot facing a much smaller panel containing three extremely versatile MFDs (multifunction displays) and with a wide-angle HUD at the top. The rest of this chapter is concerned primarily with commercial transport cockpits, but closes with

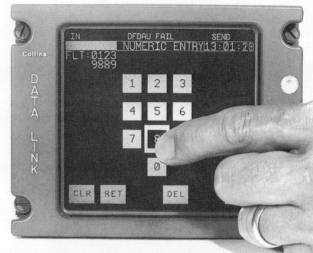
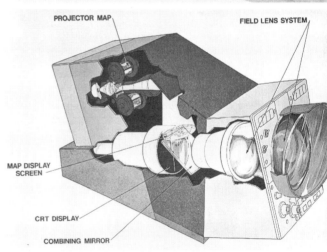

Top *The first avionic product to incorporate active-matrix LCDs is this interactive data-link display, with touch-screen control. The key touched is instantly highlighted to confirm correct entry.* (Collins)
Above *Simplified cutaway of a COMED.* (Ferranti)

a further look at helmet-mounted sights and other military display developments such as the Big Picture and the all-synthetic cockpit.

The glass cockpit revolution began in December 1978 when Boeing picked lucky Collins as sole supplier of the new instrumentation for the 757 and 767. A few weeks later Airbus Industrie contracted with Thomson-CSF and with VDO of West Germany jointly to develop similar displays for the

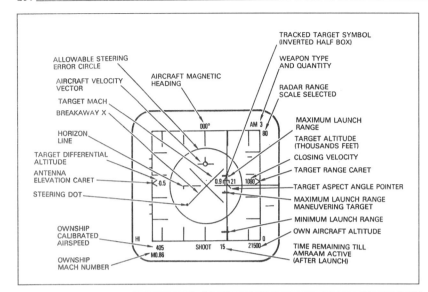

Though much of the running with displays has been made by civil aircraft, military HDDs (head-down displays) are today quite complex, even when they use traditional CRTs. This STT (single-target track) mode is one of the selectable modes of the US-derived radar proposed by AEG for the EFA.

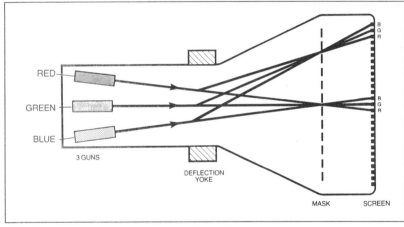

The principle of the CRT was briefly outlined at the start of Chapter 1. Slightly more complex, the traditional colour tube is of the so-called shadow mask type, with three guns. These cannot, of course, fire coloured electrons; the colours are created in the phosphor layer on the screen. (Smiths Industries)

A310. It costs years of work, at millions of pounds a year, to produce such displays. When the 757, 767 and A310 entered service these new cockpits were rather unknown quantities. In particular, to gain pilot acceptance they had to be little more than electronic versions of previous electromechanical instruments, so the full benefits of new technology could not be realized. Gradually, as pilots became familiar with them and airlines realized that they were a great improvement in reliability and maintainability over traditional displays (instead of being, as some had predicted, much worse), the pressure was on to retrofit existing aircraft and change over to glass cockpits on existing production lines. This again has demanded electronic displays not greatly different in presentation from their

predecessors, but in August 1984 Thomson-CSF was (predictably) picked by Airbus Industrie to supply displays for an all-new aircraft, the A320. At last the supplier felt emboldened to create truly capable displays, going far beyond anything previously offered to pilots. In turn, this spurred Boeing to put a modern flight deck on the 747-400 and McDonnell Douglas to put one on the MD-11, notwithstanding the fact that both are derivatives of aircraft first flown over twenty years ago.

As the pioneer glass cockpit, that of the 757/767 (they are deliberately almost identical) has two superimposed EFIS (electronic flight instrument system) displays in front of each pilot and two EICAS (engine indication and crew alerting system) displays in the centre of the panel. Each EFIS display is 6 in wide, but oddly they are not square. The upper one, called the EADI (electronic ADI) is 5 in deep (high) and the lower display, called the EHSI (electronic HSI) is 7 in deep. Each EICAS display is bigger, 7 in wide and 6 in deep. All are conventional three-gun CRTs, in principle just like a domestic colour TV. The tube has three guns all pumping out identical beams of electrons but, because of the way they are connected up, labelled red, green and blue. The three electron beams are obstructed in their travel to the face of the tube by a barrier called a shadow mask. This is thin, usually flat and extremely accurately perforated with millions of microscopic holes. The holes are arranged in an exact pattern so that, as the three beams scan rapidly to make the picture, all three converge to pass through each hole in rapid succession. On the inside of the face of the tube is a pattern of millions of dots of phosphor. They are of three types, one glowing red when struck by electrons, one glowing green and one glowing blue. They are precisely arranged to cover the whole face, so that in any direction the three colours follow in succession. The position of every dot is made accurate to within a few microns, so that, thanks to the shadow mask, electrons from the 'red' gun cannot fall on any dots on the tube face except those glowing red, and the same for green and blue. Thanks to the infinitely varying video input the effect of the pattern of RGB dots is to create a clear picture in any colour we wish, including black and white.

Modern cockpit displays are absolutely flat, mechanically tougher than domestic TVs, have foil shadow masks with a hole pitch of 0.2 mm to give superb picture resolution, of up to 80 line pairs per inch, and they can do stroke-generated (cursive) writing. Of course the obstruction of the shadow mask imposes some limitation on brightness, but as this is no longer a problem the question is academic. An advantage over rival displays is that if necessary, for example on a dark night, the shadow-mask CRT can be dimmed to zero. Today some tubes have a spectrally selective filter whose transmission characteristics are coincident with the wavelengths of the three RGB colours and much lower for other colours, and in particular almost opaque at IR wavelengths which would otherwise cause irritating distractions to anyone wearing NVGs. In brilliant sunlight a contrast enhancement filter (CEF) can be added, which attenuates light falling on the display twice (once when incident and the second time when reflected) whereas light actually emitted by the display is attenuated only once, thus improving contrast. The available brightness is determined by the power capability of the mask, and the latest so-called 'inline' CRTs — for example made by Tektronix to a design by Smiths Industries — use what are descriptively called periodic-focus guns whose power levels average 2 W/sq in, and as high as 5 W/sq in locally.

Today's most advanced airliner, the A320, still uses shadow-mask tubes but with important differences. Compared with the bigger A310 the new aircraft was designed with the benefit of the excellent experience gained with EFIS/EICAS displays, and so eliminates almost all conventional instruments. Thus the panel can be made much shallower, giving better forward view, whilst at the same time putting the pilot CRTs side-by-side (and each pilot has a perfect view of them because there is no obtrusive control yoke, only a small hand sidestick on the side coaming). Each display is bigger, all six being 184 × 184 mm (7.25 in square) compared with 159 mm (6.25 in), and the extra area has been used to display far more information. Thus, far from being mere clones of their

Typical alphanumeric colour display, in this case twin-engine pressure ratio, LP speed and exhaust gas temperature. As the numbers change, so the readouts move up or down the scales. Try designing the driver electronic circuits! (Smiths Industries)

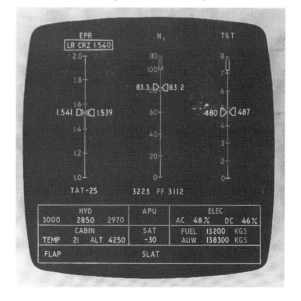

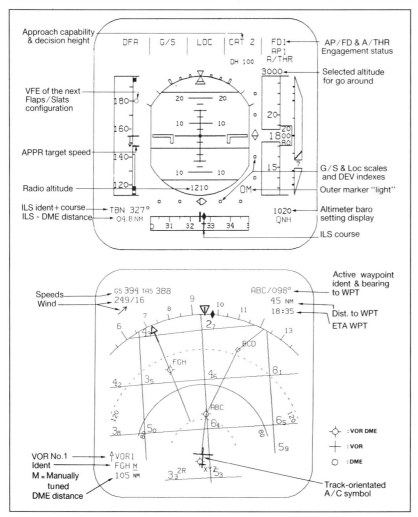

Approach capability & decision height

VFE of the next Flaps/Slats configuration

APPR target speed

Radio altitude

ILS ident + course
ILS - DME distance

DFA | G/S | LOC | CAT 2 | FD1
DH 100 | AP 1 | A/THR

AP/FD & A/THR Engagement status

Selected altitude for go around

G/S & Loc scales and DEV indexes

Outer marker "light"

Altimeter baro setting display

ILS course

Speeds
Wind

GS 394 TAS 388
249/16

ABC/098°
45 NM
18:35

Active waypoint ident & bearing to WPT

Dist. to WPT
ETA WPT

VOR No.1
Ident
M = Manually tuned
DME distance

VOR 1
FGH M
105 NM

-◇- : VOR DME
+ : VOR
○ : DME

Track-orientated A/C symbol

The first 'glass cockpit' displays that were much more than electronic versions of the traditional primary flight instruments were those of the A320. These are two picked from many operating modes for the PFD (top) and ND (bottom).

predecessors, all the displays are completely new 'instruments'. The pilot displays are called the PFD (primary flight display) and the ND (nav display). It is fair to claim that each tells the pilot just about everything he could ever want to know, the PFD (broadly) in the matter of the vertical plane and attitude and the ND in the horizontal plane. These two displays together tell the pilots far more than all the flight instruments in traditional cockpits. In the centre of the panel are superimposed displays called ECAMs (electronic centralised aircraft monitors), again 184 mm square. The upper one displays engine information and the lower one is normally dedicated to systems.

This unprecedentedly neat cockpit set a new standard. Today Boeing has followed it with a totally new flight deck for the 747-400 and Douglas for the MD-11. In each case the A320 philosophy has been followed exactly, with a PFD outboard, ND inboard and, at the centre, an engine display superimposed above a systems display. Boeing has stuck with Collins, while Douglas has given Sperry its breakthrough into the $1.3 billion a year airliner display market. The only new feature of the two huge new Americans is that the displays are even bigger, 8 in (203 mm) square, which may give a less cluttered appearance in some modes.

These glass cockpits not only look beautiful but they have revolutionized the man/machine interface. In a way impossible with electromechanical instruments, they are fed by various combinations of computers and symbol generators whose software has enormous depth and capability. Should there be a potentially serious fault, the pilot will be warned, but he can also instantly call up a synoptic picture of the local area to see what has happened. The software will tell him what to do, advise on the effects of vital actions and effects on other systems, and keep track of what is happening in real time. In theory, nothing of significance can happen anywhere in the aircraft without the pilot being informed. How far the pilot then has to take action manually is variable. In the MD-11 almost every emergency is countered automatically, though there are limitations (for example, dumping fuel has to be commanded manually).

Meanwhile, producers of older aircraft, such as the 737 and MD-80 families, have had to steer a middle course in making cockpits look newer whilst not doing anything really new that would invalidate a pilot's type-rating. At the same time, the displays in such aircraft, and in such derivative types as the ATP and Fokker 50 and 100, can provide considerable additional information, which is all useful missionary work for the technology. But the technology is moving as fast as ever. Collins put out this press release on 28 September 1987:

'Engineering development work leading toward the next generation of flight instrument display technology is ongoing at Collins General Aviation Division. Collins leadership in liquid crystal displays (LCD) for commercial applications has its roots in development performed for the Boeing 7J7 and other advanced programs. The Concept 4 avionics system has been designed to accommodate the transition to flat-panel displays with no change to system architecture or operation. Development of advanced computer algorithms and wide-range lighting modules has been progressing in parallel. Flat-panel displays offer a number of installation and operational benefits when compared to today's CRT instruments. Significantly reduced instrument depth provides greater installation flexibility. Low power dissipation of LCD flat panels reduces the heat that shortens avionics life expectancy, and display quality is not affected by sunlight.'

The several companies working on flat-panel displays are agreed that the way to go is the active-matrix LCD, and that it has a lot to offer. Smiths have built many FP displays that are only about 1 in (25 mm) thick, and thus light, and need no forced cooling. FP displays may come in as replacements for secondary displays to gain experience, prior to a possible general adoption in the mid-1990s.

For the more immediate future the buzzword is

'beam-index'. For example, Ferranti made the following announcement on 26 November 1987:

'Ferranti is now offering beam-index CRTs with the introduction of the CED 3000 series. They have been developed primarily for high-resolution colour electronic information systems and moving maps for use in helicopters and fighter aircraft. To aid visibility against reflected sunlight the displays incorporate an active contrast enhancement filter. This facility automatically adjusts the screen's brilliance to match changing levels of ambient lighting.

'The beam-index tube overcomes the various drawbacks of earlier generation shadow-mask tubes. Cursive operation is not required, as the raster mode is sufficiently bright even at the 0.3 mm linewidth possible. Much more information can be written at the faster raster writing speed than for cursive writing in the raster flyback period. Being less complex, and operating at lower power levels, the beam-index tube is inherently more advantageous. Its single gun and the absence of a mask eliminates convergence errors and provides the ruggedness of a monochrome CRT. This, together with more of the electron beam available to the phosphor screen, provides superior performance simultaneously in both brightness and resolution for raster images.'

Like the original monochrome TV tube the BI tube scans a single electron beam over the whole face. Rapid switching takes place continuously so that, for example, in the millionth of a second or less that the beam is aimed at a red spot on the face, the gun is connected to the red video channel. Less than a millionth of a second later the beam is aimed at a green dot, so the gun is connected to the green video, and so on. The positioning circuitry depends on a series of index stripes on the inside of the face. As the beam sweeps acrosss them, they emit UV light which is detected by photocells in the wall of the CRT funnel. This feedback controls the precise aiming and form of the beam, to ensure that no electrons fall outside the borders of the chosen colour phosphor stripe. Having no mask, colour purity and brightness depend critically on extremely accurate scanning and sequential multiplexing of the incoming video signals (video bandwidth must be more than six times that for a shadow-mask tube). Ferranti say 'cursive operation is not required', but so far as the author knows that is making a virtue out of necessity, because the BI tube cannot do it. Absence of a mask has been hailed as the way to a new order of brightness, but the traditional tube is fighting back and the author has not found any impartial observer prepared to

The fighter pilot of the future may wear this Agile Eye helmet, with vital flight data projected on the inner surface of the vizor, and look at the Big Picture covering the whole panel space in front of him. The touch-sensitive screen tells him just about everything he needs to know about the scenario outside. (McDonnell Douglas)

substantiate such a claim. Indeed, the BI tube has resolution problems (around 43 line pairs/in, compared with up to at least eighty). Not least, on a dark night the inability of the BI to be dimmed to zero demands elaborate switched filtering techniques to allow it to be used for night attack missions.

For the period after 1995 two further displays could supersede the CRT. The PD (plasma display) has been around 25 years, but is only now overcoming major problems. A PD is a sandwich containing a plasma, an ionized gas, many of whose atoms have lost an electron. Such a gas glows when an electric potential is applied, and to-day's PDs use AC with conductive strips inside or outside the glass anode and cathode panels. PDs can be very thin, amazingly robust and give a bright, flicker-free display. Even more exciting possibilities may be achieved with holography. Together with the AI 'pilot's associate', holography may revolutionize the man/machine interface yet again, especially in combat aircraft and helicopters where there is a need for a perfect symbiosis between on-board data, nav/aiming cues, sensor pictures, the outside real world (seen or unseen) and an artificial recreation of it.

With the demise of traditional instruments, displays are big business, and obviously will soon replace instruments in cars. Even retrofits can be major programmes. In March 1989, for example, Ferranti was awarded contracts to update the Tornado GR.1 cockpits which should be worth at least £50 million. Each aircraft will receive a bright holographic HUD, a terrain-following display using beam-index technology, a digital map generator with optical disc mass storage (with far greater capacity than current solid-state devices) and an Ada-programmed computer symbol generator. Meanwhile, designers of battlefield helicopter cockpits believe that the generation after the US Army's LHX will have a synthetic cockpit, with no outside view, and no fragile transparencies. Thus, the pilot's view will be the same day or night, in any weather. What we are not sure of is how much will be displayed in the aircraft and how much in his helmet.

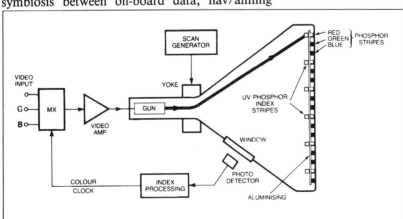

Principle of the beam-index CRT. (Smiths Industries)

14
FLIGHT CONTROL

Elmer Sperry demonstrated the first autopilot in 1912. By 1930 at least ten types of autopilot were on the market, all based on the fact that a rapidly spinning gyroscope tends to maintain its attitude. Thus, as an aircraft suffered unwanted changes in attitude, caused for example by turbulent air, valves around the gyro could be made to open and close automatically. These valves clearly could not transmit much power: usually they controlled ports in a vacuum system which deflected a diaphragm connected to a sliding piston valve in a hydraulic system powerful enough to move the aircraft flight controls to restore the original attitude, closing the vacuum ports. Alternatively the gyro could be surrounded by electrical pick-offs whose signals drove solenoids to move the hydraulic spool valve. By 1932 simple autopilots, such as the PB Deviator, were even being connected to a Marconi D/F receiver in order to fly a required course automatically, but this was a rarity.

About twenty years later, in 1952, powered flight control systems were common, in every case with an autopilot fitted; and various other adjuncts such as autostabilizers, yaw dampers and Mach trimmers were coming into use. An autostab is not very different from the most primitive autopilots, in that it attempts to maintain the aircraft in which it is fitted in the attitude commanded by the pilot. Most are relatively simple simplex (single-channel) devices, with limited authority. Should they fail or be switched off, the aircraft can be flown manually, but with a much higher pilot workload. In the case of the original production Harrier this workload, or perceiving the future need for it, occasionally proved to be beyond the pilot's capability.

To show the close relationship in principle between an autostab and an autopilot, the original Harrier autostab, comprising a pitch/roll computer, yaw computer and lateral accelerometer, was converted into a full-authority autopilot for the original Sea Harrier by adding an additional computer and sensor unit. The Sea Harrier autopilot adds to the basic three-axis autostabilization precise roll, pitch and heading hold, barometric height hold and self-test. To the author it is surprising that radar height lock is not available. In the current mid-life update to Sea Harrier FRS.2 standard an autotrim function is being added.

Yaw dampers are even more basic devices, providing very rapid corrective response to any incipient unwanted excursion in heading (yaw). This was frequently necessary on early supersonic aircraft, where attempts to fly without the yaw damper resulted in dangerous divergent control phugoids (oscillations) which were often actually augmented by the pilot getting out of step with the demand. An unusual but related problem was posed in 1954 by the Rolls-Royce TMR, better known as the Flying Bedstead, where a natural absence of stability, and tendency to tilt, was countered by fitting gyros able to sense any uncommanded rotation in pitch or roll and, via electrical pickoffs, operate the relevant high-power reaction control valve(s) to maintain a level attitude.

Powered flight control systems were developed in many forms. As we are concerned with avionics we need not worry about some aspects, but certainly must take note of artificial feel systems which attempt to give a natural feeling of force in the cockpit, and to protect the airframe against being overstressed by the pilot. At high altitude the air is so thin there is seldom any problem: the pilot could slam on full control deflection at maximum airspeed without breaking the aircraft. At low levels the air density is so high that command authority must be progressively restricted, until at peak IAS (indicated airspeed) the pilot, or autopilot, cannot move any control surface outside quite narrow

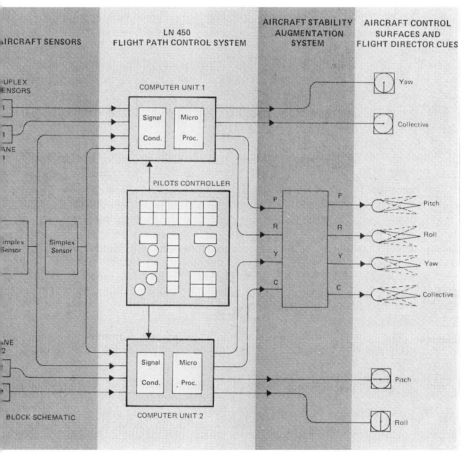

AIRCRAFT STABILITY
AUGMENTATION
SYSTEM

AIRCRAFT CONTROL
SURFACES AND
FLIGHT DIRECTOR CUES

LN 450
FLIGHT PATH CONTROL SYSTEM

COMPUTER UNIT 1

PILOTS CONTROLLER

COMPUTER UNIT 2

BLOCK SCHEMATIC

Left *To introduce the reader gently, the Louis Newmark LN450 is simpler than a full-authority autopilot but is called a four-axis (P, R, Y and C) system for helping helicopter pilots in bad-weather offshore missions. In the duplex mode Computer 1 has autopilot authority over P and R only, whilst feeding Y and C to the flight-director instruments; conversely, Computer 2 controls the Y and C autopilot channels whilst feeding P and R to the flight director.*

Right *A typical simplex (single-channel) digital flight guidance system for a fixed-wing aeroplane. Inputs are at the left and outputs at the right. Broken lines outline the two main LRU avionic boxes. Tacho is the feedback of servo-motor speed, ie of rate of surface movement. (Smiths Industries)*

limits — which are still ample for the most powerful manoeuvres. Almost all modern fast jets have a q-feel circuit, or ADC (air-data computer), which can feed in dynamic pressure as sensed at one or more forward-facing pitots. It is this which commands the flight-control authority and proportional feedback. Closely linked with the FCS (flight control system), feedback and yaw damper, there might be the third simple device mentioned earlier, the Mach trimmer. In the early 1950s almost all fighters and bombers suffered a powerful change in trim as they neared their limiting Mach number. Usually the effect was nose-down, but it could be nose-up. This could, of course, be countered by the pilot, but often the effect was powerful, and as it was repeatable it was often countered by fitting an auto Mach trimmer, sensing the Mach number and q-feel, and automatically applying just enough elevator to eliminate the trim change.

Today fighters and related aircraft are usually so

well designed, with the aid of computers and graphics displays, that their flight qualities exhibit no such unpleasant characteristics. It may therefore be disconcerting to note how many 'black boxes' they seem to need. For example, as described later, all versions of Tornado — a delight to fly in the manual mode, at any speed — have an AFDS (digital autopilot and flight director system), a CSAS (command stability augmentation system), a SPILS (spin and incidence-limiting system) on RAF aircraft, and control surfaces driven by quadruplex electrohydraulic power units.

Over the past forty years aircraft flight-control systems have developed in several directions, to solve different problems. One of the most important routes, which is a central theme in this chapter, is FBW and FBL. But in the 1960s, as explained in Chapter 11, great efforts were made to develop autopilots which, in partnership with a reliable and accurate ILS, could land aircraft automatically.

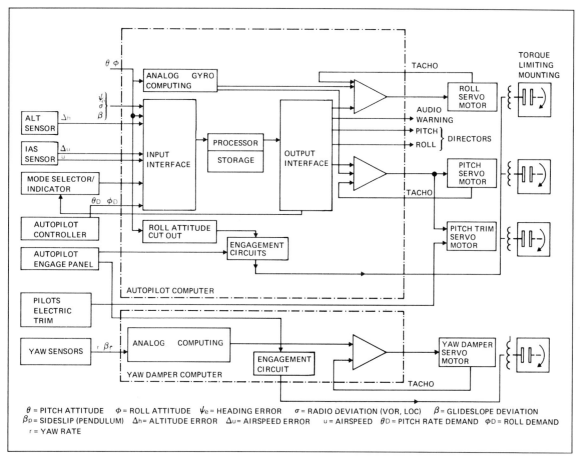

θ = PITCH ATTITUDE Φ = ROLL ATTITUDE ψ_e = HEADING ERROR σ = RADIO DEVIATION (VOR, LOC) β = GLIDESLOPE DEVIATION
β_P = SIDESLIP (PENDULUM) Δh= ALTITUDE ERROR Δu= AIRSPEED ERROR u= AIRSPEED θ_D = PITCH RATE DEMAND Φ_D = ROLL DEMAND
r = YAW RATE

With such an autopilot the weather (thick fog, for example) was no longer of importance, though it might make it impossible to drive away from the airport! Such efforts were not called upon because of any new feature or characteristic in the aircraft, so to solve the problems it was mostly a case of adding new black boxes and of providing such carefully arranged duplication that no failure could imperil the safe landing.

The first of these failure-surviving, fail-soft autoland systems, and the first to be certificated for civil operation in Cat III weather, was the Smiths SEP.5, fitted to the Trident. Any diagram of this would look incredibly complex. Most of the SEP.5 is triplexed, though the ADC, heading reference and autothrottle are dual. As explained in Chapter 11, such autopilots, linked to an AFCS (automatic flight control system) and autothrottles, put the captain in the role of passive observer during the most crucial phase of flight, an approach and land-

ing in blind conditions. Bearing in mind the reluctance previously shown by pilots even to accept a coupled ILS in visual conditions, or any other kind of autopilot-coupled mode of operation, it can be seen that the introduction of blind landing in the 1960s was a major psychological breakthrough. It occurred first in Europe, with such airlines as BEA and Air Inter. In the USA things moved more slowly, and in November 1971 J.D. Rector of Collins said:

'The rapidly advancing semiconductor device technology, and the competitive aviation marketplace, have resulted in the evolution of increased levels of automation for aircraft control. It has been our observation that the inclusion of automatic control functions in the cockpit has frequently preceded the pilot's willingness to use them.'

This move towards autolanding capability was just one of several major paths of FCS development. FBW/FBL has been mentioned, and another

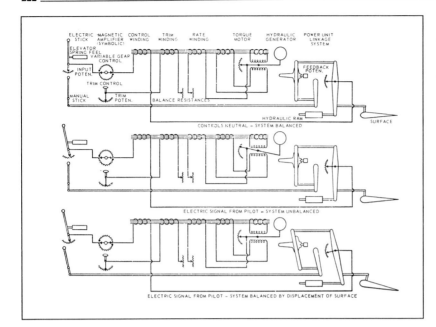

Simplified diagrams of the pitch (elevator) circuit in the V.663 Viscount, which nearly 40 years ago was the first FBW aircraft. It used the technology that was available. (Dowty Boulton Paul)

is ACT (active control technology). Though FBW/FBL has attracted the attention of the media, it has a long history and is really just one aspect of the overall process of improving the art of the FCS, and especially of ACT. Accordingly, I will run through FBW/FBL without further ado, before going on to the great variety of avionics found in a modern FCS.

The need for FBW (fly by wire) emerged in the period following World War 2, when aircraft

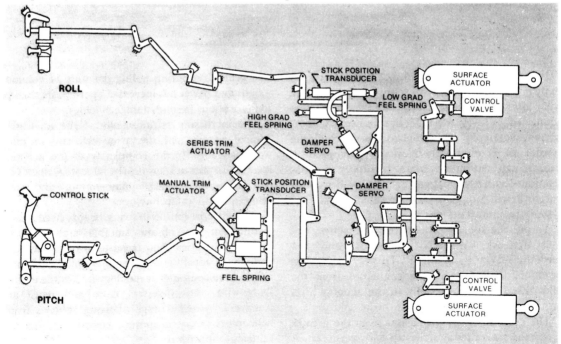

engineering was finding itself hard-pressed to meet the control demands of high-flying jets. Such problems as freezing of lubricant, the need for autostab and control functions to operate throughout each flight, the use of irreversible powered control units and, above all, the need for precise mechanical inputs at the far end of a long and complex mechanical control run, all conspired to force designers to consider electrical signalling. (Much the same thing had happened on the railways, where electrical signals fed along wires replaced literally miles of push/pull mechanical linkages to signals and points.) The author was privileged to have flown in about 1956 in the world's first FBW aircraft, the Tay-engined Viscount 663 which had been bailed to Boulton Paul to support the Valiant bomber programme. Though primitive, the system was true pioneering. The right-hand seat was 'all electric', with wiper potentiometers transmitting pilot input demands along dual electrical channels (I believe one used 28 V DC and the other, basically identical, used 110 V AC), with a feedback potentiometer at each powered surface. The left-hand seat remained permanently available for manual control by a staff pilot. Everyone liked the electrical signalling, but probably few of us regarded the aircraft as anything but a freakish one-off.

A little later the Avro 707C delta began a six-year programme at the RAE Farnborough with a Fairey simplex system on one side and manual on the other. This was a more advanced system, each axis having dual signalling circuits, rate gyros to measure change of attitude, and a lane computer to compare response with the pilot demand. This gyro/computer link not only corrected any discrepancies in normal manual control but also detected and corrected attitude changes caused by turbulence or any other external force. This was probably the first aircraft able to fly seemingly rock-steady through low-level turbulence. In turn, the 707C was succeeded by the RAE's 'Green Hunter', or Hunter Mk 12, which probably carried out more flight-control research than any other aircraft in the world until it was pranged. It had a basic quad analog system, with the safety pilot in the left seat having mechanical reversion. Elliott Brothers, now GEC Avionics, supplied what I think was the world's first digital autopilot to this aircraft.

In 1962 the basic design of Concorde was settled, one of the Anglo-French choices being to use fully powered elevons and rudder with electrical signalling. The main busbars were arranged to power two 26 V 1.8 kHz static inverters supplying the current to a quad signalling system, which was paralleled by

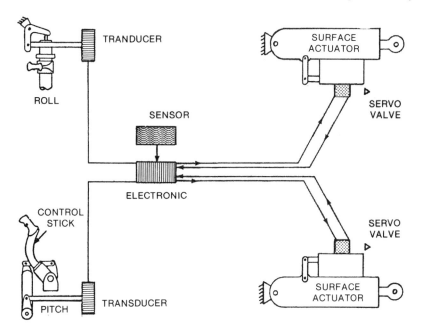

Left and right *Though purely schematic, these diagrams are based on fact, and emphasize why FBW has much to offer. The subjects are the pitch and roll circuits of the F-111 and an equivalent FBW system.* (GD Fort Worth)

a mechanical reversionary system. Apart from electric pitch trim, and a non-linearity device in the roll axis, all three axes were made similar. Pilot demand caused a displacement of a 'common point' mechanism by an amount which depended on pilot input force, trim position and feel-simulator reaction. The displacement generated an electrical signal, combined in a servoamplifier with surface feedback and with autostab signals before being sent FBW to the surface power units, designed by Boulton Paul. At the same time the common-point movement displaced a spring rod linked to a booster jack, to reduce control-column loads to an acceptable level (also used for autopilot input), and a torque limiter to limit loads in the mechanical system and protect against jamming. Each surface was driven by tandem jacks, one half of each power unit in the Green hydraulic system and the other half in the Blue. A duplicated monitoring system was added which continuously measured surface position and electrical/hydraulic system performance, and very rapidly switched channels or took other action in the event of failure.

This is virtually the FBW system still used on Concorde today, and one should not forget that, unique among commercial transports, this aircraft also has FBW controls for the powerful variable engine inlet system. Reliability of both the flight and inlet systems has been virtually 100 per cent during the 22 years the Concordes have been flying, but if modern microelectronics had been available 25 years ago Concorde's empty weight would be more than a ton lighter, and this would make a significant

difference to the economics.

In 1972 the United States got into the act, most notably with the NASA F-8C Crusader, which in May 1972 made the first FBW flight without mechanical reversion. This aircraft had simplex digital control, the first wholly non-analog aircraft in the world, the standby system being triplex analog. It was closely followed by another Government-funded programme, McDonnell's YF-4E SFCV (survivable flight-control vehicle), which was an attempt to find an FCS better able to survive battle damage. It had a physically separated quad analog system, the backup being a direct electrical path, and exhaustive bombing and gunnery tests demonstrated the superiority of the FBW system.

These encouraging results confirmed Panavia in their much earlier (1968) choice of triplex analog for Tornado, and, apart from Concorde, this was the first production FBW aircraft in the world. The basic CSAS (command stability augmentation system) comprises triply redundant pitch, yaw and roll gyros, a pitch computer and a roll/yaw (lateral) computer, plus a pilot controller and position transmitters. FBW links feed the computerised outputs to the tailerons, spoilers and rudder, with mechanical reversion for the tailerons only. The AFDS (autopilot and flight-director system) provides duplex digital trajectory control, sending autopilot command signals to the CSAS and flight-director command signals to the HUD. It can capture and hold Mach, IAS, attitude, heading, barometric or radar height, landing approach and,

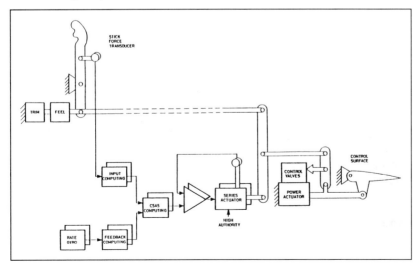

Left *One form of CSAS (command stability augmentation system) with duplex channels. The broken lines indicate a mechanical link between the stick and surface power unit.* (GEC Avionics)

Above right *A schematic diagram of the flight-control system of the Tornado ADV. Stick at lower left, pedals upper left and throttles at top (with input to hi-lift/sweep control). Small figures '3' mean triplexed signal (three channels).* (British Aerospace)

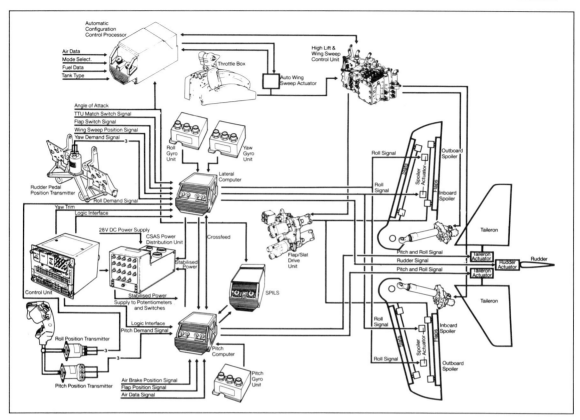

for the IDS attack Tornado, terrain-following. The F.3 interceptor has a further item, the SPILS (spin prevention and incidence-limiting system). This is a duplex computer and control panel whose function is to reduce the roll/yaw authority available to the pilot at high AOA (angle of attack) by taking the stick/pedal signals from the CSAS and scheduling each as a function of AOA; and augment the pitch stiffness to provide a more precise AOA control with a firm upper limit.

Tornado first flew in 1974, and the same year saw the first flight of the General Dynamics YF-16. This was one of the two USAF LWFs (lightweight fighters). The rival YF-17 was a stable aircraft with mechanical reversion, but the YF-16 was not only a CCV (control configured vehicle) 'relaxed stability' aircraft, but its FBW system was the first in the world to have no reversionary system whatever. The CCV concept would have been impossible to realize without modern fast-acting FCS computers, because in effect the idea is to make the aeroplane unstable in pitch. In an extreme case this would be like trying to throw a dart pointing backwards!

Traditional aeroplanes have the wing lift well behind the CG (centre of gravity), the resulting nose-down moment being balanced by a download on the horizontal tail. This download in effect adds to the weight, demanding extra lift from the wing. The tail download is especially severe just when the wing already has the hardest job, on rotation at take-off. Not only does this lengthen the take-off

CCV and RSS are acronyms taken for granted in the design of any modern fighter. Making aircraft longitudinally unstable, as in the case of the F-16, would be impossible without high-authority electronic flight controls.

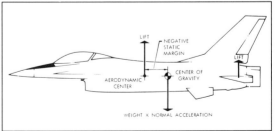

(and landing), and increase structural loadings, but it also fights against manoeuvrability in that the naturally stable aircraft tries to resist sudden changes in pitch attitude. If we dare to design for RSS (relaxed static stability), which we do by putting the CG close to or even aft of the centre of wing lift, we get an aeroplane where the basic nose-up moment is countered by an up-load on the horizontal tail; in other words the tailplane adds not to the weight but to the lift. Thus we can make the wing smaller, and the reduction in trim drag allows us to design the tail and rear fuselage to be smaller and lighter. Even more important, the aircraft is naturally unstable; any uncommanded nose-up rotation results in extra lift ahead of the CG, causing a violent runaway nose-up pitch which could be expected to tear the wings off. The aircraft is made flyable by the advanced FCS, with FBW signalling, which has great power, high authority, reacts with electronic speed and, via quad redundancy, has reliability as good as the integrity of the primary structure. Thus, via the small force-sensing sidestick controller (another innovation), the F-16 pilot gains significantly in manoeuvrability, because of the basic instability of the aircraft. Apart from this, it comes out smaller and lighter than a traditional design, burning less fuel, with more rapid acceleration, higher turn rates and able to pull more g in turns, especially at supersonic speeds.

To be precise, the F-16 is an RSS design, which means that, with its CG at about 37.7% of the wing chord, its pitch stability is close to neutral. In contrast, aircraft are now flying which are longitudinally exceedingly unstable. The first was a special research Jaguar at BAe Warton, used to support the design of the EAP and subsequent EFA. This was made roughly 3% unstable by adding weights in the tail; then huge strakes were added ahead of the wings to increase the instability to about 11%. This far exceeded anything attempted previously, and eliminated any possibility of manual reversion. The research Jaguar was designed in 1977 and tested in the early 1980s up to demonstrations of 'carefree manoeuvring' at high AOA. So far as the author knows, the only other aircraft to have equalled this degree of instability is the Grumman X-29, the first true FSW (forward-swept wing) aircraft to fly. With a thin supercritical section, the X-29's FSW appears to have demonstrated all that was claimed for it, including more lift, less drag, better low-speed handling and much more besides. After the flawless

first flight on 14 December 1984 the media homed in on the test pilot and ignored the engineers whose brainchild the X-29 was. The pilot said 'It's not fair; I'm like the quarterback who gets the glory'. At which scribe John Tierney felt moved to tell the world how the whole thing depended on the three FCCs (flight control computers) which sent their signals to the movable surfaces exactly forty times each second, fast enough always to overcome the inherent instability. No human could do this, 'So', concluded Tierney, 'the person sitting behind those computers was not exactly the quarterback. He was more like the football'. A little unkind perhaps, but it underscores that the latest aircraft are flown by avionics, not by humans.

From the viewpoint of control capability it is worth noting that the FCS tested in the AFTI/F-16 (Advanced Fighter Technology Integration) served new functions, even though this involved no new avionics. Its digital FCS controlled the normal F-16 surfaces plus diagonal ventral foreplanes which, used in conjunction with other surfaces, made possible decoupled (six degrees of freedom) manoeuvres, such as quite violent vertical or lateral movements without change in the pointing axis of the fuselage, or large changes in the fuselage axis without change in the flight path, or flat (unbanked) turns, or manoeuvre enhancement and gust alleviation. This last function is also available on the B-1B, which could accrue fatigue damage very rapidly from sustained flight at full throttle at near sea level. Accelerometers in the fuselage sense vertical and lateral movements caused by turbulent air, and send FBW signals to fast-acting power units driving canard vanes sloping down from the nose, very like those of the AFTI but proportionally smaller, to cancel out the motion before its magnitude could degrade crew efficiency or contribute significantly to structural fatigue.

A not altogether minor point is that the introduction of FBW systems means that the pilot's stick has to be connected to a transducer which converts either stick movements or, increasingly, stick input forces (without movement) into electrical signals. The design of these transducers involves technology of the very highest order, both to obtain precisely correct outputs, with exactly the desired aircraft response to varying input forces, and also because the whole unit is safety-critical, and in some situations the slightest fault could be catastrophic. The leader in this challenging field is a British company,

GEC Avionics, which is developing the sidestick transducer assembly for the Lockheed/Boeing/GD YF-22A as well as the 'primary flight controller' for the GD/McDD A-12A.

Today it is still a rarity to find a digital civil aircraft; for example Collins hailed *N800S* (a BAe 125–800) as 'the first digital bizjet' in 1985. It is interesting, therefore, to see the great complexity of the all-digital FCS developed in 1972 by what was then Marconi-Elliott Avionics for the Boeing YC-14, a large transport planned by the USAF to replace the C-130 and which impressed the author tremendously. Its FCS was just a bonus, developed in order to give precise control of the 237,000 lb aircraft at speeds down to around 90 kt, with the USB (upper-surface blowing) high-lift regime in operation, augmented by BLC (boundary-layer control) blowing of the leading-edge flaps. There were 41 separately scheduled movable surfaces, counting the rudders as three, not six. The digital FBW control system had to perform an exceptional extra range of functions, such as pitch/roll rate command, trajectory control with/without USB/BLC, throttle/flap USB speed control and DLC (direct lift control) spoilers, engine-out sensing and flap compensation (geometrically different asymmetric settings), aerial delivery, altitude/heading hold and flight-path angle, and engine-out configuration management (among other things, with FCS power switched to an emergency air-turbine hydraulic pump).

Today the only truly modern commercial transport flying is the A320. This looks deceptively normal, but any pilot converting to it will soon understand that it is a 1990s aircraft, whereas its rivals are 1960s designs. I have lost count of just how many computers are on board, but it reflects on the amazing power and compactness of modern microelectronics to note that the far less capable analog FCS of the A300 comprised seventeen main items with a volume of 151 MCU (a Modular Concept Unit is the standard unit of avionic box volume, equal to one-eighth ATR). The digital A310 cut the number to nine items, occupying 74 MCU. Today's fantastic A320 system has just four main items, occupying 32 MCU. So compact, yet the rewards are almost limitless. Once confident, you can do anything you like.

The classic case is a violent downburst, the most severe form of windshear. The system detects it in advance, but if these sensors were switched off and the unaided human pilot noticed what was happening only at the last moment, he can simply pull back on his little sidestick to the limit. The pitch attitude might go to 30° but would quickly come back to a stable 21° or thereabouts, in a stable climb at about 115 kt at AOA of 18°; in the landing configuration the last figures might be 98 kt at 19°. It would be impossible for the windshear or downburst to cause a crisis, impossible for the throttles not to match the demand, and impossible for the pilot to stall the aircraft. In the same way, you could work up to max-

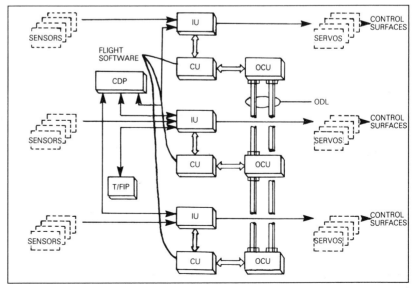

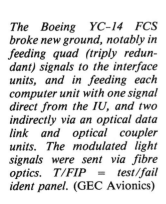

The Boeing YC–14 FCS broke new ground, notably in feeding quad (triply redundant) signals to the interface units, and in feeding each computer unit with one signal direct from the IU, and two indirectly via an optical data link and optical coupler units. The modulated light signals were sent via fibre optics. T/FIP = test/fail ident panel. (GEC Avionics)

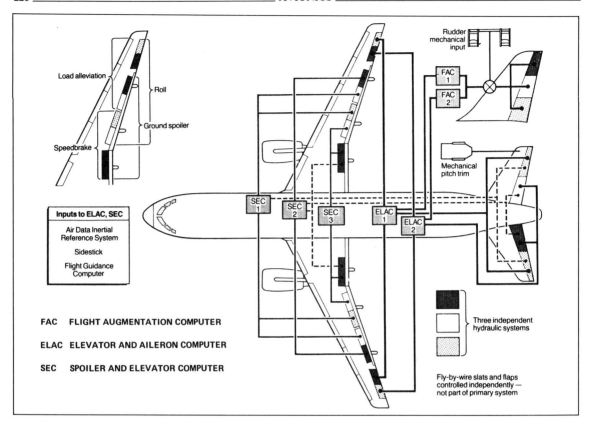

Load alleviation

Roll

Ground spoiler

Speedbrake

Inputs to ELAC, SEC

Air Data Inertial Reference System

Sidestick

Flight Guidance Computer

Rudder mechanical input

FAC 1

FAC 2

Mechanical pitch trim

SEC 1   SEC 2   SEC 3   ELAC 1   ELAC 2

Three independent hydraulic systems

Fly-by-wire slats and flaps controlled independently — not part of primary system

FAC   FLIGHT AUGMENTATION COMPUTER

ELAC   ELEVATOR AND AILERON COMPUTER

SEC   SPOILER AND ELEVATOR COMPUTER

imum permitted IAS or M_{MO} and then suddenly push the sidestick fully forward; the A320 would note what you wanted, but give you exactly what it knew to be safe. Even with almost every kind of simulated fault the A320 FCS puts other jetliners to shame.

Simplified diagrams show the basic architecture of the A320 FCS. Some of the major elements are as follow. The two FMGCs (flight management/guidance computers) perform autopilot and flight-management functions, including computations for autopilot cruise, 4D navigation, autothrust (engine control), autolanding to Cat IIIB, and vertical-profile flight performance management. The two FACs (flight augmentation computers) provide such basic functions as rudder trim, yaw damping, auto rudder steering and travel limiting, high-AOA protection and control of the speeds (upper and lower limits and manoeuvring speeds) displayed on the PFDs. The two ELACs (elevator/aileron computers) are part of the FBW system, with inputs from the sidesticks, autopilot, aileron and pitch trim, and a wide range of sensors,

outputting demands to the ailerons and elevators. (These are Thomson-CSF products, most other boxes being Sfena.) The three SECs (spoiler/ elevator computers) are similar, handling auto or manual spoiler roll control, speedbrake and (via the ailerons and two outer spoilers on each side) gust-load alleviation, as well as emergency manual pitch control and pitch trim. The idea somehow gained credence in Australia that the gust-alleviation was to enable the wing to be made weaker than it could otherwise(!); of course, it was really provided to avoid passenger discomfort and reduce the onset of fatigue. The two MCDUs (multifunction control and display units) on the central console are similar to those in other modern transports, being the pilot's management interface; they also indicate system faults, as supplied by the CFDIU (centralized fault-detection interface unit, photo on page 199) which channels all BITE data and, by scanning Arinc messages from each equipment, can trace the origin of any fault. Finally the FCU (flight control unit) across the centre of the coaming is an interface allowing the pilots to perform short-term guidance and handle some of the FMGC functions manually. This is the other non-Sfena part, coming from BGT in Germany; Honeywell-Sperry collaborated on the FMGC and MCDU.

As the Lockheed YF-22 and Northrop YF-23 are both classified, the newest fighter FCS that can be covered here is that of the British EAP technology demonstrator, developed around 1984–5 by GEC Avionics on the basis of the system developed (with a great deal of pioneering) for the unstable research Jaguar mentioned previously. Of course, the EAP again has a quad digital fully-FBW system, but experience with the Jaguar showed that instead of dual-triplex the system could be dual-dual and still remain operational after any two failures. Inputs are: stick sensors, pedal sensor, three-axis rate gyros, three-axis linear accelerometers, two dual air-data sensors, two AOA probes and two sideslip probes. Because of its instability the EAP requires a high degree of rate-stabilization about all axes, and the solution adopted is to provide four orthogonal packages, supplied by Litef of Germany, called AMSUs (aircraft motion sensor units). Each contains a strapdown set: two-axis rate gyro for pitch/yaw, two-axis rate gyro for pitch/roll (both gyros are dry tuned), and normal, lateral and longitudinal accelerometers. The primary function

of the AMSUs is to provide the FCS with aircraft rates and accelerations, but they also form a completely independent source of inertially derived attitude and heading to the standby flight instruments.

The air-data sensors obtain static and dynamic pressure from three probes, one on the nose and the others (giving redundant sources of reduced-accuracy data) on the canards. The overall system architecture is shown here, where AOA and sideslip inputs are identified as α and β. These are required to enhance pitch and lateral laws for carefree handling, but are not essential for safe flight. Thus the α and β inputs can be: one, fail operative; two, fail passive. This is achieved with two AOA probes and two sideslip probes, interfaced one-to-one with the four FCCs (flight control computers). The fail-operational capacity results from Jaguar experience, where it was found that sideslip can be determined from the difference between left/right AOA and vice versa.

The FCS avionics are up front, whereas most surface power units are at the rear. Each of the latter has a tandem hydraulic drive controlled by electrohydraulic first-stage actuators, half the quad actuator being in one hydraulic system (called H_1 in the diagram) and the other half in the other system.

Above left *Basic architecture of the FCS of the Airbus A320, the only totally new commercial jet and a yardstick against which future rivals will be judged. The hi-lift system (slats and flaps) is not included.*

Right *Simplified architecture of the EAP FCS. The quad (triply redundant) portions are obvious. Engine inlet control and nosewheel steering are coupled into the same system.* (British Aerospace)

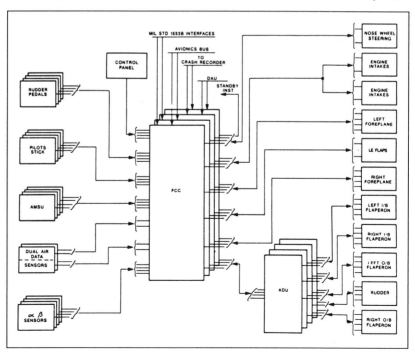

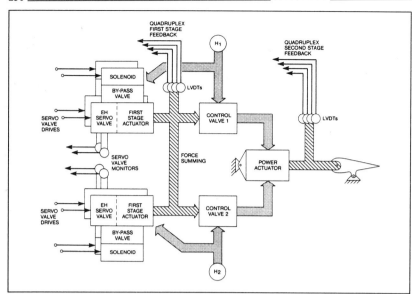

Left *Simplified block diagram of a single EAP primary actuator. LVDT = linear variable differential transformer (or transducer).* (GEC Avionics/Dowty Boulton Paul)

Below right *Internal configuration of an EAP ADU (actuator drive unit). TTL = transistor/transistor logic.*

To survive a second failure it is clearly necessary to detect, locate and isolate at least one of the lane failures. This required the addition of servo valve (spool position) monitors and solenoid-operated bypass valves to isolate a failed lane. Two-way serial data links join the four FCCs to the four ADUs (actuator drive units), supplied by BGT of Germany. The ADUs are non-intelligent; they do not have to take failure logic decisions or majority-voting decisions, but merely transmit (in both directions) information on the five aft control surfaces, before and after any two failures.

For the immediate future there are several new types of FCS in prospect. One uses DD (direct-drive) actuators and servo valves, which dispense with hydraulic amplification of the input signal and instead use electric actuators to drive the main power valve(s) directly. EHS (electrohydrostatic) systems use electric signalling, and electric power, to control and to power small localized and self-contained hydraulic power units at each surface. In the all-electric FCS hydraulics are eliminated, and very powerful electric actuators, with samarium-cobalt magnets, drive the flight-control surfaces under electronic control.

Many aircraft fitted with a simple manual FCS may still have an SWS (stall warning system). Almost all comprise some form of AOA sensor, typically sensitive over the range $\pm 25°$, a simple computer (the Conrac SWS computer weighs only 0.85 kg) and an indicator. Most incorporate provision for sensing flap position, which of course affects V_s, and some can incorporate a stick-shaker to give unambiguous warning. A few more sophisticated systems incorporate a stick pusher, which forcibly rotates the aircraft into a nose-down attitude, and an even smaller number (such as incorporated in the FCS of the BAe 146) sense not only the AOA and boundary of the safe-flight envelope but also the rate at which the limiting safe value is approached.

A basic input to any FCS, or even a simple SWS, is an ADS (air data system). In recent years such companies as Pacer and Rosemount have developed ADSs suitable for helicopters, STOVL and tilt-rotor aircraft, in which the local flight vector may make a large angle (up to 180°) with the fore/aft axis. Omnidirectional or orthogonal ADSs necessarily measure the dynamic q head along two or three axes, a computer then calculating the airspeed and direction of flight, as explained in the final chapter.

As several other topics, such as windshear warning, were covered in Chapter 10, the last subject to be addressed here is FBL, fly by light. Using light transmitted along an FO (fibre optics) data link can reduce weight, power and heat dissipation, transmit data much more rapidly (typically 10,000 times faster than electric signals along copper wires and 100 times faster than RF along coaxial cables), and reduce, almost to the point of elimination, interference between the FCS and other systems, or between external influences, such as EMP (electromagnetic pulse) interference and the FCS. It also opens up new possibilities in simple and direct feedback of actuator position and rate, either linear or rotary. Several workers have expressed the opinion that the ability of FBL systems to ignore severe EM interference, to function reliably in all-composite airframes, and to eliminate the need for secure and frequently inspected screening, will make their early introduction inevitable.

The first FBL system known to the author was demonstrated on a Calif A-21J jet sailplane in 1979 by what was then Lockheed-Georgia Co. This was a simple system in which pilot demands were digitized and sent along three 100 ft single FO cables to the servo electronics, giving closed-loop control in the pitch axis only. In 1985 Westland received an MoD contract to develop and fly an FBL system on a Sea King, but no further announcement has been made. Again in connection with helicopters, the various contenders for the USA's LHX programme have universally agreed to use an Adocs (advanced digital optical control system), but again not much hard fact had emerged as this was written in early 1989. Thus, oddly, the only FBL system I can say much about is the GEC Avionics system first flown on an

Airship Industries Skyship 600 on 23 October 1988.

A non-rigid airship is large, flexible and almost totally non-metallic. It is almost impossible to transmit control forces over great distances through so flexible a structure. Moreover, the big airship proposed with Westinghouse for the US Navy requires very accurate autostab and autopilot functions, besides carrying super-powerful radar and operating at a height where it would be prone to lightning strikes. On the other hand, things in airships do not often happen in milliseconds, so the pilot can be a decision-taking element in the loop and the FCS architecture can be relatively simple, with one lane operative and a parallel lane on standby. Another simplifying feature is that, as airspeeds are low, control-surface moments are modest and can be provided by small electric actuators adjacent to the surface.

The Skyship 600 pilot in the ventral gondola controls trajectory via four tail controls, two rudders and two elevators, some 140 ft astern. Sensors on the yoke send analog signals which are digitized in the FCC (in a more sophisticated production system the signals would be shaped according to the mode of flight). The microprocessor outputs one signal for each surface, which is reconverted back to an analog voltage which is passed to the FO signal transmitter and encoder (with the present system the computer can be bypassed). The encoder converts the voltage to a digital word and adds discrete bits, for example to command nav lights on/off. Additional bits are added to enable the validity of the signal to be checked. The digital word is converted to light pulses, and transmitted to the ADUs (actuator drive units). These contain duplicated signal reception and conditioning circuitry, the servoamplifier drives for the duplex drive motors and triplex position pickoffs forming the local servo-loop closure. The ADUs also gather and collate data describing the health of the complete local system. The two channels have independent power supplies, and it is probable that in a future system the electric power could be generated locally.

Longer-term possibilities are exciting. The obvious next-generation FCS will have an FO data bus able to make use of the enormous increase in bandwidth and signal-carrying capacity. Moreover, whereas at present there have to be electrical connections between sensors, computers and surfaces — for example, the yoke input pickoff — optical sensors are now being developed which can

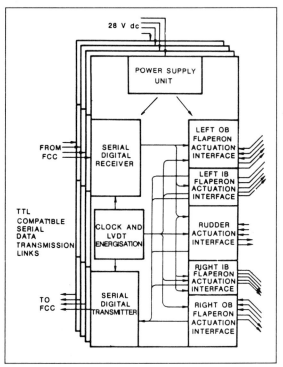

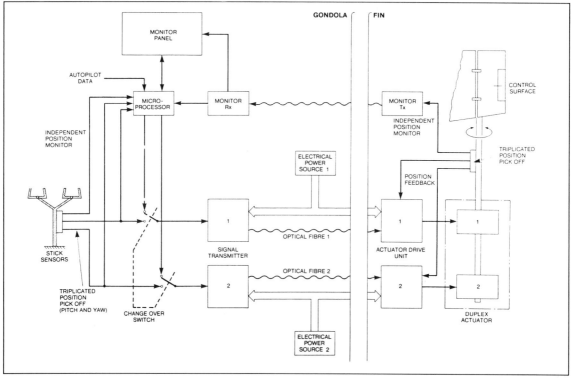

GONDOLA   FIN

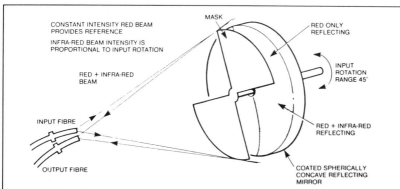

CONSTANT INTENSITY RED BEAM
PROVIDES REFERENCE

INFRA-RED BEAM INTENSITY IS
PROPORTIONAL TO INPUT ROTATION

RED + INFRA-RED
BEAM

INPUT FIBRE

OUTPUT FIBRE

MASK

RED ONLY
REFLECTING

INPUT
ROTATION
RANGE 45°

RED + INFRA-RED
REFLECTING

COATED SPHERICALLY
CONCAVE REFLECTING
MIRROR

Above *Schematic architecture of the Skyship 600 FCS. The FCC is labelled Microprocessor.*

Left *The first LI-LO (light in, light out) sensor to be developed for use in an FCS is the FORPT. This explains the principle.* (GEC Avionics)

eliminate the need for everything but light from the system. A diagram shows one of these 'light in, light out' sensors, called an FORPT (FO rotation position transducer). Its only moving part is the input shaft, carrying a fan-shaped mask rotating in front of a concave mirror. This mirror is coated with an interference filter, such that some parts reflect a particular wavelength, the mask and coating having the same shape. Input light of two wavelengths — red and IR — is TDMd (time-division multiplexed)

and sent to the FORPT, where it is reflected by the mirror out again along the output fibre. As the shaft/mask rotates, the IR output is varied, while the red output is unchanged. This gives an accurate measure of shaft position, in a device that is electrically passive, inherently robust and reliable and immune to variation in attenuation of the FO links. Many other types of passive sensor are being developed.

15

COMPUTERS

The last chapter in this book is probably the most significant, the most difficult to write or comprehend, the most exciting, and indeed the most of almost everything. There are hundreds of people walking around today — in, at the most, five countries — who hold in their heads the details of the complex inter-relationships between particular sub-systems in future aircraft. They are the programmers, and it is their task to design the software. To some degree they can claim to be the successors to the traditional 'aircraft designer'. The latter used to write down everything in rows of fat dog-eared design manuals. These volumes gathered dust throughout the lifetime of the aircraft, because they were the ultimate design authority. Today the software is so complex it can be conceived in the human brain but hardly written down at all, and if it were to be written down it would be absolutely meaningless to almost every ordinary mortal, even a traditional aircraft designer.

Where possible I have tried to ease the problems by filling in a bit of historical background, but in this chapter it is hard. At a rough guess I suppose the number of solid-state logic gates — simple switches which are the basis of modern airborne computers — was zero in 1958, about 10,000 in 1960, 1 million in 1970, 10,000 million in 1980 and maybe 10,000 billion today. If that doesn't underscore the problem, I don't know what would!

Some of the earliest uses of airborne computers were electronic control boxes for engines, of which the Ultra system for the Proteus engines of the Britannia comes first to mind (1951). This was an analog system (Chapter 1), which both sensed engine parameters — such as compressor rpm and turbine inlet temperature — in the form of continuously varying voltages, and applied control in the same way. But this was antedated by the much more complex computer needed by the German A.4

(V–2) ballistic missile, and which functioned flawlessly on the first full-range flight on 3 October 1942. This computer was electromechanical, because at that time this was the only available technology able to function reliably in a missile environment.

In the postwar development of long-range missiles, such as the American Jupiter, Snark, Navaho, Triton, Atlas, Thor and Titan, computers unquestionably posed the greatest problems and consumed more development man-hours than any other single topic (this is ignored in most popular histories of such weapons). One has to remember that most computers at this time were analog in nature, and that instead of solid-state devices they had to use vacuum tubes. I believe the first digital computer to fly was developed by Remington Rand Univac, in 1955, and used subsequently in Titan I. Other companies active in the field were AC Spark Plug, Bosch Arma and, especially, the Autonetics Division of North American Aviation. NAA built their first computer in 1949. This XN-6 was the first of about six stages of development which led in 1956 to the N-6B digital inertial navigation system for SM-64 Navaho, but this was cancelled. By this time Autonetics had the strongest airborne-computer team in the world, and though solid-state electronics was in its infancy it was being used very widely by this company as early as 1955. In that year design was completed for Verdan, and this was one of the landmarks in the story of avionics.

Some wag suggested Verdan stood for 'very effective replacement for dumb-ass navigators', and there was a grain of truth in this. Actually it meant 'versatile digital analyser', and from this time onwards anyone could see in basic form how to design a digital computer that could fly in aircraft such as the XA3J (later A-5) Vigilante, guide missiles such as Hound Dog, or even do industrial

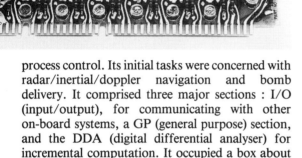

Microelectronics of 30 years ago, when everything comprised discrete components soldered on to a PCB. These boards from a Verdan computer are (upper) a logic board with 130 diodes, and (lower) a flip-flop board with 24 diodes and 32 transistors.

process control. Its initial tasks were concerned with radar/inertial/doppler navigation and bomb delivery. It comprised three major sections : I/O (input/output), for communicating with other on-board systems, a GP (general purpose) section, and the DDA (digital differential analyser) for incremental computation. It occupied a box about the size of a small suitcase (19.5 × 15.5 × 8 in), weighing 82 lb (37 kg). Typical circuit boards are illustrated. They contained about 1,000 diodes and 1,500 transistors (almost all these 2,500 devices were

germanium), 3,500 resistors and 670 capacitors. Main storage was on a magnetic disc, with a capacity of 1,664 words. As the disc rotated (on what I believe to have been the first-ever production air bearings) at 6,000 rpm the processing speed was 100 per second, or 0.1 kHz.

I have described Verdan because it shows where we had got to thirty years ago, when computers first became important in aircraft. At that time many non-flying computers — in those days relatively huge — were of the analog or hybrid types, but these were never important in aircraft. Virtually all airborne processors have been digital, operating with discrete 'bits' of data. And today we could do the work of Verdan, only about 500,000 times faster, with a single silicon chip not much bigger than a thumbnail.

We first encountered digital technology in Chapter 1, where it was explained that digital devices do not operate on continuously varying voltages but on streams of discrete 'bits', in exactly the way that we assemble letters to make a word. I said in Chapter 1 that the simplest analog computer is the slide-rule, and the simplest digital computer the abacus, though an abacus is mechanical. One of the fundamental reasons for making an electronic computer digital is that it enables us to make our computer out of simple devices which are bistable, in other words they exist in either of two stable states. Like the simplest electrical switches, they can be 'on' or 'off'. We call these devices logic gates. To build a modern computer we just need a few million of them. But before describing how gates work we must briefly look at binary notation.

We happen to count in tens; it came about because most of us have that number of fingers/ thumbs. Perhaps this is the only defect of the human body, because if we had 12 fingers/thumbs our number system would be better. But suppose we had no fingers, just two thumbs? Then, perhaps, we would count in binary notation, which is counting

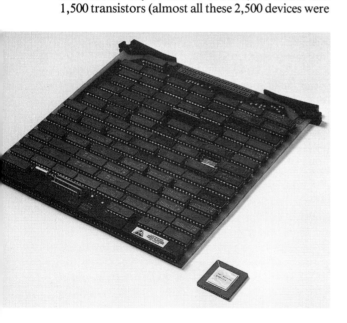

In 1970 this big processor circuit board was considered a marvel of compact design. Today it has been replaced by the single logic gate shown beside it.(Collins)

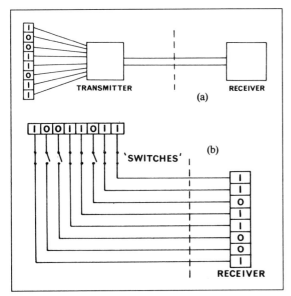

Digital data transmission can be serial (a) or parallel (b). The latter is obviously faster, but needs more conductive channels.

in twos. The very first number in binary code is 2^0 ($= 1$). The next number is 2^1 ($= 2$), followed by 2^2 ($= 4$). Next comes 2^3 ($= 8$), followed by 2^4 ($= 16$), 2^5 ($= 32$) and so on. Thus the numbers 1 through 11 expressed in binary code are: 0, 10, 11, 100, 101, 110, 111, 1000, 1001, 1010 and 1011, the number in each case being read from right to left. Thus, 100 becomes 1100100, 1,000 becomes 1111101000, and 1,024 (2^{10}) 10000000000. This probably seems very laborious, and most of us would hate to do our sums in binary; but it is just fine for digital computers. This is because every number can be expressed in terms of two things only. We call them 0 and 1, but we could just as well call them 'off' and 'on'. Using binary, a digital computer can process streams of numbers, each looking perhaps like 00101100011010001110110000101, millions of times faster than the eye can blink. Some superfast computers can accept instructions at the rate of 10^{11} binary digits (bits) per second. If we ourselves began accepting instructions at the rate of six a minute, 12 hours a day, 365 days a year, we should take on board No 10^{11} in just 60,000 years' time!

We call the incoming stuff data. It may come from a sensor, or from an on-board system, or from any of a thousand other places in a complex aircraft. No matter whether the original is a set of

numbers, or names (such as the names of nav waypoints) or a mix of letters and numbers, the data arrive in the form of streams of 0s and 1s, or rather in the form of tiny signal pulses representing 1s and missing or absent pulses representing 0s. Each pulse or non-pulse is called a bit. Every group of eight pulses is called a byte. Bytes are then combined to form words — machine words, totally unrelated to ordinary words — so that each word may have 8, 16 or 32 bits.

Thus we feed the computer with data made up entirely of two kinds of input. We then build our computer from millions of logic gates, each of which can be acted upon by a 0 or a 1, or more strictly by a 'pulse' or a 'no pulse'. The commonest of these logic gates are the AND, the OR, the NAND, the NOR and the inverter. In their simplest form (except for the self-descriptive inverter) these have two inputs and one output. In practice gates can be quite complicated, with many inputs. I have shown in schematic form the circuits for an AND and an OR gate; the reader can easily devise the others. As its name suggests, the AND gate gives a '1' output only if it gets a '1' at both inputs (or all 32 inputs if there are that many). In contrast, the OR gate gives a '1' output if it receives a '1' input anywhere. The NAND and NOR are the exact opposite: a NAND always gives a '1' output unless it receives a '1' at every input, while a NOR always gives a '0' output unless it receives a '0' at every in-

Some basic logic gates. Broken lines show switching functions, commanded by sending a 0 or a 1. Individually microscopic, these are the building blocks of today's processors.

name	symbol	operation
AND		
OR		
NOT (inverter)		output

put. An inverter just changes incoming '1s' into '0s' and vice versa. All these logic gates are constructed, usually in epitaxial silicon, with arrangements of devices which can range from a single n-MOS (metal oxide and silicon) or junction transistor up to quite complex groupings, depending on the number of inputs and other factors. Usually there may be a transistor, a diode and a resistor (for example).

In the 1960s each gate was a device in itself, separately packaged and connected into the computer by soldering or wrapping numerous wire/terminal connections. By the 1970s numerous gates were being connected into more complex devices called logic modules, again all formed into a single silicon chip. Such modules might comprise from ten to 200 or more gates, and they are given such names as adders, compilers and shift registers. These are the basic building blocks of the arithmetic part of a computer. Adders, for example, can add together endless streams of numbers, each expressed as a long row of binary 0s and 1s, and never make a mistake, but in many cases the module is designed to operate on the data passing through it, so that the output may appear superficially to bear no resemblance to the input. For example, if the inputs are an endless succession of radar heights there is no point in adding them or subtracting them; in this case what we want to know are how close we are to the ground, what is the rate of change (positive or negative is crucial) and how is the rate of change changing. All this could be done by one module on quite a small chip.

A proper computer also has at least one further module, called a memory. This does no processing but merely stores data and, especially, the program. By this time the reader will no longer need telling that avionics is a fast-developing technology. In a popular book written in 1971 it was explained that to store data one can use 'punched cards, paper tape, magnetic tape, magnetic cores, magnetic drums and discs or vacuum tubes.' To today's avionics engineer nearly all of this sounds prehistoric. Certainly more than 99 per cent of today's avionics memories are formed just like the logic gates in expitaxial silicon, MOS or a similar microscopic piece of semiconductor.

We have already met several kinds of memory. Perhaps the commonest kind is the RAM (random-access memory), so named because it is possible to read or write almost instantaneously in any part of it. Another very common one is the ROM (read-

only memory), any part of which can be read repeatedly but cannot be altered, because the contents are 'burned in' during manufacture. Among many others, some we have already encountered are the PROM (programmable ROM), Eprom (ROM electrically programmable, or alterable by UV light), Eeprom (electrically erasable ROM), Earom (electronically alterable ROM), Novram (non-volatile RAM) and Uverom (UV-erasable ROM). Volatile memories lose their contents if power is switched off. All these memories can be formed in a single chip, or even a small part of a chip. At a rough guess, excluding packaging, the volume required for any given memory storage is today one ten-millionth what it was in 1960, and the end is not in sight. On the other hand, the smaller we can make our computers, the bigger are some of the problems, as described later.

For the past ten years the buzzwords in airborne computers have been 'microprocessor', 'LSI' and 'VHSIC'. The two acronyms mean, respectively, large-scale integration and very-high-speed integrated circuit. So far as the author knows, none of these terms can be precisely defined, but microprocessor is the general term for a computer formed in a single chip. In a year or two more than half the airborne computers will be micros, and they already probably account for more than half the computers in today's aircraft fitted with twenty computers or more. Perhaps by year 2000 single-chip computers will account for 80 per cent or more of all computers built for airborne applications. LSI and VHSIC are more or less synonymous, and refer to large chips containing from 5,000 to over 250,000 components. Of course, these terms do not refer only to computers, but when ICs get as big as this they usually do serve a computing or management function. As an aside, the point may be made that such circuits would be almost impossible to design without the prior existence of very capable computers. In other words, it takes computers to design, manufacture and test computers.

It also takes computers to produce software. So far this topic has been avoided in this book, and this is partly because many people find it difficult to understand. Another word which is approximately synonymous with software is program. As in 'analog' we must note the spelling, which is the same in all English-speaking countries.

Of course, software is complementary to hardware, the latter meaning all the tangible parts of a

A typical avionics processor, RAMS (Racal Avionics management system) Type 5401 is one of a family of related LRUs designed to interface with different systems, which may be analog or digital. After disconnecting the multipin connectors on the front, the whole LRU can be pulled from its racking, the side removed and any circuit board pulled out, as shown. Different applications merely mean changing some of the cards.

computer. If a medical student were to hold aloft a human brain, he would have merely the hardware. To be of any use, a brain has to be alive, and filled with software (thoughts), comprising memory and experience, desires and objectives, and knowledge, including knowledge of how to solve problems. Some people have likened a computer to a complicated but uninhabited city, and the software to the people who make everything tick. Without a program a computer could not add 2 and 2.

We have already seen how seemingly laborious some computer operations are, especially the need to express everything in terms of either 0 or 1. This extends powerfully to the writing of programs. Things we do in our head in a fraction of a second, automatically taking care of numerous potential pitfalls, may take a computer thirty or more steps, laboriously written out so that nothing, absolutely nothing, is left to chance. Major computers, even those in airborne applications, may have a program made up of 250,000 separate steps. Herein lies the biggest problem confronting both the makers and users of advanced computers.

Like all other data inside a computer the software has to be made up of seemingly endless streams of 0s and 1s. These are assembled into bytes and words, though quite soon we detect various kinds of hierarchy. First, the software is made up of different forms of instruction called by such names as routines, assemblers, compilers and narrators. Second, it is almost always divided into two parts. The basic software is provided by the equipment manufacturer. This is machine-oriented and enables the user (any user) to use the computer. It comprises such parts as diagnostic programs, I/O (input/output) conversion routines, compilers and programs for file- or data-management. In contrast, application software is user-oriented, and more often than not it is compiled by a subcontracted software house or even by the user himself. It is related totally to the computer's specific application(s). Third, the entire software has to be written in a language that the machine can understand.

We do not need to spend too much time on software, but I would like to emphasize what I wrote earlier: that software, and especially SQA (software quality assurance) is probably the fastest-growing engineering discipline in the world. Since the first edition of my *Jane's Aerospace Dictionary* I have collected more than 2,600 terms relating to software, of which probably 2,500 date from 1985 or later. Hundreds relate to such topics as SQA, Software simulations, the SDE (software development environment), Software for complex real-time systems, Automated tools for software, Software for IKBS (intelligent knowledge-based systems) and many more. This may give readers just a faint idea of the gigantic worldwide demand, which is made all the more acute by the fact that almost everyone — certainly most British school-leavers — has never heard of it.

I touched on the problem of language. Inevitably this has to be written at different levels, though any one program is probably written all in one language. At one extreme are various machine codes, instantly understood by the computer but totally meaningless to any ordinary human. At the other extreme is plain English, or other everyday

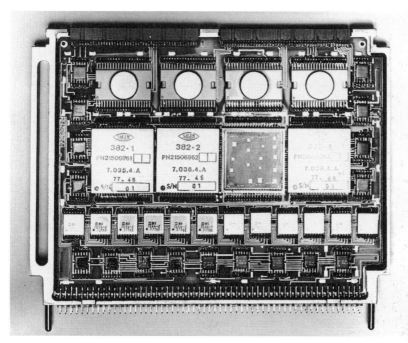

This Sagem UT 382–50 processor fits on to a single circuit board. Processing speed is 300K (300,000 operations per second). France will probably eventually have to adopt Ada, but the preferred French military HOL remains a language called LTR.

Right *A typical example of duplicative systems management is seen in the CMS-80 which manages the avionics aboard the AH-64A Apache helicopter. This is the control/display unit, compatible with NVGs. (Collins)*

language, understood by people but not by the machine (I do not believe anyone has yet thought it worth while creating a computer that understands such a language). In between come the computer languages used for today's software, which are known as HOLs (higher-order languages). These languages are still almost meaningless to the man in the street, but they are very much easier to understand than low-level machine codes. Programmers can learn most of them relatively painlessly and quickly, the structure of the program (often called the architecture, though this word is also used to describe the structure of avionics systems) is clearly visible, facilitating modifications, and the software is no longer machine-dependent but universal.

There are at least 250 HOLs in current use, but half a dozen account for about 80 per cent of the lines of software in modern aircraft. Obviously, what the world has needed has been a common universal HOL. It will have been obvious that the author takes a jaundiced view of the fact that whatever is chosen in the United States pretty soon becomes the world standard, because this has given us VOR, TRSB and other things criticised in this book. In the field of HOL it has given us Ada. This is the end-product of a big effort started by the US Department of Defense in 1975. Eventually a French HOL devised by CII Machines Honeywell-

Bull was selected and used as the basis for Ada, which has subsequently been adopted essentially as the world standard, at least in the sphere of defence. The author is not a programmer, and so can only express the opinion of experts, but it seems that Ada is a mighty achievement, but one that will cause millions of furrowed brows well into the next century and may possibly not work at all. For example, we in the UK are going to throw away our own Coral 66/Mascot which is easy to learn, truly portable and seems to have no shortcomings, and adopt the universal Ada which is desperately difficult to learn, is almost certainly not portable (in other words you can't take software from one application and use it to program a similar device in a different kind of vehicle) and bristles with problems, many of them stemming from the language's sheer complexity. I read of fresh problems every few days. Maybe if nobody starts a war for thirty years everything will be fine.

Certainly Ada does nothing to solve the central crunch-question, which is that, while processors become ever smaller, faster and more capable, so do their software problems multiply. A cynic could predict that in 2025 we shall have one man churning out fantastic microprocessors — designed by computers and made by computers — and five million highly paid programmers all over the world trying to provide the software. Certainly, and this is an entirely serious statement, there will soon be more people making and debugging software than making computers. There are many reasons for this. An obvious one is that, the greater the capability of the computer, the greater the length and complexity of the program. Suppose you had to write down a *complete* list of all your own experiences and resulting instructions, such as 'If a piece of metal is bright orange and glowing it is probably very hot; you should not touch it. If you see a fly on a window you should not kill it with a hammer...' You might end up with several billion lines, and this is the kind of length we are talking about, but with the big difference that the software lines tend to be consecutive and inter-related.

Another part of the problem is that with today's awesomely capable computers the communication problems are also awesome. The programmers form the essential bridge between the computers and the customers, but often the latter do not know how to express their exact requirements — note, they have to be exact — in a way that the programmer can understand and translate into software. Time after time the problems are totally unexpected, and do not surface until months later, and in at least two recent cases after catastrophic aircraft accidents. It is probably fair to say that every program for a modern computer starts off riddled with various kinds of difficulty. These may be caused by simple errors, or by the programmer not quite understanding some aspect of the computer's tasks, or by overlooking various details of the problem, such as the finite time aircraft or systems take to respond to demands, or the need to tell a system to ignore a demand whose magnitude is zero. Debugging the software is unquestionably the hardest and most protracted task in the entire process of creating a new aircraft.

This is especially the case where the computers are essential for safe flight, as is now becoming universal for commercial, business and military aircraft. It is fair to claim that, with the software we now have in advanced aircraft, the debugging can never be perfect. The most we can hope for is to get the program very nearly perfect, and if possible without any 'bugs' that could have serious consequences. This is not good enough for certification authorities, so the answer is to provide duplicative redundancy, and — a fairly new idea — dissimilar redundancy. Thus, we use triplex or quad channels,

and get a different software house or team to write the program for each channel. Not only is the software configuration likely to be quite different in the three or four channels but the actual statements and instructions may be expressed in different ways, which virtually precludes any duplication of an error. Even then, some odd combination of circumstances may cause catastrophe: for example the crash of the first Saab Grypen has been traced to software.

This notion of coupling computers together is also of fairly recent origin. Only thirty years ago no non-American fighter in service even had a computer. Coupling them together gradually emerged as a sensible idea in the late 1960s, when it was realized not only that ever-bigger central processors could no longer cope but also that one could do much better than link everything with looms of thousands of cables, which were heavy and so complex that building wiring looms became one of the most labour-intensive and costly tasks in aircraft manufacture. Any modification caused severe problems, even with every wire tagged and labelled. The advent of all-digital aircraft opened the way to today's architectures based on data buses.

The word bus was first used in aircraft in 1931 to mean the main feed cable of an electrical power system. Aircraft engineers still use it in that context,

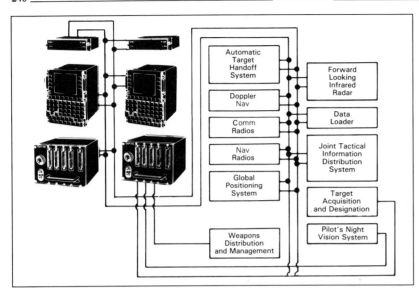

Left *Architecture of the CMS-80, with twin buses. (Collins)*

Below *Most bus systems require that wires be cut at connections, very much like wiring a house. Boeing's DATAC, which was planned for the propfan 7J7, simply couples subsystems by electrical induction by clamping a transformer round the bus.*

so a data bus ought to have its full title. There is nothing very complicated about it; it is just the main highway along which data travels. Some data buses are already optical fibres, conveying light, but every production data bus known to the author is a twisted-cable pair, invariably electrically screened and with the screen (shield) grounded (UK = earthed) at all breaks and ends, to eliminate electronic interference in either direction (in or out).

There are two buses that are fast becoming world standards. Naturally they are American, though both were as good as avionics engineers could make them when they were invented in 1975-7, and both have proved amenable to progressive improvement. Hopefully they will endure until all inter-LRU communication is optical. They are called Arinc 429 (civil) and MIL-STD-1553B (military).

Arinc 429 was first used on the 757, 767 and A310. It is a single-source, multi-sink bus, in other words only one LRU (black box) can transmit data along the bus but everything connected to the bus can receive it. Usually the transmitting unit is at one end of the bus, so all traffic (flow of data) is in one direction only. This is a drawback, in that twice as many cables are needed to equal the performance of a two-way system. As the data flows along the bus it encounters side branches called stubs which supply the data to the subsystems or subsystem computers. Each of these has several input ports, each connected to a different bus, but only one output port. There is thus one Arinc 429 bus for each computer or subsystem processor in the aircraft. Some of the

latest airliners contain over 150 Arinc 429 buses, many running in a common loom and others physically separated to provide extra safety. Small specialized dedicated computers called bus controllers organize and control the flow of data along each bus. With Arinc 429 the maximum number of receivers on each bus is twenty, though the French Digibus (formerly Ginabus) can accept 32.

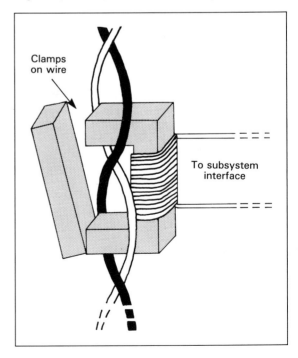

Clamps on wire

To subsystem interface

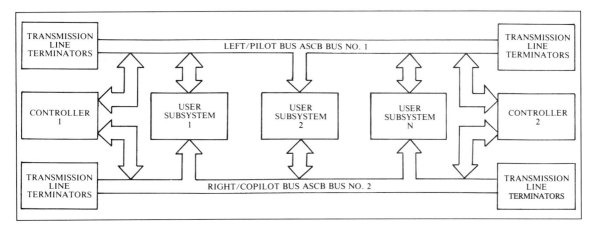

Each signal is modulated in what is called bipolar RTZ (return to zero) format, which means signals are formed by switching between three states (voltages). The hi state can be ± 13 V, the lo state ± 5 V and the null state ± 2.5 V. In any bit interval a hi returning to a null represents a logic '1', a lo to a null being a '0'. Data can be sent in one of two data-rate bands, the high rate being 100K bits/s and the low rate 12 to 14K bits/s. All words are 32-bit. Bits 1–8 form a label, and 9–10 the source/destination identifier. Bits 11 to 28 or 29 are available to carry the data. Bits 29 or 30 to 31 form the sign/status matrix and the final bit is the parity digit. The gap between words must be at least four bits.

A few special word formats can be provided, the most common being to convey latitude/longitude data. There are numerous subsidiary Arinc specifications which exactly define particular input signals. Arinc 547 defines the characteristics of the signal from a VOR, Arinc 561 defines characteristics of an inertial system, Arinc 568 the signal from a DME, 571 the signals from an inertial system, and 575 those from a DADC (digital air-data computer). Arinc 453 defines the high-speed bus linking a weather radar to its display: generally similar to Arinc 429, it accepts words other than 32-bit length. Certainly the author believes there is a need for a civil bus handling data much faster than 100K bits/s. One such product, the ASCB (avionics synchronous control bus) by Sperry, carries data at the rate of 600K, but is used only on that maker's (now taken over by Honeywell) equipment, on such aircraft as the ATR 42/72, Dash-8 and ATP. For the immediate future the SAE (Society of Automotive Engineers) has canvassed widely for opinions and has drafted a baseline design for a

Architecture of ASCB specifies duplicate buses and controllers. All subsystems are informed that a new frame is starting every 25 ms (0.025 s); the subsystem responses contain the usual addresses, as well as checksums of numerical data.

two-way bus handling 20M bits/s, with a choice of coax or FO transmission, serving up to 64 terminals with VHSIC technology, with integrated data and audio capability and a message length of up to 4,000 16-bit words.

This compares with a maximum message length of 32 such words for MIL-STD-1553B, which in terms of number of aircraft is by a very wide margin the most important digital bus in the world. Work began on it around 1972, and the standard was defined and published in 1975, the F-16 using it from the start. Other early users include the updated B-52G/H, B-1B, Space Shuttle, F/A-18, EH 101 and EAP. Like VOR, 1553 did not set its sights too high, so it worked from the start and is fast becoming the globally accepted system except in France, where Digibus looks like being entrenched for the foreseeable future.

The original 1553A described a single twisted-cable pair, invariably screened by at least one layer of shielding with earthed connections at all breaks and terminals. It can have a maximum length of 100 m (328 ft) with 32 stubs, conveying data in both directions (thus called 'multi-source, multi-sink, bi-directional') terminated by a resistor at each end. Data are sent at 1 MHz (1M bits/s) as biphase pulse-coded, pulses being sent out at from 18 V to 27 V peak-to-peak, the detectable voltage at any stub being 6–9 V. All words are 16-bit, plus a parity bit preceded by two sync pulses which bring up total

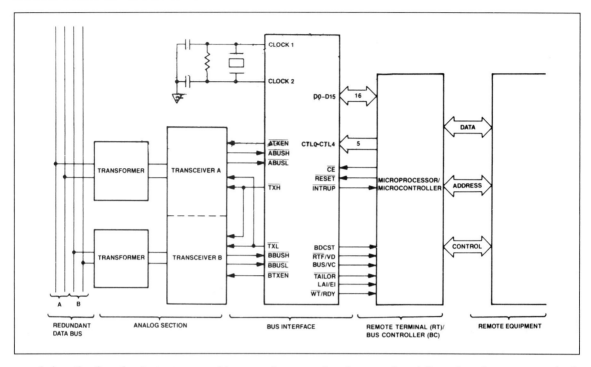

word length (ie, time) to twenty bits, so the transmission rate is 50K words/s. There are three types of word: command words can be generated only by the bus controller, status words can be generated only by the remote terminals, and data words can be sent in any message. Even the descriptions of these words occupy one of the big volumes needed to define the whole system.

The 1553A bus was updated in 1978 by 1553B, itself since several times updated. The most important feature of 1553B is that, should the bus controller or a main computer for any reason fail to function, bus control functions can be passed to different remote terminals. Another addition is a broadcast mode which warns all terminals to be ready to receive data, ensuring that the data do reach all destinations. Many 1553B architectures are of dual or even triple redundant type. The objective, of course, is to ensure that the aircraft's 'nervous system and brains' keep working even after major parts have been damaged. Clearly you cannot just have parallel sets of twisted wires. You need a great deal of bus controller intelligence to ensure what can be fantastically complex forms of failure-survival. For example, the system may have to deal with several places where buses are severed, other places where they are shorted out (by wires touching

each other, or the airframe) and remote terminals intent on pumping out degraded or garbled data. It is part of the task of the software to test data for validity and screen out anything clearly suspect, but I think we still have some work to do to make data buses survive the various failures caused by combat damage.

It is clearly not possible to illustrate the complete architecture of the avionics in a modern combat aircraft, but two contrasting diagrams give a very broad-brush idea. One shows the central portion of the single bus used on the Hawk 200, which is an extremely efficient retrofit on an aircraft that began life as a trainer with no digital bus at all. The other shows some of the features of a parallel-bus system developed by a British company as a retrofit to upgrade light fighter and attack aircraft (in particular the A-4 Skyhawk). Looped overbridges signify crossings without contact; for example radar video goes straight to the CIU, and video from the seeker head of the AGM-65 (Maverick) attack missile goes straight to the DP, in both cases bypassing a bus. Of course, in other applications it would be simplicity itself to tie in such extras as a doppler or a radar altimeter, linked to both buses. The Hotas box shows the stick and (enlarged) the multi-finger grip on top of the throttle. The DTM (data-

Left *A typical MIL–STD–1553 terminal. The central interface has 48 pins. That marked ATXEN, for example, is No 17 'Bus A transmit enable'.*

Right *The MIL–STD–1553 bus architecture provides for any degree of complexity of connection between buses, operating devices, microcomputers, bus controllers and remote terminals. The basic unit of data is the word, and this shows the formats of the three kinds of word, usually sent in this sequence: COMMAND (Transmit command, Receive command or Mode command), STATUS and then DATA (any number of words, possibly thousands). Then follows an interrecord gap followed by the next COMMAND word. Times 1 to 20 are µs.* (Rockwell)

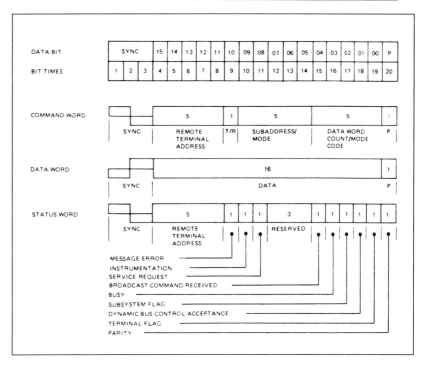

transfer module) is not part of the aircraft, as explained in Chapter 7. Another major item missing from this diagram is an EW (electronic-warfare) suite, which varies widely between customers. As explained in Chapter 9 EW devices have to be tied into the main bus system, but careful checks and interlocks are needed to ensure countermeasures are not triggered at inopportune moments.

I think this gives an outline of modern airborne computers and how they are linked into digital systems extending to every part of the aircraft. I had thought of going on to discuss such things as air-data systems, fuel-system management, stores management, cargo/CG management and Fadec (full-authority digital engine control), but decided that, at this point in the book, they might appear somewhat 'old hat'. Accordingly, I will give only a brief overview of some of these subsystems, merely

A simple example of a 1553B aircraft is the British Aerospace Hawk 200, which has a single bus whose central section (without controllers) is illustrated. INU = inertial navigation unit.

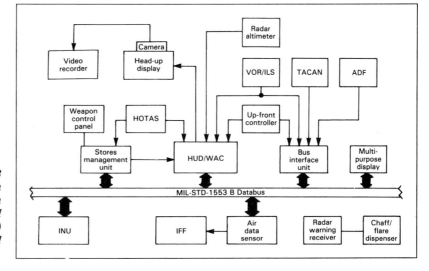

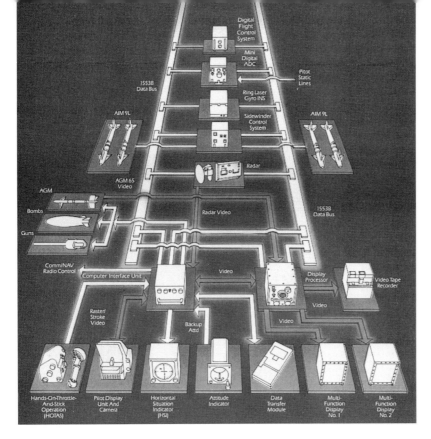

Labels in figure:
Digital Flight Control System; Mini Digital ADC; Pitot Static Lines; 1553B Data Bus; Ring Laser Gyro INS; Sidewinder Control System; AIM 9L; AIM 9L; Radar; AGM 65 Video; AGM; Bombs; Guns; Radar Video; 1553B Data Bus; Comm/NAV Radio Control; Computer Interface Unit; Video; Display Processor; Video Tape Recorder; Raster/ Stroke Video; Backup Attd; Video; Video; Hands-On-Throttle-And-Stick Operation (HOTAS); Pilot Display Unit And Camera; Horizontal Situation Indicator (HSI); Attitude Indicator; Data Transfer Module; Multi-Function Display No. 1; Multi-Function Display No. 2

Simplified arrangement of a dual-bus system installed as a retrofit to upgrade the A-4 Skyhawk. There are many other options, but the basic architecture and flow directions would not alter. (Smiths Industries)

in order not to omit them entirely.

The leading air-data system supplier is GEC Avionics, whose SCADC (standard central air-data computer) is a family of closely related TRUs each tailored to one of forty-odd different aircraft applications but with high commonality. This commonality is made possible by the software, which recognizes the host aircraft type from a code wired into the aircraft connector pins and immediately selects the output parameters, ranges and scalings (for example, an F-111 can input much greater total pressures than a C-5B). Precision pressure measurement is provided by the STA (static transducer assembly) and TTA (total ditto), each of which is a Solartron oscillating cylinder fed from the static or pitot (pressure) sources. The resulting frequencies are exactly measured by the TIM (transducer interface module). Isolated analog signals, which duplicate existing interfaces, are generated on the synchro interface (SIM), synchro transformer (STM) and potentiometer interface (PIM) modules. Any special interfaces are provided by the unique interface module (UIM). Use of the circuits on all output modules is governed by aircraft-dependent data held on the configuration control module (CCM). The 1553B bus interfaces are processed by the remote terminal module (RTM), which the air-data processor (ADP) feeds via an RT subaddress. The

key to the SCADC is to be found in the modularity of the software governing the Z8002 microprocessor, which is the heart of the ADP.

This gives an inkling of how far we have come since the first ASI (airspeed indicator) was connected to a pitot/static system. In the same way, we no longer just let the pilot play with a throttle lever connected by push/pull rods and levers to the fuel control on the engine. Today we are a thousand times more complex, yet the whole idea is to make the pilot's task simpler. Electronic engine control goes back a long way, but became complete only very recently. The first Fadec in service was developed by DSIC (Dowty and Smiths Industries Controls) for the Pegasus engine of the various subtypes of Harrier II.

This is a demanding application. In hovering flight the safety of the aircraft depends upon the single engine, there being no lift from anywhere else. The engine has four vectored nozzles which can be pilot-controlled in combat. The engine has four thrust ratings, the highest of which is Short Lift Wet; each has its own rpm and temperature limits, and also time limitations. The Fadec must also control acceleration rates and fan speed limits. Altogether the demands overstretched traditional hydromechanical controls, which required an excessive number of maintenance man-hours if they

Block diagram of a typical thrust-management system for a commercial jetliner (DC-10). It includes such features as alpha floor (limitation of AOA) and limitation of speed with flaps extended.

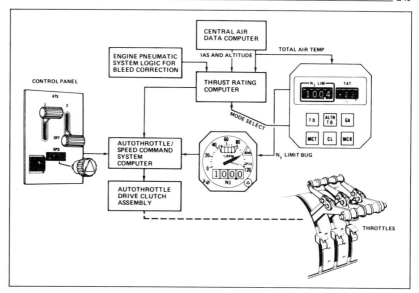

A greatly simplified Fadec architecture, together with a photograph of the actual box on a Pegasus engine. (DSIC)

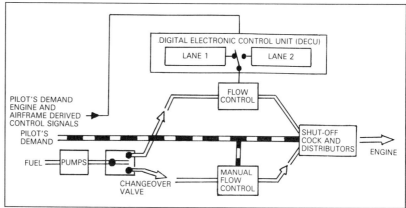

were to keep in trim.

The Harrier II Fadec is shown greatly simplified. There are really two parallel redundant control lanes from the pilot's throttle to the duplicated DECUs, with cross communication between lanes to make it almost certain that any fault will be detected. A lane-selection logic unit takes a failed DECU off-line. Inputs comprise dual throttle-position transducer signals and two parallel sets of engine and aircraft parameters. Throttle position gives a demand signal which is interpreted as fan speed, so that the throttle directly controls engine LP rpm. The pilot's lever transducer signal is converted in each processor channel into an engine fuel schedule related to altitude, AOA and compressor speed. The selected schedule, to zero the input demand, accelerates the engine at a controlled maximum rate up to the limits imposed by AOA, shaft speeds and JPT (jetpipe temperature). A new computing cycle is completed 28 times per second. The output signal controls the stepping motor which operates the fuel metering valve.

Advantages of a Fadec are numerous, but vary with aircraft type. A Harrier II may have to make a free take-off from a short deck, and engine spool-up time can be critical. A hydromechanical engine control can hold acceleration tight against the limiting boundary only by very rigorous maintenance and frequent adjustment, which burns a lot of fuel and causes severe environmental disturbance. Variations in ambient temperature or fuel specification exacerbate the problem. The Fadec gives perfect acceleration, needs no adjustment, and automatically compensates for every variable. It also controls maximum-rate spool-down after landing, compensates for engine-bleed transients, and monitors for all engine faults, or rather incipient faults. With a hydromechanical system any change to the engine or operating regime calls for time-consuming modifications back at the maker's factory, but with a Fadec nothing need be changed but the software, done (often in minutes) on the flightline. The Fadec also happens to be 20 lb lighter, but the biggest gains are in precisely repeatable top aircraft performance and reduction in pilot workload.

Third and last of the examples I have picked of computer-controlled subsystems is the FQMS (fuel-quantity measuring system). To me it is extraordinary that even very expensive cars invariably still use a resistance bridge network operated by a float. This takes no account of variation in fuel, and almost always gives a different indication depending on the attitude of the car (steeply uphill or steeply down). Similar systems began to be thrown out of aircraft by 1949, though you still find them in some light aircraft. In their place we have tried various ideas, even including putting a radioactive source round each tank and measuring radiation at a receiver near the bottom. The idea that survived is to use capacitance probes, sometimes two or three in each tank. These are concentric tubes. When the tank is empty, the space (dielectric) between the tubes is air, or rather air mixed with fuel vapour. When the tank is full, the dielectric between the tubes is fuel. This results in an enormous variation in the capacitance of each probe between tank full and tank empty, and modern systems can measure the result with an accuracy consistently better than 1%, though this presupposes that the aircraft attitude is not wildly different from that in cruising flight.

Early capacitance systems used AC, but in recent years there have been changes. The first was a progressive switch to DC, to eliminate the need for screening (shielding) and improve S/N (signal to noise) ratio. In the past twenty years all advanced aircraft have adopted digital microprocessor-based systems which, as everywhere else, add almost nothing to weight and offer many advantages. We can take the A320 system (Smiths Industries) as an

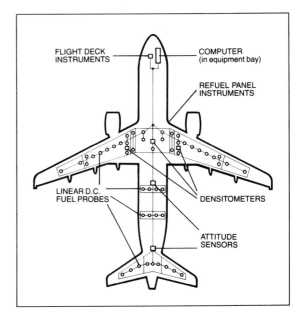

Below left *Simplified geometrical layout of a modern FQMS (A320). Every variation is taken care of.* (Smiths)

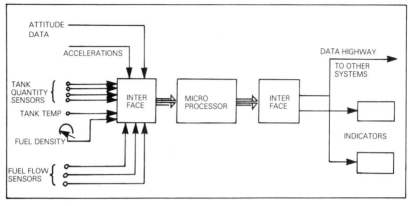

Right *To show the A320 FQMS fully would take pages; this is a simplified outline of typical architecture for a digital system.* (Smiths Industries)

example. This has a triplex power source and dual-channel digital architecture throughout. The same system is used in the first 21 aircraft, A320-100s with two tanks, as in all subsequent aircraft, which are A320-200s with three tanks. All probes are of the linear DC type, with software profiling to give an exact output despite the irregular shapes of the tanks. As fuel is pumped aboard it passes through a sensor, called a cadensicon, whose output is stored in the FQMS computer memory. It measures and averages the density and electrical permittivity of the fuel. There is also a small compensator probe in the bottom of one of the tanks which senses the actual permittivity of the fuel, which varies with temperature (and the wing skin can reach minus-60°C in cruising flight). All these signals are sent to the FQMS computer, together with exact aircraft pitch/roll attitude signals which are continuously available from the Arinc 429 bus. These data are compared with tank profile information stored in the memory, so that all necessary corrections are continuously applied to the apparent mass of fuel.

The first stage of each FQMS channel is an analog multiplexer fed with the outputs from the tank-probe signal conditioning circuits. The output from the multiplexer is fed to an A/D converter whose digital output is then read by the dual microcomputers. Linked in multiplex, these operate on a multi-input algorithm from which they derive individual tank masses and total mass. These values are Arinc 429 encoded and sent to the 'glass' flight deck and to the refuel/defuel panel indicators under the wing. The FQMS can shut off refuelling at any preselected mass, automatically distributes fuel correctly between tanks, continuously supplies aircraft gross weight and CG position to the Arinc 429 bus (needed by the FMGC, flight-management guid-

ance computers), gives early indication of any fuel imbalance likely to upset CG position, automatically identifies and isolates any fuel-system fault (for example, output from a faulty tank probe is ignored), and incorporates Bite and self-diagnosis testing.

The software for an FQMS is straightforward, unless we wish to measure fuel mass during air combat, and in the case of the A320 the whole system can be exactly calibrated away from the aircraft. Once installed, it is exceedingly unlikely ever to be as much as 1% out. But software for real-time complex systems can be among the most challenging things ever created by man. For this reason anyone who runs a seminar on software is likely to get a full house. In the past year I have been notified of 23. Taking one at random (sponsored by State of the Art Ltd) I find that one subsection dealing with toolkit-based SDEs (software development environments) covers such things as Extended Unix, Unix shells, Apollo domain and DSEE, transparent version management, Dapse and Apse base technology, ERA data modelling, Arcadia, tool building and invocation, and much more. There's even a section on SUN NEWS which I'm sure does not have a page 3! What I find distressing is that so many people should be unemployed, when if they were conversant with these subjects they could start at not less than $60,000 a year.

People who write programs make an increasing contribution to humanity. There are numerous examples of so-called 'expert systems' which are specifically designed to make the fullest use of the lifetime of experience of its author; Boeing has a library of hundreds of such systems which retain the knowledge of engineers who have retired. Near-relatives are so-called IKBSs (intelligent knowledge-

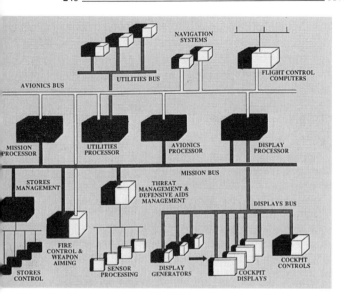

Typical simplified architecture for a combat aircraft, using a multi-bus system. Many of the local processors are embedded (form part of the LRU which they control), and these form the black parts of the otherwise white boxes. (Computing Devices Co)

based systems) where physically small systems can have seemingly fantastic capabilities, all made possible because we can put a powerful microprocessor on to a single tiny chip. Of course, different countries have different national strategies. In the Soviet Union virtually all the money goes into military software, with (until recently, at least) no significant interest into spin-off to civilian applications. In the USA most of the Federal money goes into quasi-military things like SDI and stealth, but with a very keen interest in domestic and consumer spin-off. In Japan, Hong Kong and Singapore the money goes entirely into civil — especially consumer — applications, with the sure knowledge that the chips and software will also find other applications. And in the UK we have a tiny handful of talented companies who, against terrible odds, eke out a living pecking round the edges.

Avionics today is certainly the fastest-growing branch of aviation and one of the fastest-growing industries in the world. To someone like the author it is a full-time job merely trying to keep up with what is happening. As I write this chapter, two press releases have just come in from McDonnell Douglas which typify the sort of things the USAF thinks its fighter pilots (for example) will need. One begins:

'An artificial intelligence system that could help pilots of future fighter aircraft make critical combat decisions faster and more efficiently has been demonstrated at McDonnell Douglas. The system, demonstrated 14 February 1989 in a piloted air-combat simulator, is part of the Pilot's Associate programme sponsored by the Defense Advanced Research Projects Agency (DARPA), Washington DC. The programme is managed by the US Air Force's Wright Research and Development Center.

'During the simulated air-to-ground mission, several unexpected surface-to-air missile (SAM) threats and redirection to a new target forced the pilot continually to re-evaluate the situation and flight path. Pilot's Associate provided the pilot with choices that allowed him to acquire the target and hit it accurately, then return to base safely.'

The other begins:

'McDonnell Douglas is working under a $17 million US Air Force contract to develop and test Integrated Controls and Avionics for Air Superiority, for fighter aircraft. The ICAAS programme, which uses advanced software and parallel processing computers, is designed to help fighter pilots contend more effectively with Soviet aircraft.

'ICAAS will help pilots assess tactical situations faster and with greater precision. The system will analyse air-to-air threats and present pilots with a prioritised list of tactical options, then give pilots steering cues to fly the profiles they select. The programme builds on previous McDonnell Douglas projects that used advanced cockpit displays to give fighter pilots improved situational awareness. ICAAS introduces a new capability called situational assessment. "Situational awareness tells you what's going on, while situational assessment tells you what to do about it," said George Vetsch, Chief Engineer and Manager of McDonnell Douglas' ICAAS programme. "It's one thing to see four advanced planes coming at you, and another to know what to do about them. ICAAS will help the pilot select the best tactics and use his weapons more effectively".'

With hindsight it seems remarkable that in April 1957 the British Secretary of State for Defence should have laid down as universal official policy that henceforth there would be no more human pilots in British combat aircraft. He cancelled all the new RAF fighters and bombers, and apologetically noted that the Lightning had 'unfortunately gone too far to cancel'. Today we have computers which, quite literally, are a billion times more capable, yet I have just seen an article (*Interavia* 11/1988) which begins, 'Can a computer occupy the *third seat* [my italics] in the new generation of transport aircraft?' It's OK chaps, your jobs are not at risk.

GLOSSARY

This glossary includes terms and acronyms which appear in this book repeatedly and are explained only on their first appearance.

AAM Air-to-air missile
AC Alternating current
A/D Analog to digital
ADC Air-data computer
ADF Automatic direction finding
ADI Attitude director indicator
ADR Accident data recorder
ADS 1 Automatic dependent surveillance
    2 Air-data system
aerial Antenna is preferred
AEW Airborne early warning
AF Audio frequency
AFCS Automatic flight control system
AFDS Autopilot and flight-director system
AHRS Attitude/heading reference system
AI 1 Airborne interception (radar)
    2 Artificial intelligence
AIDS Airborne integrated data system
alphanumerics Information written in letters and numbers
analog Expressed in continuously variable values, not in separate 'bits'
antenna Device for radiating or receiving EM radiation
AOA Angle of attack, the angle at which the wing meets the airflow
Arinc Aeronautical Radio Inc
ASI Airspeed indicator
ASV Air to surface vessel
ASW Anti-submarine warfare
ATC Air traffic control
Awacs Airborne warning and control system
az/el Azimuth and elevation

binary Expressed in terms of two digits only, such as 0 and 1
BIT Built in test (E adds equipment)
bit Single unit of data or information in binary system, eg 0 or 1 (binary digit)
BVR Beyond visual range

C-band From 3.9 to 6.2 GHz
C^3 Command, control and communications (CM adds countermeasures; I adds IFF)
CAT Clear-air turbulence
CCD Charge-coupled device
CDU Control/display unit
centimetric Operating at a wavelength of a few centimetres
CFAR Constant false-alarm rate
CFDS Centralised fault-display system
CG Centre of gravity
chaff Radar-reflective clouds composed of billions of small hair-like reflectors
chip Single completed device (possibly containing thousands of gates etc) formed in monocrystalline substrate
CIS Co-operative independent surveillance
clutter Radar echoes from targets in which we have no interest
CMT Cadmium mercury telluride
CNI Communications, navigation, identification
CPGS Cassette preparation ground station
CPI Crash position indicator
CPU Central processor unit
CRT Cathode-ray tube
CSAS Command/stability augmentation system
CSMU Crash-survivable memory unit
CVR Cockpit voice recorder
CW Continuous wave

D/A Digital to analog
d_a Radar resolution in azimuth

DADC Digital air-data computer
dB Decibel
DBS Doppler beam sharpening
DC Direct current
DDM Difference in depth of modulation
DE Directed energy (weapon)
DECM Defensive electronic countermeasures
DECU Digital electronic control unit
D/F Direction finding (or finder)
DFDR Digital flight-data recorder
digital Operating on discrete bits (0s and 1s), opposite of analog
DME Distance-measuring equipment
DOA Direction of arrival
d_r Radar resolution in range
DTM Data-transfer module
DTS Data-transfer system
duty cycle Proportion of time a radar is transmitting
DVI Direct voice input

EAR Electronically agile radar
ECCM Electronic counter-countermeasures
ECM Electronic countermeasures
Eeprom Electronically erasable programmable read-only memory
EFIS Electronic flight instrument system
EICAS Engine indication and crew-alerting system
ELD Electroluminescent display
Elint Electronic intelligence
ELS Emitter locator system
ELT Emergency locator transmitter
EM Electromagnetic
EMP Electromagnetic pulse
EO Electro-optical
ESM Electronic support (or surveillance) measures
EW Electronic warfare
EXCM Expendable countermeasures

FA Frequency agility
Fadec, FADEC Full-authority digital electronic control
FBL Fly by light
FBW Fly by wire
F_c Carrier frequency
FCC Flight control computer
FCS Flight (or fire) control system
f_d Doppler frequency
FDC Flight director computer
FDR Flight data recorder
FET Field-effect transistor
FFT Fast Fourier transform

FH Frequency hopping
FLIR Forward-looking infra-red
FM Frequency modulation
FMGC Flight-management guidance computer
FMICW Frequency modulated interrupted continuous wave
FMS Flight-management system
FO Fibre optics
FOR Field of regard
FOV Field of view
FQMS Fuel-quantity measuring system
F_r PRF
frequency agility Ability to hop extremely rapidly and randomly from one frequency to another

GA General aviation, ie not airline or military/naval/army
GaAs Gallium arsenide
Gbit/s Gigabits (thousands of millions of bits) per second
GHz Gigahertz (thousands of millions of cycles per second)
GMTI Ground moving target indicator
GPS Global positioning system
GPWS Ground-proximity warning system
GS, G/s 1 Groundspeed
     2 Glideslope of ILS

HDD Head-down display
HF High frequency, 3,000–30,000 kHz
HMD Helmet-mounted display
HMS Helmet-mounted sight
HOL Higher-order language
hole Notional carrier of unit positive charge
Hotas Hands on throttle and stick
HSI Horizontal-situation indicator
HUD, Hud Head-up display
Hudwac HUD weapon-aiming computer
HUMS, Hums Health and usage monitoring system
hyperbolic Generating a fixed pattern of (invisible) hyperbolic pathways in the sky
Hz Hertz, cycles per second

IC Integrated circuit
ICNI Integrated CNI
ICNIA, Icnia Integrated CNI avionics
IFE Inflight entertainment
IFF Identification friend or foe
IFM Instantaneous frequency measurement
IFOV Instantaneous field of view
IIR Imaging infra-red

IIS Infra-red imaging system
IKBS Intelligent knowledge-based systems
ILS Instrument landing system
INEWS Integrated electronic-warfare system
INS Inertial navigation system
IO Integrated optics
I/o Input/output
IP Initial point
IR Infra-red
IRCM Infra-red countermeasures
IRLS Infra-red linescan
IRS Inertial reference system
IRWR Infra-red warning receiver

JTIDS Joint tactical information distribution system

K 1 Degrees Kelvin
 2 Thousand, thus 96K = 96,000 bits
Kbit/s Thousands of bits per second
KE Kinetic energy
kHz Kilohertz, thousands of cycles per second
klystron Velocity-modulated electron tube for generating microwaves
kV Kilovolts, thousands of volts
kVA Kilovolt-amperes, measure of AC power

laser Device for generating beam of coherent light (many species)
LCD Liquid-crystal display
LCF Low-cycle fatigue
LED Light-emitting diode
LEF Light-emitting film
LF Low frequency, 30–300 kHz
lidar Light (laser) radar
LLTV Low-light TV, ie works in near-darkness
LO Local oscillator
LOC Localizer of ILS
Loran Long-range navigation
LOS Line of sight
LRU Line-replaceable unit
LSI Large-scale integration
LW Long wave

MAD Magnetic anomaly detector
magnetron Device for generating microwaves from rotating magnetic field in metal cavity
MAR Multiple-access receiver
Mbit/s Millions of bits per second
MCU Modular Concept Unit
MF Medium frequency, 300–3,000 kHz

MFD Multifunction display
MHz Megahertz, millions of cycles per second
microelectronics Solid-state electronics in which devices are microscopic
micron One millionth of a metre
microsecond One millionth of a second
microwaves EM radiation between RF and far-IR, about 1–300 GHz
MLC Mainlobe clutter
MLS Microwave landing system
MMIC Monolithic microwave integrated circuit
MMS Mast-mounted sight
MOS Metal-oxide silicon
mrad Milliradian, thousandth of a radian, just over one-twentieth of a degree
MTBF Mean time between failures
MTBO Mean time between overhauls
MTI Moving-target indication
MTOW Maximum takeoff weight
MW Megawatts, millions of watts
mW Milliwatts, thousandths of a watt

n-type With preponderance of electrons
ND Navigation display
NDB Non-directional beacon
noise Unwanted incoming EM radiation of random power, frequency and direction
ns Nanosecond, one thousand-millionth of a second
NVGs Night-vision goggles

OBS Omni-bearing selector
OCM 1 On-condition monitoring
 2 Optical countermeasures
ORS Offensive radar system

p-type Preponderance of holes
PA Public-address
PCB Printed-circuit board
PCM Pulse-code modulation
PD Pulse doppler
PDES Pulse-doppler elevation scan
PDM Pulse-duration modulation
PDNES Pulse-doppler non-elevation scan
PDS Passive detection system
PDU Pilot display unit
PFD Primary flight display
PN Pseudonoise
PNVS Pilot's night vision system
Pods Portable data store
PRF Pulse repetition frequency
PRI Pulse repetition interval, interpulse period

PROM Programmable read-only memory
PSP Programmable signal processor

radar Device or technique for using RF waves to give information about presence, location, velocity or form of remote objects
RAM 1 Random-access memory
     2 Radar-absorbent material
rate Rate of change of a variable, denoted by dot above symbol for quantity
RBC Rapid-bloom chaff
RC Radar computer
RCS Radar cross-section
RF Radio frequency, 3 kHz–300,000MHz
RLG Ring laser gyro
RMI Remote magnetic indicator
R-nav Area navigation, ie not forcing aircraft to follow particular tracks
ROM Read-only memory
RSP Radar signal processor
RTI Radar target indicator
RVR Runway visual range
RVSP Radar video signal processor
RWR Radar warning receiver

SAM Surface-to-air missile
SAR Synthetic-aperture (or array) radar
SARH Semi-active radar homing
SEAD Suppression of enemy air defences
SHF Super-high frequency, 3,000–30,000 MHz
Si Silicon
sideband Radio frequencies, often unwanted, produced by modulation above and below tuned frequency
sidelobe Radar beams emitted at an angle to the main beam (mainlobe); usually just a nuisance
sigint Signals intelligence
silent Emitting no radiation
SLAR Side (ways) looking airborne radar
SLC Sidelobe clutter
S/N Signal-to-noise ratio
SOJ Stand-off jammer
S/P Serial/parallel
Stalo Stable local oscillator
STOVL Short takeoff, vertical landing
STT Single-target track
suite Complete avionics installation for (usually light) aircraft

SWS Stall warning system

TA Terrain avoidance
Tacan Tactical air navigation
TCAS Threat alert and collision-avoidance system
TDM Time-division multiplex
TDMA Time-division multiple access
Tercom Terrain contour matching (or mapping)
Terprom Terrain profile matching (or mapping)
TFOV Total field of view
TFR Terrain-following radar
TICM Thermal-imaging common module
TRA Terrain-referenced avionics
TRSB Time-referenced scanning beam MLS
TTA Total-terrain avionics
TTG Time to go
TWS 1 Track while scan
     2 Threat warning system
TWT Travelling-wave tube
TX Transmitter, transmission

UHF Ultra-high frequency, 300–3,000 MHz
UV Ultra-violet

V_d Doppler velocity, ie range rate
VASI Visual approach slope indicator
VDU Visual display unit
VFO Variable-frequency oscillator
VHF Very high frequency, 30–300 MHz
VHSIC Very high-speed integrated circuit
VLF Very low frequency, 3–30 kHz
VLSI Very large scale integration
VOR VHF omni-directional range
VVR Voice and video recorder

W Watts, measure of power
waveguide Conductor of microwaves and other EM radiation which travels through air or other medium surrounded by conductor
WXR Weather radar

X-band Obsolete but still popular definition of radar frequency band about 5.2–10.9 GHz, about 3 cm wavelength

μ Greek mu, symbol for microns
μs Microseconds

INDEX

Also published by Patrick Stephens Limited

THE AIRCRAFT COCKPIT

From stick-and-string to fly-by-wire

L.F.E. Coombs
Foreword by Bill Gunston

The aircraft cockpit has evolved beyond all recognition since the dawn of flight — from nothing more than a cradle among the struts and wires of the early flying machines to the digitalized 'front office' of today's airliner or the futuristic environment of the fighter pilot.

In the first book of its kind, L. F. E. Coombs surveys the evolution of the pilot's place from the first powered flight of 1903 to the present, and on into the future. Significant civil and military aircraft types are selected to show the more important changes as aviation science and technology have progressed. Instruments and controls form a central element — how they originated, why they are where they are, and the differences they have made — together with consideration of 'the human factor', the pilot, and in due course crew, and their problems and responsibilities.

Detailed coverage is given to the origins of many design standards (such as which side the pilot sits) and early important aids to safety and regularity of flight, among them the development of radio systems for navigation and guidance, and of instruments for 'blind flying'.

Cockpits of the First and Second World War receive particular attention, corresponding to the advances in controls and instruments that the two wars brought about. Following the emergence of the closed cockpit which replaced the open cockpit in the 'thirties, developments of five decades are examined culminating in the digital computer technology, electronic colour instruments and flight management and control systems, including fly-by-wire, of the 'eighties. Even more advanced control and instrument concepts are already being evaluated for the future, and are also described and illustrated.

L. F. E. Coombs writes from long professional experience of the subject and at an understandable level, drawing together a wide range of information. Illustrated with almost 200 photographs and some beautifully clear diagrams, here is a book for enthusiasts, students, pilots, and anyone with an interest in aviation.

WORLD ENCYCLOPAEDIA OF AERO ENGINES

Fully revised second edition

Bill Gunston

This second edition of the *World Encyclopaedia of Aero Engines*, conveniently arranged in alphabetical order and complete with new entries, photographs and updated information, describes and lists every major aeroplane engine manufacturer throughout the world. From the earliest piston engines of the Wright brothers from Dayton, Ohio in 1903 through the pre-First World War ABC, Hall-Scott and Curtiss to the latest Rolls-Royce jet 535-E4 and the multi-national collaborative projects, every significant engine is included. Engine development has been critical to the evolution of aircraft design and each engine is placed in its historical context. The author discusses all the important design features and wherever possible every unit is illustrated — thus bringing to light many rare and previously unpublished photographs. Thorough research has also uncovered a large number of hitherto virtually unknown facts about many Russian and even American engines which are described in detailed histories of all the world's major engine-producing companies, including the tight-lipped Soviet design and construction bureaux.

There is another side to the creation of any human-designed system as complex as an aero engine — there is scope for triumph and catastrophe, violent argument, crises and nagging doubt. The author has not ignored the human element in aero engine history and some of the personal struggles that resulted in engines like the Rolls-Royce Merlin or the Pratt & Whitney PT6 are to be found under the relevant company entries.

The first edition of this remarkable and comprehensive guide was published in 1986 to considerable critical acclaim: this new edition continues to fill a major gap in aeronautical history and represents a vital addition to any aviation enthusiast's shelves.

'A very worthwhile book' *Air Pictorial*
'A most valuable reference work on the subject' *Motor Sport*
'A unique, timeless reference' *Pilot*
'An excellent book' *Air International*

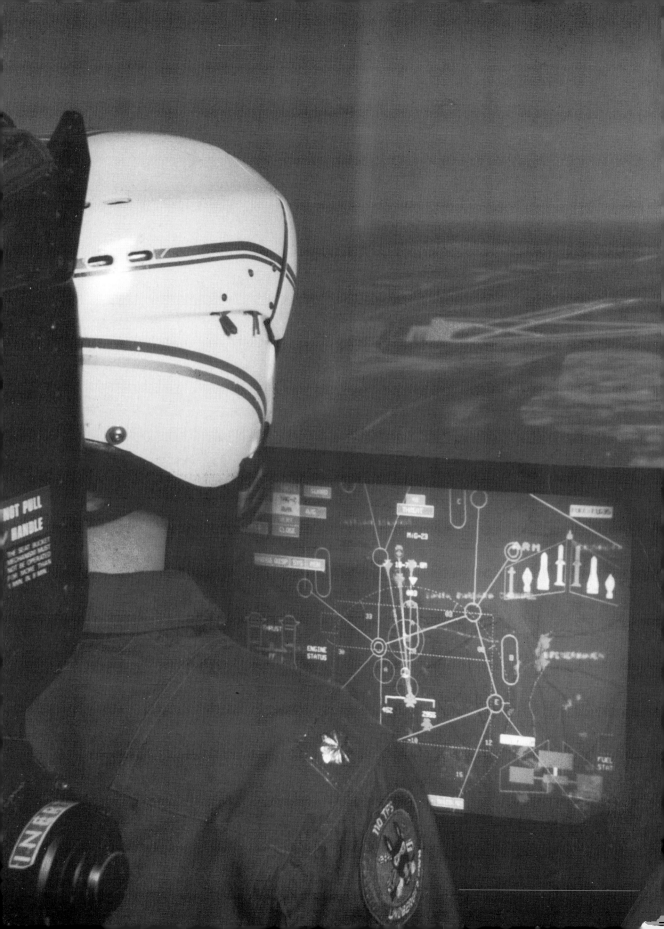